Af
Hours…

When business and pleasure combine…

Three passionate novels!

In July 2006 Mills & Boon bring back
two of their classic collections, each
featuring three favourite romances
by our bestselling authors...

AFTER OFFICE HOURS...
The Irresistible Tycoon
by Helen Brooks
A Professional Marriage
by Jessica Steele
Marriage on the Agenda
by Lee Wilkinson

MARRYING THE MILLIONAIRE
by Lynne Graham
An Arabian Marriage
The Disobedient Mistress
The Heiress Bride

After Office Hours...

THE IRRESISTIBLE TYCOON
by
Helen Brooks

A PROFESSIONAL MARRIAGE
by
Jessica Steele

MARRIAGE ON THE AGENDA
by
Lee Wilkinson

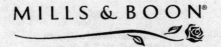

MILLS & BOON®

*Harlequin Mills & Boon Limited,
Eton House, 18-24 Paradise Road, Richmond, Surrey, TW9 1SR*

AFTER OFFICE HOURS...
© by Harlequin Enterprises II B.V., 2006

*The Irresistible Tycoon, A Professional Marriage and Marriage on
the Agenda were first published in Great Britain by Harlequin
Mills & Boon Limited in separate, single volumes.*

The Irresistible Tycoon © Helen Brooks 2001
A Professional Marriage © Jessica Steele 2002
Marriage on the Agenda © Lee Wilkinson 2001

ISBN 13: 978 0 263 84965 3
ISBN 10: 0 263 84965 1

05-0706

*Printed and bound in Spain
by Litografía Rosés S.A., Barcelona*

THE IRRESISTIBLE TYCOON

by

Helen Brooks

Helen Brooks lives in Northamptonshire and is married with three children. As she is a committed Christian, busy housewife and mother, her spare time is at a premium but her hobbies include reading, swimming, gardening and walking her old, faithful dog. Her long-cherished aspiration to write became a reality when she put pen to paper on reaching the age of forty, and sent the result off to Mills & Boon®.

Don't miss Helen Brooks' exciting new novel
The Italian Tycoon's Bride
out in September 2006 from Mills & Boon Modern Romance™

CHAPTER ONE

'Kim, I'm not at all sure that this is the right step to take, I'm really not. You've enough on your plate as it is; you know that.'

'I've no choice, Maggie, and *you* know *that*,' Kim answered steadily.

'But...' Maggie Conway stared helplessly at her friend as she ran out of words.

'Look, just be an angel and pick up Melody after school, okay? I shouldn't be much later than five but you know how interviews are; they might keep me waiting for a while.'

'No problem,' Maggie said unhappily.

'Thanks. I don't know what I'd do without you,' Kim said with heartfelt warmth as she gave Maggie a brief hug.

Kim was still thinking about her last words as she left the comfort of Maggie's spacious, open-plan apartment and stepped into the crisp frosty air outside the big Victorian house which had been converted into several self-contained flats.

Maggie was an unlikely-looking angel, being as round as she was tall with a shock of vibrant curly ginger hair and freckles covering every inch of her skin, but an angel she was nevertheless, Kim told herself silently as she walked briskly to the bus stop. How she would have got through the last two traumatic years without Maggie's unfailing support and good humour she didn't know.

She reached the bus stop just as the bus drew round the corner and, once seated, stared unseeingly out of the window, quite oblivious to the overt stare of the young, good-looking man sitting opposite her who clearly couldn't take his eyes off the golden-haired beauty on the other side of the aisle.

Maggie had stepped in as unpaid childminder when the need arose—as it did frequently—confidante, stalwart friend, advisor and a whole host of other roles, Kim reflected warmly. The only good thing to come out of her relationship with Graham—apart from Melody, of course—was that he had introduced her to Maggie.

Graham… Kim's soft full mouth tightened and her brown eyes narrowed for a moment before she forced her thoughts away from the spectre in her mind.

This wasn't the time to think of Graham, not with such an important interview looming, she told herself firmly, straightening in the seat and squaring her slender shoulders. She understood the competition for the post of secretary to the chairman and managing director of Kane Electrical was fierce, and she needed to be focused and clear from the outset.

It was another fifteen minutes before the bus dropped her on the outskirts of Cambridge and almost outside the huge site which Kane Electrical occupied, and within five minutes she was standing in Reception explaining to the model-slim, beautifully coiffured receptionist that she had an appointment with Mr Lucas Kane at half-past two.

'Right.' The girl's expertly made-up eyes had made a swift summing up of the tall, discreetly dressed woman in front of her, and now she gave a practised smile as she said blandly, 'If you would like to take a seat for a moment I'll tell Mr Kane's secretary you're here, Mrs Allen.'

'Thank you.' Kim had flushed slightly under the scrutiny. Her winter coat was a good one, but not new, neither were her shoes and handbag, whereas the receptionist's expertly cut grey silk suit screamed a designer label and her hair could only have been cut by one of the most expensive salons in Cambridge.

Still, she wasn't going to let this girl or anyone else intimidate her, Kim told herself fiercely as she took the proffered seat and sank into inches of soft leather upholstery. She might not be wearing the very latest fashion or have her hair styled by Vidal Sassoon but she was an excellent secretary, as her references confirmed.

She raised her small chin abruptly and stared straight ahead, her hands resting in her lap and her knees demurely together, before a restrained commotion at the side of her—as a tall, dark man with what could only be described as an entourage swept into the building—brought her head swinging round.

Whether it was the receptionist's less than tactful appraisal, or the fact that everyone on the perimeter of the man seemed to be falling over themselves to get his attention, Kim didn't know, but she found herself staring at the back of the personage in question with unmitigated dislike.

He certainly knew how to make an entrance, she thought waspishly, and he was so full of his own importance he was almost bursting with it! How she disliked the fawning and obsequious servility that went with wealth and power in some quarters.

The party was making for the lifts at the far side of the reception in a subdued furore of which the man leading seemed totally unaware, and Kim still had her eyes fixed on his back, her face expressing her feelings only too clearly, when he suddenly turned and to her shock and surprise looked straight at her.

She was conscious of a pair of rivetingly hard, metallic silver-grey eyes taking in the whole of her in a stunningly swift perusal that was quite devastating before she could wipe her face of all expression, and then she saw dark eyebrows rise in mordant disdain. The message was un-mistakable.

He had recognised what she was thinking, recognised it and dismissed it—and her—as beneath his contempt, she thought as her face turned scarlet. And she couldn't blame him, she really couldn't. If nothing else she had been un-forgivably rude.

In the split second before the lift doors opened and the man turned to enter Kim's mind raced, but there was no time to do anything but watch him disappear. The doors closed, there was the faintest of purrs as the lift ascended, and that was that.

She was aware of sinking back in the seat and it was only then she became conscious she had been holding her-self rigid. How embarrassing! She shut her eyes for the briefest of moments and swallowed hard, glancing across at the receptionist, who was speaking to someone on the telephone. What must he have thought? But then he'd left her in no doubt what he had thought, she added with a touch of dark humour.

She was looking at the receptionist without seeing her now, her mind continuing to dissect every moment of the little drama which had unfurled so unexpectedly. Who was he? Obviously someone important: one of the directors of the firm maybe?

An awful thought occurred to her but she pushed it away immediately. No, it wouldn't be him—not Lucas Kane, she told herself firmly. That would be too disastrous, and if nothing else she was due some good fortune—well over-due, as it happened.

'Mrs Allen?'

Kim came out of her rueful musing with a little jolt to find a tall, rather formidable-looking woman standing in front of her.

'Good afternoon.' A hand was extended and as Kim rose

she made a suitable reply, shaking the other woman's hand. 'I'm June West,' the woman continued, 'Mr Kane's secretary. If you would like to come with me...'

'Thank you.' As they walked towards the waiting lift Kim glanced at the other woman from under her eyelashes. June West was the person the successful applicant would have to follow, and if Lucas Kane's present secretary was anything like as efficient as she looked they would have their work cut out. It didn't help Kim's confidence an iota.

'Mr Kane is running a little late.' As the lift doors closed, June turned to her with a polite smile. 'We've had one panic after another this morning.'

Kim nodded, smiling in turn before she said, 'Is that usual? The panics, I mean?'

'I'm afraid so.' June was looking hard at her. 'As his secretary you would have to be used to working under pressure most of the time and making decisions for yourself. Would that be a problem?'

Being under pressure and making decisions for herself? That had been her life for the last two years—and before— Kim reflected silently. 'No. No, it wouldn't.'

'Good.' The smile was warmer now. 'I've worked for Mr Kane for the last ten years and I can honestly say there's never been a dull moment. It hasn't always been easy, and the job is certainly not your average nine-to-five, but he's a very fair employer and prepared to give and take, if you know what I mean.'

Kim didn't, not really, but she nodded and said, 'Can I ask why you are leaving?'

'Of course. Sensible question.' The lift doors had opened and now Kim followed the tall figure into a hushed corridor as June said over her shoulder, 'I'm getting married and my future husband lives and works in Scotland. He's got his own business; I met him through Kane Electrical, actually, as he's one of our suppliers, so it's not feasible for him to make the move.'

'Congratulations,' Kim said with genuine cordiality.

'Thanks.' As June opened a door and waved Kim through, she added quietly, 'I'd given up on meeting the man of my dreams, to be honest, but whoever said life begins at forty was dead right as far as I was concerned.'

So June was forty, and she had obviously been a career woman dedicated to her job and Kane Electrical for the last decade—she had been right about the other woman being a hard act to follow if nothing else, Kim thought ruefully.

'This is my office.'

They were standing in a large, beautifully decorated room with ankle-deep carpet and the very latest in office furniture and equipment, Kim noted.

'And through there—' June inclined her head to a door behind her desk '—is my private cloakroom. Mr Kane has his own leading off his office along with a dressing room and small sitting room. He sometimes sleeps over when things are particularly hectic,' she added quietly.

'Right.' This was way, way out of her league. Kim kept her face expressionless but her thoughts were racing. The best she could hope for was to get through the next twenty minutes—or however long the interview with Lucas Kane lasted—without making a complete fool of herself. He was clearly looking for a personal assistant-cum-secretary who would eat, breathe and sleep Kane Electrical, and she just couldn't give that degree of commitment with Melody to consider.

But she had stated quite clearly she had a four-year-old daughter on her CV, she reminded herself in the next instant, divesting herself of her coat before taking the seat June indicated and watching the other woman disappear through the interconnecting door in to her boss's domain.

She wouldn't have got this far if he objected to his secretary having a life outside of work, would she?

She glanced round the opulent room again and her stomach swirled. She was amazed she *had* got this far if she was being honest, she admitted silently. It had been the thought of the huge salary such a post would command—nothing more and nothing less—which had prompted her to send off her CV when she had seen the position advertised at the end of September, just over four weeks ago now.

She hadn't heard anything at all for three weeks and then she had received a letter, written on embossed, thick linen notepaper, stating she had been selected for the initial short list to attend an interview on Monday, 30th October, at 2.30 p.m.

Which was today, now, this very minute! *Oh, help.*

'Mrs Allen?' June had opened the interconnecting door again and was smiling at her. 'Mr Kane will see you now.'

She knew, just a moment before she walked through the door, who would be seated within the room beyond. It was in that split second Kim acknowledged she had had a presentiment the moment she had stared into the cold silver eyes in the lobby below. He had *looked* like a millionaire tycoon; it had been in his walk, his bearing, the turn of his head, even the way his eyes had held hers in such arrogant contempt and disregard.

'Mrs Allen...' A tall, broad-shouldered figure rose from behind a massive grey desk at her approach, but the clear autumn sunlight streaming in through the huge plate-glass window behind him blinded Kim for a moment and turned Lucas Kane into a dark silhouette. And then, as she reached the chair which had been placed in front of the desk, she blinked, and he came into focus. Alarmingly into focus. All six feet four, and then some, of him!

'How do you do?' He was smiling as he enclosed her

small paw in his long fingers, but it was definitely a croc-
odile sort of smile, Kim noted helplessly. He had obviously
realised who she was earlier and had been looking forward
to this moment with some relish. 'Please be seated, Mrs
Allen.'

She wasn't going to give him the satisfaction of stutter-
ing and stammering, and she knew she wouldn't be able to
speak clearly until she had had a moment or two to pull
herself together, so she smiled in what she hoped was a
cool, contained sort of way and sank gracefully into the
chair. If nothing else it eased her trembling legs!

There hadn't been time to look beyond the granite stare
which had pinned her down in Reception, but now, to add
to the agitation and shock that had her heart thumping like
a sledgehammer, she could see Lucas Kane was disturbingly attractive. Not handsome, the rugged chiselled face
and impressive muscled body was too aggressively male
and ruthlessly compelling to ever be labelled such, but he
had something that went far beyond good looks.

'You understand you are one of four applicants on a final
short list?' he asked expressionlessly without looking at
her, his eyes on the papers on his desk as his hand flicked
over a page of what she assumed was her CV.

His hair was very black, almost a blue-black, she noted
silently, and cut so short as to be harshly severe. And then
he raised his head, and the curiously silver eyes shaded by
thick black lashes compelled a response.

'Yes, I do, Mr Kane,' she managed evenly.

'So what makes you think I should choose you over the
other excellent candidates?' he drawled smoothly, but with
an edge that told her the incident in Reception was not
forgotten or forgiven.

She had had the answer to just such a question drilled
into her during the business management degree she had
taken at university, and had even encountered it first-hand

when she had applied for her last job, just over two years ago, but now, in the face of Lucas Kane's cruelly mocking scrutiny, something hot and contumacious rose up in Kim's chest.

'That's for you to weigh in the balance and consider, surely, Mr Kane,' she answered coolly.

The silver eyes iced over a fraction more; her tone of voice clearly hadn't been to his liking. 'Is it, indeed?' It was soft and low but with an underlying sharpness that suggested velvet disguising pure steel.

He had expected a stock answer—she had read that in the brief dart of surprise the silver-grey eyes had been unable to conceal—but she wasn't playing any sort of game with this man. If he wanted to conduct a straightforward interview that was one thing, but she wasn't going to be intimidated by Lucas Kane or anyone else.

He stared at her for another moment or two and she forced herself not to drop her gaze, and then he flicked the intercom on his desk.

'Yes, Mr Kane?' June's voice sounded so wonderfully normal it made Kim want to get up and fly into the outer office.

'Coffee, June, for Mrs Allen and myself.'

Kim had been half expecting him to tell his secretary that the interview was finished, or ask June to show her out—anything, in fact, but request coffee for them both. She found she badly wanted to smooth her hair but restrained the impulse to fiddle with the thick shining braid coiled tightly on top of her head, knowing the intuitive, razor-sharp mind on the other side of the desk would recognise the nervousness behind such a gesture.

'Or perhaps you would prefer tea?' The brilliant gaze had fastened on her again after the brief respite.

'Coffee will be fine, thank you,' she answered carefully, keeping her voice in neutral.

'So, Mrs Allen...'

His voice was very distinctive, she thought shakily as she watched him settle himself comfortably in the vast leather chair and lean back slightly, crossing one long leg over the other knee as he surveyed her unblinkingly. Deep and ever so slightly husky, with the merest trace of an accent she couldn't quite place.

'Are you a career woman?' he asked softly.

There was only one answer she could possibly give to such a leading question, given the circumstances; a reply in the affirmative was what he was expecting and what she must make—the knowledge was screamingly obvious. 'My work is very important to me, Mr Kane, yes,' Kim said quickly. But not necessarily for the reasons he supposed, she added silently.

'And I see you got a First at university. That must mean you worked hard but had a natural aptitude for the subject too?' he commented thoughtfully.

She couldn't read anything from either his tone or his face but somehow she felt a punchline was on the way, and she couldn't quite keep the wariness out of her voice when she said, 'Yes, I suppose so.'

She saw the firm hard mouth twitch slightly, as though he was enjoying some private joke of his own, but his voice was still very even—almost expressionless—as he continued, 'So why did you get married immediately on graduating from university, and moreover start a family within months, if you intended to make the most of your excellent qualifications and carve a career for yourself? It doesn't quite seem to add up, Mrs Allen.'

Flipping cheek! She thought about making some facetious reply and passing off what she considered an extremely intrusive question, but he had hit her on the raw—possibly because she had had cause to bitterly regret the marriage almost immediately—so her voice was cold when she replied, 'Whether it adds up or not, that is what happened, Mr Kane, and it is my business, no one else's.' Okay, so she'd blown it good and proper, she thought sickly, but she didn't want his rotten job anyway!

She expected a cutting retort, something stinging to put her in her place, but even as she had started speaking he had straightened in his seat and was bending over the papers again, his voice businesslike as he said, 'Did you meet your husband at university?'

'Yes.' It was succinct in the extreme but he didn't look up.

'And I see you were widowed barely three years later. That must have been hard for you.'

There was nothing she could say to that and so she kept quiet, but he obviously didn't expect a comment as he continued immediately, 'That would have meant your daughter was two years of age when you became a single-parent family?'

'Yes.'

'Tough break.'

There was a smokier quality to his voice as he spoke, a trace of warmth evident in the deep husky tones for the first time, and it unnerved her. Kim didn't know why it bothered her but it did, and she suddenly found she was acutely aware of the formidable breadth of his shoulders and the muscled strength evident beneath the superficial veneer of expensive cloth.

It took all coherent thought clean away, and in the pause which followed Lucas Kane raised his dark head, his piercing eyes narrowing on her troubled face. 'You find it painful to talk about this, Mrs Allen?' he asked quietly.

Kim nodded—it seemed the safest option—but she was heartily thankful he had misunderstood the reason for her evident agitation.

'I think you can appreciate I have to ask whether you

have suitable arrangements in place should the need arise for you to work late or even be away from home for a few days?' he continued expressionlessly after another brief pause. 'Such occurrences are not unusual in this office.'

'Yes, I do.' This was more solid ground and Kim's large chocolate-brown eyes expressed the sentiment to the perceptive metallic gaze watching her so closely, although she was unaware of it.

'Melody was in full-time nursery care for two years before she started school in September and she loved it,' Kim said quickly, 'and she's just sailed into school. The school provides an after-hours club for children with working parents which finishes at five-thirty, but if ever I'm unavailable to pick her up a good friend who lives close by and works from home steps in. If I had to go on a business trip, Maggie would love to have her for however long it took.'

'How fortuitous.'

It was even and spoken without any expression but somehow Kim felt an implied criticism in the smooth tone. Her eyes narrowed and she stared hard into the tough masculine face in front of her, but other than ask him outright if he had a problem with the way she organised her affairs she could do nothing but say, coolly, 'Yes, it is. I'm very fortunate to have a friend like Maggie.'

'You don't have family living near?'

'No. My...my husband was an only child and his parents had him late in life. They're now in their sixties and his father is in poor health so they rarely travel from Scotland, where they live.'

'And your family?' he persisted relentlessly.

What this had to do with her aptitude to do the job, she didn't know! 'I have no family,' she said shortly.

'None?'

He sounded faintly incredulous and she supposed she couldn't blame him. 'I was orphaned as a young child,' she said matter-of-factly. 'I lived with an elderly aunt for a time but when she died and left her estate to her own family I was put in a children's home.'

The silver-grey eyes flickered briefly.

'So,' Kim continued quietly, 'I suppose I might have some distant relatives somewhere but I wouldn't go so far as to call them family, and I certainly have no wish to trace any of them. I've made my own life and that's the way I like it.'

He leant back in the chair again, his eyes never leaving her face. 'I see.'

Exactly what he saw Kim wasn't sure, but she felt she had as much chance of being offered this job as a snowball in hell.

'Since your husband died you have worked for Mr Curtis of Curtis & Brackley, is that right? And the firm went into liquidation four weeks ago.' He was reading from her CV again and the relief of having that laser-sharp gaze off her face was overwhelming.

'Which is when I saw this job advertised,' Kim agreed.

'Mr Curtis seems to have thought a great deal of you. He has written what I can only describe as a glowing reference.'

And she had earned it. Hours of overtime a week; calls in to the office to deal with minor panics at weekends; interrupted holidays—Bob Curtis had had no compunction in wringing every last working minute he could out of her. But the salary had been good and Curtis & Brackley had been practically on her doorstep and just down the street from Melody's nursery. But it had been the memory of trailing from interview to interview, in the span between Graham's death and securing a job, that had induced her to put up with almost anything.

Bob had been kind enough in his own way and she had found the running of the small office exerted no great pressure or stress; indeed in the last six months she had been becoming increasingly bored.

'It was a nice family firm to work for,' Kim said now as she realised Lucas Kane was waiting for a response.

'Kane Electrical is not a nice family firm,' came the dry reply as the eagle eyes flashed to meet hers again. 'Do you think you are capable of making the transition?'

It wasn't so much what he said but the way in which he said it, and again it caught Kim on the raw, calling forth a terse reply that was not like her, she thought confusedly even as she said, 'I wouldn't have wasted your time or mine in applying for the position if I didn't, Mr Kane.'

She saw the dark brows frown and his mouth tighten, but June chose that precise moment to knock and enter with the coffee, and Kim had never been so pleased to see anyone in her life. She knew she was flushed, she could feel her cheeks burning, and she acknowledged her tone had not been one which a prospective employee would dream of using to their future employer, but it was *him*, Lucas Kane, she told herself in silent agitation. She had never met such a patronising, arrogant, downright *supercilious* man in all her life.

'Do you own a car, Mrs Allen?'

'What?' She had just settled back in her seat after accepting her cup of coffee from June and was bringing the cup to her lips when the question, barked as it was, made the steaming hot coffee slurp over the side of the china cup into the saucer as Kim gave an involuntary start.

'A car?' he repeated very distinctly.

The tone was now one of exaggerated patience, and it brought the adrenalin pumping again as she took a deep breath and forced herself not to bite back, instead speaking calmly and coolly as she said, 'No, I do not own a car, Mr Kane.'

'But I see you have passed a driving test. Are you a

confident driver?' His eyes were like narrowed points of silver light. 'Or perhaps I should ask if you are a competent one?' he added silkily.

'I'm both confident and competent,' she answered smartly. 'Maggie has me on her insurance so I borrow her car when I need to.'

'Ah, the ever-helpful Maggie.'

She *definitely* didn't like his tone, and she had just opened her mouth to tell him so, and to point out what he could do with his wonderful job, when he said, 'If you were offered this post and accepted it a car would be provided for your use. A BMW or something similar. I don't want my secretary trailing about waiting for buses that arrive late, or being unable to get from A to B in the shortest possible time.'

She stared at him, uncertain of what to say. Was he telling her all this so that she would be aware of what she had missed when he turned her down? she asked herself wretchedly. She wouldn't put anything past Lucas Kane.

'And there would be a clothing allowance,' he continued smoothly, his gaze running over her for a second and reminding her that her off-the-peg suit—although smart and businesslike—was not in the same league as the couturier number June was wearing. 'There is the occasional function here in England which requires evening dress, but certainly on the trips abroad you will require an array of clothes.'

If she had been flushed before she knew she was like a beetroot now. He had put it fairly tactfully, she had to admit, but the end result was that he considered her an office version of Cinderella! But clothing for herself *had* been the last priority since Graham had died, in fact she couldn't remember buying anything new since then, apart from items of underwear. She just hadn't been able to afford it…

'Yes, I see.' She forced the words out through stiff lips

and then took a hefty sip of the hot coffee, letting it burn a fortifying path down into her stomach.

He didn't have a clue how the other half lived, she thought savagely, shading her eyes with her thick lashes so he wouldn't see the anger in her eyes. For the last two years she had lain awake nearly every night doing interminable sums in her head, even though she knew the end result would be fruitless.

Her marriage had been a nightmare but Graham's death—following a drinking binge when he had fallen through a shop plate-glass window—had unleashed a whole new set of horrors. Her husband had left debts—frightening, mind-boggling debts, as far as she was concerned—and, Graham being Graham, he hadn't been concerned about tying her into the terrifying tangle. She had been so *stupid* in the early days of their marriage; she'd trusted him, signed papers without enquiring too much about the whys and wherefores, and the payments she'd believed had been as regular as clockwork just hadn't happened.

Not only that but he had borrowed from friends, business colleagues, *anyone* who would lend him money to finance his failing one-man business and—more importantly, to Graham—his alcohol addiction.

She had known, once she had become pregnant with Melody, there was something terribly wrong. The handsome, charming, flashing-eyed Romeo from university days had changed into someone she didn't recognise, but she had put it down to work stress, the unplanned pregnancy—she had become pregnant following a stomach bug which had made the Pill ineffective—all manner of things but the real cause.

She had loved him, made excuses for him—fool, fool, *fool*. And all the while the debts had been mounting, debts she was now struggling to pay off, month after painful month, as well as providing for her daughter and herself.

Maggie had been great. The two thousand pounds Graham had borrowed from her had been written off as far as Maggie was concerned on the day of the funeral, but there were plenty of others who hadn't been so magnanimous.

She was constantly torn all ways. She wanted Melody to have nice clothes, good food and a happy environment, but although she had struggled to make the best of the tiny bedsit she had rented since the funeral it was hardly the best place in the world in which to bring up a young child. And the debts diminished so slowly. She couldn't believe how slowly.

'I take it you could start immediately, Mrs Allen, should you be offered the post?'

Kim had been so entrenched in the morass of the past that her eyes were almost bewildered when she raised them to meet Lucas Kane's.

'Yes, I... Yes.' Pull yourself together and act like the efficient secretary he's looking for, she told herself bitterly. You can't afford to be choosy about who you work for, even though you disliked this man on sight. Not that she had any chance of securing the post; he had made that very clear.

'And would you accept the position, should it be offered?' he asked softly.

She stared at him, her stomach muscles tightening as she acknowledged again that she felt he was playing with her. And she had had enough of that—manipulation, half-truths, deceit—to last her a lifetime.

'Oh, I'm sorry, I should have mentioned the salary before now.' His voice was very cool as he mentioned a figure that was three times as much as she had been getting at Curtis & Brackley.

Kim gaped at him. She knew her mouth was partly open,

that was the worst of it, but she was too stunned to do anything about it.

'I believe in paying the best for the best, Mrs Allen.' His mouth was twisted in a quizzical smile. 'But if you worked for me you would earn every penny; ask Miss West if you don't believe me. I demand absolute loyalty, unquestioning allegiance to Kane Electrical... You get my drift?'

His derisive expression was mocking but in this instant Kim found she didn't care. Her mind was turning cartwheels in working out what such a financial bonus would mean and, on top of a car, a dress allowance... But she hadn't been offered the job. She came back to earth with a wallop.

'I...I think with such a generous package you would be within your rights to expect complete commitment and dedication from your secretary, Mr Kane,' she managed at last. And how!

'You do? Good. A meeting point at last.' His voice was very deep and quiet and for a moment the portent of his words didn't register. And then, as the covert censure hit, Kim flushed hotly.

The silver gaze ran over her pink face, the golden-blonde of her upswept hair bringing the charcoal-brown of her eyes into greater contrast, and then Lucas Kane stood up abruptly, thrusting his hands into his pockets as he turned to look out of the huge window behind him.

'You haven't answered my question, Mrs Allen.' His voice was remote, distant.

'I haven't?' Her mind was whirling and for a second she couldn't grasp what he was getting at.

'I asked you if you would accept the position if it was offered,' he reminded her evenly, still without turning round.

She stared at the big figure in front of her, part of her mind conceding that he must be one of the tallest men she had ever met and certainly the most disturbing, and then she found herself saying, 'Yes, I would accept it, Mr Kane, if it was offered.'

He was quite still for another moment and then he turned, slowly, to glance at her still sitting primly on the chair in front of the desk.

She was one hell of a beautiful woman. The thought came from nowhere and he found it intensely irritating. Beautiful, but with an air of wary vulnerability one moment and steel-like hardness the next. Nothing about her seemed to add up and he was sure she was keeping plenty from him—as far as skeletons in the cupboard went he wouldn't be surprised if she had several rooms full of them.

From all she had said it sounded as though the kid was nothing more than an appendage to her life; women like her should never have children of their own. It was a sweeping statement and he recognised it as such, which further irritated him.

Damn it all, he knew nothing about her and her private life was no concern of his. As long as she did her job, that was all he was interested in. The thought caught him, tightening his mouth still more. Anyone would think he was offering her the job and he still had two of the other applicants to see yet, one of whom appeared to be a second June—if that were possible.

'So, thank you for attending this interview, Mrs Allen, and we'll be in touch within a day or two.'

It was a clear dismissal and Kim rose immediately to her feet, only to find she didn't quite know what to do with the coffee cup.

'May I...?' He moved round the desk and again she felt that little curling in her insides as the sheer breadth and height of him dwarfed her. At five foot ten she wasn't used to feeling so tiny and it was disconcerting to say the least.

'Thank you.' As he reached for the coffee cup she was

careful not to let her fingers touch his although she couldn't for the life of her have explained why. He was so close now she caught the faintest whiff of delicious and probably wildly expensive aftershave, and the effect of it on her sensitised nerves was enough to make her take a hasty step backwards, almost falling over the chair behind her as she did so.

Great. That was all she needed. Wouldn't he just love it if she fell flat on her face in front of him? It was enough to put iron in her backbone and a tight smile on her face as she gathered up her bag and coat, and said steadily, 'Goodbye, Mr Kane. I'll wait to hear from you.' And they both knew exactly what his decision would be, didn't they? she added with silent bitterness.

'Goodbye, Mrs Allen.' There was a bite to the words; he had obviously noticed her involuntary recoil and hadn't appreciated it, Kim thought wretchedly, humiliation adding more depth to the colour staining her cheeks.

The two or three steps to the interconnecting door seemed like miles, but then she was outside in June West's office and Kim was amazed how utterly normal everything seemed. She had just endured one of the most—no, probably *the* most—unnerving experiences of her life and June West was sitting typing away at her word processor as though nothing had happened. But then she dealt with Lucas Kane every day of her life. The thought was astounding and Kim found herself looking at the other woman with new respect as she made her goodbyes and escaped to the lift.

What had made her say she would take the post if it was offered? As the lift whisked her silently downwards, Kim stared at her reflection in the mirrored wall in horror. Well, she knew why—filthy lucre! She gave a weak grin and the dark-eyed girl staring at her grinned back.

Not that her agreement was any cause for concern—

Lucas Kane was as likely to offer her the job as a trip to the moon. She nodded to the thought, faintly comforted but still trembling slightly.

She didn't know how anyone could survive working for such a man; he was too cold, too ruthless and overtly powerful to be human.

But the money *was* good. She shut her eyes for a second, thinking of the speed in which the remainder of Graham's debts could be settled if she had a salary like the one Lucas Kane had mentioned coming in every month. She and Melody could think about moving out of the grotty little bedsit they were forced to call home, and with a car—a BMW, he had said, hadn't he?—travelling would be a pleasure.

The lift glided to a halt and her eyes snapped open. Enough daydreaming. She stepped into the foyer and walked determinedly towards the far doors without looking to left or right. It wasn't going to happen—furthermore, she didn't *want* it to happen, she told herself firmly.

She would soon get another job and eventually, one day, she would be clear of the burden which hung like a great millstone round her neck. And she had Melody. She thought of her daughter's sweet little face and felt a flood of love sweep through her, dispelling all the heartache. Yes, she had Melody, and compared to Lucas Kane with all his millions that made her the richest woman on earth.

CHAPTER TWO

'So, ALL in all an unmitigated disaster, then?' Maggie said with forced brightness. 'Never mind, pet; on to the next one, eh? I get the car back from the garage tomorrow, so if you want to borrow it you can. Friday's the next interview, isn't it?'

Kim nodded. She was standing drinking a hasty cup of coffee in Maggie's ultra-modern kitchen before she left to pick up Melody from the Octopus club her daughter attended after school. 'At the accountant's on the corner of the street where I live, actually,' she answered with matching brightness, 'so I shan't need the car. The accountant's would be much handier than Kane Electrical, travel-wise.'

'Absolutely.'

'And it's a small place—just three or four work there, I think—so it's bound to be friendlier than a big firm like Kane's.'

'Definitely.'

'Oh, Maggie.' Kim put down her flamboyant mug painted with enormous red cherries abruptly and stared into her friend's bright blue eyes. 'All that money, and a car and *everything*.'

'Don't forget Lucas Kane goes with the deal.' Maggie was trying to find something positive to say about the lost chance of the century.

'I could put up with him,' Kim answered miserably. 'If it meant being able to move out of the bedsit and get somewhere with a garden for Melody I could put up with just about *anything*.'

'I know.' Maggie put a sympathetic hand on Kim's arm

for a moment. 'But anyone has only got to see you two together for a minute to know that Melody has something all the money in the world can't buy. There's an awful lot of kids with gardens and a nursery full of toys who have rotten childhoods, lass, with parents who don't give a damn.'

Maggie's Northern accent was always at its strongest when she was in earnest about something, and now Kim smiled into the round homely face as she said, 'Thanks, Maggie. You're one in a million.'

'Just repeat that in Pete's ear, would you? *Loudly!*'

Pete was Maggie's boyfriend of five years' standing who was incredibly inventive in avoiding any mention of commitment and settling down, much to Maggie's increasing exasperation. He worked as a stockbroker—a successful one, by all accounts—and occupied the flat above Maggie's, which was how the two of them had first met.

'I thought you were going to have a chat with him over the weekend? Lay it on the line about how you feel?' Kim said quietly, forgetting her own troubles for a moment as she looked into Maggie's sky-blue gaze. Pete commuted into London every day and arrived back at the flat well after eight each night, so any serious talking was always left until the weekends.

'I was.' Maggie shrugged her meaty shoulders disconsolately. 'But he wasn't feeling well—a touch of flu, I think—and I was snowed under with work anyway, so it perhaps wasn't the right time.'

Maggie was an interior designer and her star was rising in the career sense if not in her lovelife.

'He doesn't know how lucky he is, that's the trouble,' Kim said stoutly, finishing the last of the coffee in one gulp and placing the mug on Maggie's gleaming worktop.

'I've been thinking the same thing myself,' Maggie agreed wryly. 'Working from home is great in all sorts of ways but he knows I'm always here, no matter what, just waiting for him to come back from the City. The way he carries on sometimes, you'd think he was a Viking returning from a far distant land—he's such a drama queen! In his opinion, he's the high-flyer taking chances, on the cutting edge and all that, and I'm good old dependable Maggie with nothing to do but get ready with his pipe and slippers.'

'The short, sharp shock treatment might wake him up, if you can think of something not too life-threatening,' Kim advised with a grin. 'I'm sure he does love you, Maggie.'

'Ah, but how much, lass—that's the sixty-four dollar question, isn't it? I'm getting on for thirty; I can't wait around for ever!'

'I must go; Melody will be out soon.' Kim gave Maggie a quick hug and made for the door. 'Ring me later if you fancy a chat.'

'Even if it's just to moan about Pete?'

'Course. What else are friends for?'

Kim found herself sprinting the last hundred yards or so along the cold streets to the school, although there was no need; she was in plenty of time. She had always made sure—no matter how hectic or difficult her day or how heavy her workload—that either she or Maggie was there before time to pick up Melody.

Melody's huge, thickly lashed brown eyes were searching for her the second her daughter walked out of the school doors, and as the small face lit up and a little red-mittened hand waved frantically Kim felt a lump in her throat at the unabashed love on the tiny face so like her own.

'Mummy! Mummy!' Melody fairly flew across the playground and into Kim's waiting arms. 'Guess what? I'm going to be Mary in the Nativity and have a white dress and tinsel in my hair. Mrs Jones picked me specially.'

'That's wonderful, darling.'

'She said she can trust me not to be silly,' Melody continued solemnly. 'Cory Chambers was *very* silly today; she stuck a crayon up her nose and Mrs Jones couldn't get it down and Cory was crying her head off. Mrs Jones had to get her mummy.'

The chatter continued during the ten-minute walk to their bedsit, situated in a terraced street which was grim by any standards. A young married couple and several students occupied the other four bedsits the narrow, three-storey house contained, with a shared bathroom for all occupants on the top floor next to Kim's room.

The fact that the bathroom was right next door for Melody and that their elevated position cut out the possibility of noisy neighbours overhead were two small advantages in their somewhat miserable surroundings, but Kim fought a constant war against mould and damp, ancient plumping and poor lighting. It wasn't so bad in the summer, but the two winters they had spent at the house had been abysmal.

Kim had made their home as bright and attractive as she could with the minimum of expenditure, making bright red curtains and a matching duvet cover and cushions for the bed-settee she shared with Melody, and scattering several rugs over the threadbare carpet, but nothing could hide the general run-down ambience of the old building.

Once home, and with Melody settled in front of the fire with a glass of milk and a biscuit, happily watching her favourite TV programme, Kim set about preparing the evening meal. But in spite of all her efforts to the contrary she found she was constantly replaying every minute of the interview earlier that day over and over in her mind.

It had been a travesty. Her eyes narrowed and she sliced a hapless carrot with uncharacteristic savageness. From the second her eyes had met those of Lucas Kane in the reception area she hadn't stood a chance. The moment she had seen who was seated behind that desk she should have turned right round and marched out with her head held high. Instead… She gritted her teeth and another carrot met the same fate as the first.

Instead she had sat there and answered his barbed questions as though she wanted his precious job, and let him walk all over her in the process.

No—no, she hadn't, she argued in the next instant. He hadn't had it all his own way, and besides, she *did* want the job. She wanted it so much she ached with it—or, rather, she wanted what the position as secretary to the chairman and managing director of Kane Electrical would do for Melody, for them both.

But it wasn't going to happen. She added two pieces of chicken breast to the vegetables and popped the casserole in the dilapidated oven the bedsit boasted. And in spite of the huge financial rewards it was probably just as well. She couldn't even begin to imagine herself working for Lucas Kane.

At eight that evening, when the telephone rang in the hall downstairs and Juliana—one of the students—banged on Kim's door to say a Mr Lucas of Kane Electrical was asking for her, Kim found herself having to do just that very thing.

'This is Mrs Allen.' She didn't like the fact that her voice was so breathless but hoped he would put it down to the fact that she lived on the top floor—something Juliana had apparently pointed out to him, according to the raven-haired Italian girl.

'Lucas Kane, Mrs Allen.' The deep husky tones were just as compelling over the telephone and she could just picture him, eyes like silver ice and mouth a hard line in the darkly attractive face, sitting at that massive desk in what must now be a deserted office block. Not that he had to be there, of course, she amended silently. He could be calling her from home, wherever that was. 'I hope I'm not interrupting anything—you don't have guests?'

Guests? Once she and Melody were ensconced in the limited space within the bedsit, there was barely room to swing a cat, Kim thought drily. 'No, Mr Kane, I don't have guests.' Her voice was better this time; less of the Marilyn Monroe and more of a Katharine Hepburn briskness to it.

'Good.' It was cold and crisp, very much like the man himself. 'I'm ringing you to offer you the job, Mrs Allen,' he said, without any preamble. 'If you haven't changed your mind, of course.'

'I... You—' Pull yourself together, woman, she told herself silently. He's obviously looking for a secretary who can string two words together! 'That's wonderful, Mr Kane,' she managed faintly.

'Then you accept?'

'Yes—yes, I do, and thank you. Thank you very much indeed.' She forced herself to stop babbling, realising she had gone from one extreme to the other, and took a long breath before she said more slowly, 'When would you like me to start, Mr Kane?'

'Well, that was one of the points in your favour, Mrs Allen, the fact that you can begin immediately,' he said coolly. 'June is understandably anxious to join her fiancé as soon as she can and oversee the arrangements, the wedding being in the spring, but even allowing for the possibility you are an exceptionally quick learner—' did she detect a note of covert sarcasm there, Kim wondered, or was she getting paranoid about this man? '—it will take several weeks to pick up all the strings.'

'You want me to start tomorrow?' she asked with a calm she was far from feeling.

'I was going to suggest Monday, to give you time to make any provision for your daughter which might be necessary, but if you are able to come into the office tomorrow that would be excellent. June normally arrives about nine-ish, so any time after that would be fine.'

There was no trace of emotion or feeling in his voice and the lack of humanity was disconcerting, to say the least. As his personal assistant-cum-secretary, she was going to be working very closely with this intimidating machine—could she handle it? Kim asked herself frantically, before answering in the same instant, Don't be silly, of course you can handle it. You can't miss the chance of a lifetime through sheer cowardice.

'I'll be there, Mr Kane,' Kim said steadily.

'Good. I'll get Personnel to draw up a contract and arrange for a car to be delivered some time tomorrow so you can have it to drive home. Any particular colour you'd like?'

She almost said, Colour? before she bit the word back, but her hands were beginning to shake and her stomach was swirling with a mixture of amazement and delight at how suddenly her circumstances were changing and bone-chilling shock at her temerity. 'I don't know,' she said dazedly. 'This is all rather sudden.'

'Has your daughter got a favourite colour?' The deep, dark voice was as expressionless as ever, but the content of the question totally threw Kim in view of the robot asking it.

'Blue,' she faltered weakly.

'Just as well it's not shocking pink—BMW might have objected,' came the dry response. 'Blue it is, then, and I'll see a child's seat is fitted, of course. Goodnight, Mrs Allen.'

'Goodnight, and thank you for letting me know so promptly,' she said quickly, her head spinning.

'A pleasure.' It was soft and smooth, and although Kim told herself his reply was just a formal nicety, something in the silky tones sent a trickle of awareness down her spine.

He would be one sexy customer in bed. The thought—coming from nowhere as it did—horrified Kim so much it was just as well the phone had gone dead at the other end because she was quite unable to speak or move for a good thirty seconds.

Was she mad? she asked herself as she replaced the receiver with elaborate carefulness and then put both hands to her burning cheeks. Lucas Kane was her new boss and that last thought had been inappropriate to say the least. And machines weren't sexy. Powerful maybe, frightening sometimes, and certainly cold and efficient, but definitely not sexy.

She stood for a moment more and then, as her agitation subsided slightly and the full knowledge of what the new job package would mean swept over her, she took the stairs two at a time, bursting into the bedsit and doing something unheard of—waking Melody from a deep sleep and dancing round the room with her daughter's tiny body held tight in her arms.

The next morning was one of frosty brilliance, and when Kim awoke to a crystal-bright world and gazed out over the white sparkling rooftops as she fixed a hot drink for herself and Melody her heart was singing.

This was a new shiny beginning; even the weather confirmed it. She would start looking for a new place to live—a small ground-floor flat with a garden, maybe, or even a little house—this very weekend. She was going to be earning a small fortune; she could soon pay off the remaining debts, as long as she was careful, and then her life would be her own again. No more robbing Peter to pay Paul, no more working out how to make a pound stretch into two or three—oh, life was *wonderful*.

Once she had got Melody off to sleep again the night before she had phoned Maggie with the good news. Maggie had immediately offered to pop round early the next morning and take Melody to school, so Kim could arrive at Kane Electrical in plenty of time—the buses being unreliable at the best of times—and Kim had gratefully accepted her friend's kind offer.

So it was that Kim arrived outside the huge building just as June West drew into the 'Reserved for the secretary of the managing director' spot, and the two women walked into Reception together.

'Nervous?'

June was smiling sympathetically as she spoke and her voice was warm, and Kim smiled back weakly as she answered, 'A little. Well, a lot, really. My previous job wasn't anything like as high-powered as this one.'

'Don't worry, you'll be fine.' June was watching her closely and now, as the two women entered the lift and the doors glided shut, she added in a low tone, 'I shouldn't really be telling you this but there were dozens after the position, you know. Some were better-qualified than you, some were more experienced, but Lucas chose you and that means, as far as he's concerned, you are the best for the job.'

Kim knew June had meant her words to be uplifting but they had the opposite effect. All she could manage, as the lift doors opened to disgorge them into the exalted upper sanctum, was, 'You call him Lucas? Not to his face, surely?' She hadn't got Lucas Kane down as being on first-name terms with his secretary somehow.

'Sure.' June grinned at her conspiratorially. 'You'll find him quite different to the public image, once you get to know him, and he hates to stand on ceremony in private. Of course, in front of other colleagues and business clients, it's Mr Kane and Miss West, or in your case Mrs Allen.'

'Right.' Oh, help!

'He's a good boss to work for, Kim, take it from me,'

June continued easily as they walked along the corridor. 'I wouldn't have stayed ten years otherwise.'

'How...how old is he?' Kim asked nervously.

'Thirty-seven. He took over the business when he was only twenty-five. His father, who founded the firm, got sick—cancer, I think, leukaemia or something to do with the blood, anyway—and had to have months and months of treatment. Lucas stepped in; he'd been with the firm for four years, since leaving university, but when he took charge he did so well, apparently, that his father decided to retire and let him take over permanently, and since then the business has gone from strength to strength. It was only a tenth of its present size when I started.'

June opened the door into her office, lowering her voice as she glanced towards the interconnecting door, and added, 'He's got a reputation for having the Midas touch, and admittedly he does have brilliant business acumen, but his competitors don't see the endless hours he puts into the business while they're off swanning round a golf course or having holidays in the Caribbean. He deserves every little bit of success he's had. I don't know anyone who works so hard.'

'I appreciate the accolade, June, but just in case the tenor changes I think I'd better point out the cleaners seem to have knocked the switch on the intercom again.'

The voice was dry, very dry, but as June glanced at her Kim saw the older woman's face was quite unabashed and her expression was reflected in her voice when June said, 'Whoops, that was a near thing, Lucas. Another minute and your ears might have begun to burn.'

'My ears are incapable of burning, June, as you very well know.' It was even drier. 'Do I take it Mrs Allen is with you?'

'Yes, she's here,' June confirmed quickly.

'Then I would like a word with her, before you start

addling her brain with a hundred and one facts,' the dark voice said evenly. 'And a cup of black coffee, when you're ready.'

'Coming right up.' June flicked the switch on the intercom and smiled breezily at Kim as she indicated for her to go through into Lucas Kane's office, and Kim found herself thinking—as she had done at the interview the afternoon before—that she would never, ever—not in a million years—*ever* be able to mirror the relaxed approach June apparently had in dealing with her formidable boss.

She quickly slipped out of her coat, smoothed down her already sleek and shining hair, caught in a neat and somewhat severe pleat at the back of her head, and took a deep breath as she walked across the room and opened the door into Lucas Kane's office.

'Good morning.' The devastating silver-grey eyes were waiting for her and in spite of all her preparation for this moment Kim's heart bounded in her chest. 'You haven't changed your mind, then?'

'Changed my mind?' She stared at the big figure seated behind the desk in surprise. 'Of course not, Mr Kane. I told you I would be here this morning.'

'And you always do what you promise?' he asked smoothly, his pearly gaze narrowing on her flushed face.

'Yes, I do.'

There was a slight bristle in the words which Lucas registered with hidden amusement, but his voice betrayed nothing of what he was feeling when he said, 'Good. We'll get along just fine in that case, Mrs Allen.'

He rose from behind the massive desk as he spoke and Kim forced herself to show no reaction at all when he perched himself easily on the side of it, the hard lean body giving the impression of a coiled spring just waiting to pounce.

'The car, a blue BMW, will be delivered before four o'clock.' His tone was steady now, almost bored. 'That will

give ample time for you to be able to familiarise yourself
with the controls and ask any questions you feel relevant.'

'Thank you.' She didn't know what else to say.

'I trust your daughter will be satisfied with the colour
when she sees it.'

Kim glanced sharply at him then but the sardonic attractive face was expressionless, as was his voice when he
continued, 'Over the next few weeks you will learn how
this office works and what makes me tick, Mrs Allen.'

Her wide open eyes blinked once but she didn't make
the mistake of rushing into speech and the carved lips
twitched a little. 'Let me save a little time and lay down
some ground rules which I'm sure will benefit us both?'

It was in the form of a rhetorical question but Kim nodded nevertheless, it seemed to be expected somehow.

'As I mentioned yesterday, I expect—*demand*—absolute
loyalty from those close to me; anything less is unacceptable. As my secretary and personal assistant, you will be
privy to all manner of confidential information, both with
regard to business and my private life. I expect you to be
unconditionally discreet in both areas.'

He had nodded at her to sit down when he had settled
himself on the edge of the desk and Kim was thankful of
it now; she felt utterly overwhelmed by the sheer magnetism of the man who was now her boss. Her *boss*. Her
stomach turned right over and she swallowed hard. 'Of
course, Mr Kane.'

'Lucas.' He leant back slightly, the blue-black of his hair
accentuated by the white sunlight behind him. 'If you are
serious about working with me, the second thing you have
to learn is that all formality stops at that door.' He nodded
to the interconnecting door behind her. 'You are my eyes
and ears in this organisation and beyond, a valuable second
opinion and ally who must be completely frank within the
confines of these four walls.'

'And if my opinion doesn't fit in with yours?' she asked with a careful neutrality that hid her jangling nerves.

He said nothing for a second, just looking at her with piercing eyes, and then he smiled. The first real smile she had seen. 'I'm not looking for you to agree with me, necessarily,' he said quietly, 'but if you do disagree I expect your comments to be logical and well informed. I have enough sycophantic boot-lickers around already; I don't need another one, Kim.'

It was the first time he had said her Christian name and, ridiculous though she told herself it was, it did something strange to her insides. Something she didn't care to examine. *He was too close.* The thought came from nowhere and she told herself sharply she was acting like a skittish schoolgirl, not a mature woman of twenty-six.

To combat the weakness she forced herself to smile back, her tone light as she said, 'Dare I ask if I can remind you of that in the future?'

The smile grew, turning the aggressively male face of hard angles and planes into a more mellow whole, and Kim watched, fascinated.

'I have the feeling you will do so with or without my blessing,' he said lazily, before levering himself off the desk in one easy movement and seating himself in the massive leather chair again. 'Observe much, say little and keep your wits about you during the next few weeks, Kim, and you'll do just fine. It's nice to have you aboard.'

'Thank you.' It was a clear dismissal and Kim rose a trifle flusteredly, hoping her tension didn't show. He was the most disturbing man she had ever met, but she had to find a way of coping with how she felt—and fast. This job was too fantastic an opportunity to blow.

It was that thought which enabled her to leave Lucas's office with measured steps, her blonde head high and her face deadpan.

It would be all right, she assured herself, standing aside

to let June pass into the Holy of Holies with the coffee. She had June to soften her absorption into the role of secretary to Lucas Kane and the other woman would be around for some weeks yet. After that...

Her heart began to thud and she clucked her tongue at herself, annoyed at her nervousness. After that she would be just what he wanted her to be—an efficient, cool, capable machine who ran his office like clockwork. *She could do this.* If nothing else, her time with Graham, not to mention the searing aftermath, had shown her she had hidden resources she had never dreamt of.

When she thought of that nightmare funeral, which had occurred the day after she had found out she was not only destitute but thousands and thousands of pounds in debt, she knew nothing could ever be as bad again.

But she had come through that, and not crawling on her belly, either—she'd carved out a reasonable life for herself and Melody and it was going to get better and better from this point on. She was in charge of her own destiny—hers and Melody's—and the vow she had made standing in the pouring rain at the side of the newly dug grave still held good. Never again would she put her trust in any one man; she had learnt a hard lesson but she'd learnt it well. Men said one thing with their lips but their mind was thinking something else. They could be sweetness and light in company—with everyone else—but in the privacy of their own home turn into the devil incarnate.

She was autonomous now—blessedly, gloriously autonomous—and nothing, *nothing*, would ever persuade her to be anything else. And this job would ensure her material security in a way she had never imagined; it was her chance of a lifetime.

Secretary to Lucas Kane? Kim glanced at the closed door, beyond which she could hear the low murmur of voices. She was going to be the best secretary he'd ever had or die in the attempt!

CHAPTER THREE

OVER the next few weeks Kim worked as she had never worked before. She made copious notes of everything June told her, taking reams of paper home each night and sitting up until well past midnight, memorising anything and everything which was relevant. She acquainted herself with every file, every company, every individual who played a role in Lucas Kane's business life until she had more facts and figures in her head than June did.

One of Melody's schoolfriends lived directly opposite her daughter's school and Kim came to an arrangement with the child's mother that in return for the payment of a small fee she could drop Melody off at just gone eight every day, enabling the blue BMW to purr into Kane Electrical's car park every morning before half-past eight.

Kim had imagined, the first day, that it would be just her and possibly the caretaker in the building, but Lucas's sleek, champagne-coloured Aston Martin was already in residence when she had pulled up and it continued to be so every morning.

He had come to the door of his office on her early arrival and gazed quizzically at her for a moment or two, but beyond a request for one of the endless cups of coffee he consumed all day had made no comment.

Christmas had come and gone, and Kim had gulped slightly at the size of her very generous Christmas box from Lucas in the form of a cheque, and in the second week in January she and Melody had moved into the small but charming two-bedroomed cottage she had found not far from her daughter's school.

And then the Monday of the third week was upon her, the first day June wouldn't be there to cushion her from any minor panics, the other woman having left for Scotland the previous weekend. And Kim found she was as nervous as a child on its first day at school.

She'd gone to extra trouble with her appearance, the clothing allowance having enabled her to buy a new wardrobe consisting of several stylish, neatly tailored suits, blouses and accessories which perfectly projected the image Lucas Kane's secretary needed to give, and Kim knew the dove-grey suit and salmon silk blouse complemented her English peaches and cream colouring.

Nevertheless, her soft brown eyes were wide and faintly anxious as she checked the coiled braid on the back of her head, her thick straight fringe just brushing the tops of her fine eyebrows.

'Nothing has changed in the last forty-eight hours,' she told the efficient-looking reflection softly. 'You've been working for him for the last week or so with June doing little more than observing; you can handle anything now.'

Kim had to remind herself of that last comforting assurance in the next minute or two.

Over the last weeks she had slipped into the pattern of serving Lucas coffee as soon as she arrived in the office, but when, after the normal customary polite knock, Kim opened the door, it wasn't the usual immaculately attired and perfectly groomed tycoon she had grown accustomed to who looked up from his desk.

Lucas had obviously been asleep until she had woken him, and now, as he straightened and peered at her from bleary eyes, Kim's heartbeat went haywire.

It wasn't the fact that he hadn't shaved or brushed his hair, or that his dishevelled appearance bore evidence to the fact that he had slept in his clothes that had her insides turning cartwheels.

At some time during the last hours he had discarded his suit jacket along with his tie, and now his open shirt revealed a deep V of tanned flesh sprinkled with dark curling body hair and a muscled—devastatingly muscled—male chest of Olympic athlete proportions.

He worked out. He very clearly worked out. Kim was glued to the spot, the tray with the coffee and plate of biscuits wobbling dangerously in her hand. And he was... Well, he was something else, she admitted with silent shock. Clothed, he was pretty intimidating and all male, but partly clothed... No wonder June had told her that the fast car went with equally fast, glamorous women and a love 'em and leave 'em personal life where work—always—came first.

'Not that it seems to put them off,' June had murmured confidentially. 'Of course, the circle he moves in are all of the same mind, I guess, so that helps. Lucas has never been one for the dumb blonde type female; he goes for brains as well as beauty. The last one was a lawyer, the one before that a mogul with her own business—they all seem to find him irresistible.'

She hadn't made any comment at the time although she had silently told herself that irresistible was definitely *not* a word that came to mind when she thought of Lucas Kane, but now, if nothing else, she could appreciate what drew and held such women.

Taken off his guard like this, and with his office mode in abeyance for once, she was seeing the raw animal magnetism she had sensed once or twice—well, a lot more than once or twice, she admitted ruefully—in all its deadly power.

'Hell, what's the time?' The silver eyes were clearing even as he spoke and granite was replacing the faint smoky hue that had been so stunningly sexy.

'Eight-thirty.' It was succinct but all she could manage until her hormones sorted themselves out.

'Is that coffee? You're an angel.' He leant back in the chair and stretched magnificent muscles before raking back his hair, none of which did Kim's equilibrium any favours. 'I've been here most of the weekend; the Clarkson deal blew up in our face and needed some quality time.'

'Right.' Kim nodded in what she hoped was an informed, efficient sort of way and wondered if he was aware he was half naked. If he was it clearly didn't bother him.

She placed the coffee and biscuits on the desk in front of him and prayed her face wasn't as flushed as she feared it was.

'But I've got it nailed.' He reached for one of the biscuits and ate it in a hungry bite before reaching for another.

'When did you eat last?' she asked carefully.

'Eat?' The crystal-bright eyes that could be so piercingly intent were vague. 'I don't remember. Saturday, I think.'

'Fancy some bacon sandwiches?'

'Bacon sandwiches?' He stared at her interestedly. 'Don't tell me you can provide those at a moment's notice, Kim?'

'Almost.' She was fighting sexual arousal and it made her voice stiff. 'There's a little man on the corner who comes every morning in his mobile and does a roaring trade, apparently. Bacon sandwiches are his speciality.'

'Then I'd like six rounds from your little man,' Lucas said promptly, 'with lashings of brown sauce.'

She inclined her head, as she imagined the estimable June would have done in the same circumstances, and forced herself to turn and walk towards the door. 'I'll be ten minutes or so,' she said evenly over her shoulder and she didn't look back.

She was fifteen minutes, and when she knocked for the second time that morning on Lucas's door and walked into his office, her boss had transformed himself—courtesy of the small bathroom and dressing room, which were part of his executive suite—into his usual cool and impeccable self. But in spite of the fresh charcoal suit and pale blue shirt with matching tie, all Kim could see was a mental picture of acres and acres of finely honed muscled flesh and it was disconcerting, to say the least.

It didn't help that his hair was still slightly damp from the shower and his freshly shaved face more relaxed than usual, either, and the hot prickle of overt sexual awareness that had hit her so forcefully earlier didn't seem to want to die the death she was willing on it.

'Six rounds of doorsteps with what looks like a pound of bacon in them,' she said as expressionlessly as she could. 'Eat them while they're hot.' She handed him the plate as she spoke.

'You sound like my mother.'

His *mother*? She narrowed her eyes and smiled sweetly. 'Don't tell me you are one of those men who have a mother fixation,' she said coolly before she thought too much about it and didn't dare voice the tart retort which had sprung to mind.

'I don't think so.' He was eyeing her with what could only be termed a glint, but a glint of what Kim wasn't sure. 'My mother is a wonderful woman and ideally suited to my father, but…no, I don't think so.' He took a bite of one of the sandwiches and closed his eyes in ecstasy.

'How come I haven't had bacon sandwiches from your little man before?' he asked almost petulantly.

'Because you didn't ask?' she suggested daringly.

The silver eyes fastened on her, pinning her to the spot, and Lucas smiled slowly. 'I only have to ask?' he drawled lazily.

She might have known she had no chance of winning in a war of words with him! Kim was disturbingly aware that something had shifted in the last few minutes, something that had been bubbling away under the surface from the first moment she had laid eyes on Lucas Kane—something that couldn't, mustn't, have expression. 'I'll get you another cup of coffee.' She had turned and swept out of the room before he had time to take another bite.

Lucas smiled faintly to himself. There was more, much more, to his efficient, beautiful new secretary than met the eye; he had known that from the beginning. And was that why he had been tempted to choose Kim above other more qualified, experienced candidates?

The thought didn't sit well with him and the smile turned into a frown. He had chosen Kim Allen because she was the most suitable applicant—qualifications and experience weren't necessarily the be-all and end-all of a working relationship, he told himself sharply. There had to be a spark, a cutting edge, a quality that was undefinable but which told you any association would be healthy and productive without becoming dull or boring. He had never wanted a mindless android who wouldn't say boo to a goose. That was why he had chosen Kim. And her qualifications were pretty good too, as was her experience.

June had had it—they had enjoyed some very real altercations in their time, he assured himself firmly, ignoring the little voice of honesty which suggested he was comparing chalk to cheese.

He was suddenly uncomfortable with his thoughts and, reaching for another sandwich, having finished the first, he turned his mind to the Clarkson file sitting in front of him, dismissing all further thoughts of Kim with the single-minded ruthlessness that had made Kane Electrical so successful in the last decade.

It took Kim a good deal longer to get her unregenerate thoughts under lock and key, but once she had succeeded she determined they wouldn't escape again. Lucas Kane could prance around naked if he so desired and she wouldn't turn a hair, she told herself on the drive home that evening.

She had to admit he had a certain something, a darkly seductive something—in fact it was a relief to acknowledge it and bring it out into the open, she assured herself firmly. He *was* a compellingly attractive man—most powerful, wealthy men had an aura that set them apart from the crowd—but it didn't make them easy to live with or likeable.

And she didn't have to like him; as long as she could respect his business acumen and flair and enjoy her work, that was all she wanted. His lifestyle and the way he conducted his personal relationships was absolutely no concern of hers; the fact that he embodied everything she most disliked in a man in that area didn't mean she couldn't work with him. He saw her as part of the office machinery, not a woman, and that made all the difference.

She was well satisfied with her reasoning by the time she drew up outside the school gates and parked the car, walking down the concrete drive and standing to one side of the big wooden doors as the first desultory snowflakes began to fall out of a laden sky.

By the time Melody emerged with one or two other children—the teacher standing just behind them and checking each child had its respective escort—the snow was coming down in thick fat white flakes that sent the children into transports of delight.

'Mummy, it's *really* snowing!' Melody danced up to her, her small face alight. 'Can we build a snowman in the garden?'

'Maybe tomorrow, if it snows enough,' Kim agreed warmly. The cottage had a delightful garden with a large lawn surrounded by mature trees and shrubs, and Melody had already commandeered a small corner of it, announcing she was going to plant her own herb garden in the spring.

She would, too, Kim thought fondly as they walked to the car. Anything she set her mind to, Melody did; her small daughter was bubbling over with confidence and vitality and thankfully had no memory of the last terrible months Graham had put them through before he had died.

She refused to dwell on thoughts of her late husband, concentrating on Melody and asking her small daughter about her day, but once Melody was in bed and the cottage was quiet she found the memories flooding in in spite of all her efforts to shut them out.

She had thought she loved Graham—she had been *sure* she loved him—but the old adage that said you never knew someone until you lived with them had certainly been true in her husband's case, she reflected bitterly.

The handsome, bright, only son of aged doting parents, Graham had been spoilt outrageously from the cradle. In spite of their fairly limited means, Graham's parents had endeavoured to give their charismatic offspring everything he wanted, even financing the one-man business he had set up after finishing university, although it had taken every last penny they had.

She hadn't been aware of that at the time; she hadn't been aware of many things which had come to light after Graham's death.

She hadn't known he had a drink problem at university—everyone drank, it was part of the culture, and Graham had been adept at hiding his addiction from her. And by the time it became apparent he was an alcoholic she had been pregnant with Melody and desperate to make her marriage work for the sake of their unborn baby.

Graham's business had failed almost immediately—it couldn't have done anything else with the lack of time and effort he had put into it—and with his parents unable to bail him out he had started borrowing from all and sundry, using his compelling charm and attractiveness to get him what he needed. He had always had the ability to be irresistible when he had put his mind to it.

Kim glanced up suddenly from the task of darning the hole in the pocket of Melody's school coat.

Irresistible. The word had suddenly switched on a light in her mind and now she understood why she was thinking of Graham after months of being able to shut him out. 'They all seem to find him irresistible.' Those were the very words June had used about Lucas.

Kim's soft mouth straightened into a hard line and her dark brown eyes narrowed unseeingly across the cosy sitting room. 'They' all might find Lucas Kane irresistible, but this was one female who had received very powerful antibodies against such a disease, she told herself savagely, acknowledging in the same instant that the little episode in Lucas's office that morning had bothered her more than she had admitted.

He was the first man who had even remotely stirred her sexual awareness since Graham had died, but now she had recognised the fact and the danger it represented she would be on her guard against herself twenty-four hours a day. It wasn't that she thought he would be interested in her in a personal way—she almost laughed out loud at the thought of the ruthless and focused Lucas Kane harbouring romantic inclinations towards his secretary—but she didn't want to be attracted to any man, ever again, and certainly not one cast in Graham's mould.

She had never told anyone about those last awful twelve months with Graham, the humiliations she had suffered at his hands, and she never would. She didn't have to. She was answerable to no one and that was the way she liked it. Melody was the only important thing in her life and, thanks to this new job—she couldn't bring herself to say thanks to Lucas Kane—she was going to be able to give her daughter the kind of lifestyle she hadn't imagined was remotely in her grasp just a few months ago. And nothing—*nothing*—must interfere with that.

She nodded sharply to herself, her eyes focusing once more on the small red coat in her hands, and as she set to again with renewed vigour her lips were still drawn uncharacteristically tight.

The next morning there were several inches of snow and the world had been transformed into a winter wonderland, much to Melody's delight, but the BMW regally ignored such trifles as snow-packed roads and icy conditions.

Once Kim had dropped Melody off and was on her way to work she found herself thinking, as she had done more than once in the last few weeks, how fortunate she was to have such a powerful and comfortable car at her disposal. No more struggling along glassy pavements with wet feet or sitting in a cold bus which had arrived late and was filled with the musty smell of damp humanity.

As usual Lucas was already in his office when she arrived. She had the feeling that if she went into work at five in the morning she would still find him there.

She assumed the routine the hiccup yesterday had interrupted, taking his coffee into him once she had divested herself of her coat and quickly smoothed her hair in her small cloakroom.

'Good morning, Kim.' He didn't raise his head from the report he was studying as he spoke and his voice was polite and cool.

Kim answered in the same vein, placing the tray on the desk and forcing herself to walk smoothly out of the office without allowing her glance to linger on the dark bent head and harshly carved lines of his face, but, annoyingly, she found her heart was beating a tattoo as she sat down in front of her word processor and the hand that raised her coffee to her lips was shaking slightly.

She was glad they had reverted to the businesslike working relationship of the previous weeks, of course she was, she told herself silently. So why did she feel his cool remoteness was almost like a slap across the face? *Ridiculous.*She nodded irritably to the thought. She was being absolutely ridiculous—it must be the time of the month or something.

She grimaced to herself, drank the coffee in several burningly hot gulps and got down to work.

At five past ten Kim put through a call from the managing director of Clarkson International, and at ten past Lucas put his head round the door. 'One of those tapes on your desk is a breakdown of the Clarkson contract so far. Concentrate on that first, would you, Kim? I need it for twelve. And we're lunching with them today at one, by the way, so book a table for four at Fontella's.'

Kim stared at him, her mind racing. 'Do you mean you want me to accompany you?' she asked politely, her face and voice hiding all signs of agitation.

'Yes, and you'll need to bring your notebook and pencil, and get a financial report from Accounts. We might need that.' He was totally in work mode, his distant voice indicating he was thinking about several things at once. She had noticed that about him before; it was one of the many accomplishments he had that added to the notion he wasn't quite human.

'Right.' She nodded efficiently and then, once the door had closed again, sat staring vacantly across the room. A business lunch with clients, that was all it was. She could handle this. This sort of thing was going to happen time and time again so she might as well get used to it.

The breakdown was on Lucas's desk at half-past eleven and Kim was waiting—outwardly serene and inwardly disturbed and uptight—at twelve-thirty when he buzzed her to say they were leaving. Her stomach muscles had tightened as the deep dark voice came over the intercom, but when he emerged from his office a few moments later she was all cucumber-cool efficiency.

'We're meeting them at Fontella's so I'd like to get there a few minutes early.' He took her arm as he spoke, ushering her out of the door with his usual fast, capable way of doing things. She caught a whiff of the expensive aftershave he wore, the feel of his height and breadth all around her as they entered the lift at the end of the corridor, and it was then she carefully moved away and put a little space between them.

'What's the matter?'

'I'm sorry?' She stared at him as he leant against the carpeted panelling and looked at her quizzically, but she couldn't stop her cheeks flushing with colour. She had thought her cautious withdrawal had been sufficiently diplomatic and discreet to be unnoticed, but she might have know that razor-sharp brain would have detected it.

'You didn't like me touching you,' he stated evenly, his narrowed eyes like twin points of silver light. 'Why? Is it me or are you the same with all men?'

Any other man, *any other man*, might have registered her unease but wouldn't have confronted her on it. The thought hit Kim at the same time as the hostility at his astute assessment of her, and her voice was icy when she said, in direct answer to the challenge, 'I don't like physical contact, as it happens.'

'I'll forgo the joke about your daughter being born through immaculate conception,' he drawled drily, 'and repeat my question. Do you have a problem with me, Kim? If so, it needs to be brought out into the open and dealt with. I'm not in the habit of jumping on unsuspecting females; neither do I believe in mixing work and pleasure. Is that plain enough for you?'

This was awful, horrific. Kim had never felt so embarrassed in her life. She stared at him and then as the lift glided gently to a halt she saw the gleam in his eyes. It could have been anger, it could have been irritation or a whole host of things, but to her utter humiliation she rather suspected it was dark amusement. And if nothing else it restored her fighting spirit in a way nothing else could have done.

'I really don't know what you are talking about,' she said with painful self-dignity. 'I merely stated that I don't like physical contact, that's all.'

'I don't consider taking your arm physical contact in any real meaning of the words.' It was cool, firm and completely without emotion. 'So you had better get used to it, okay? I'm not about to watch every movement I make in case I offend you, Kim, so get your head round that and save us both a lot of trouble.'

Her mouth had widened slightly in a little O of surprise and when the lift doors opened in the next instant and his cool hand cupped her elbow she offered no resistance at all. They were through Reception and out into the front car park within seconds, and he guided her over to the gleaming Aston Martin without speaking, opening the passenger door for her with a courtesy she suspected was entirely natural.

Kim sank into the luxurious confines of the powerful car and watched him helplessly as he walked round the sleek low bonnet. She hated him. She really hated him, she told herself bitterly. He was the most unfeeling, callous, hard brute of a man she had ever met—and that included Graham. No amount of money was worth this.

'Kim?'

She had continued staring straight ahead, her cheeks

burning, after he had slid into the car, and when after a long moment or two he spoke, very softly, her head jerked in surprise to meet the silver-grey of his eyes.

'I handled that very badly. I'm sorry,' Lucas said quietly.

If the ground had suddenly opened beneath them and engulfed the car she couldn't have been more surprised.

'You hit me on the raw,' he admitted softly. 'I didn't like being put in the position of feeling like some sexual pervert. I've never had that happen to me before.'

'Lucas, I...' She had gone all hot inside and had never felt more out of her depth. It wasn't just his apology, surprising though it was, but the disturbing fact that he was closer than he had ever been and his overall maleness was swamping her to a point where she felt breathless.

He was so big and dark and *masculine* and in this present mood, with his deep voice slightly husky and smoky and his amazing eyes intent on her face, the magnetism that was an intrinsic part of his dangerous attractiveness was heightened tenfold.

'Was it your marriage?' he asked, with a gentleness she would have sworn he was incapable of.

Oh, hell, what did she say now? She said the only thing she could in view of the fact that he had abased himself so utterly. 'Yes.' It was tight and stiff. 'It was my marriage.'

'I'm sorry.'

He really sounded as though he was, but, having turned to look through the windscreen once more, Kim didn't dare meet those devastating arctic eyes again. 'It's all right.' It was inane but all she could manage. 'Shouldn't we go now?'

'Did he hurt you? Physically, I mean?' There was a strange note in Lucas's voice and Kim wasn't to know her ruthless, cold, unemotional boss was in the grip of feelings new to him.

The silence stretched and lengthened until it was so taut

Kim felt she would either scream or faint. She did neither, merely saying, in a small, chilled little voice, 'I don't want to be rude but I can't discuss it, Lucas.'

She didn't expect him to let it go without a fight but he surprised her for the second time in as many minutes when he started the engine without another word, pulling out of the company car park with a savagery that made the car growl as he murmured, 'Without knowing any of the facts, and in direct variance to the notion that you shouldn't speak ill of the dead, I'd say you were well rid of the—' He stopped abruptly. 'You're well rid of Mr Allen,' he finished tightly.

How right he was. She gave a peculiar little laugh. 'I know it.'

'How did it happen?' For a moment she glanced at him, at the harsh set face frowning at the road ahead, uncertain of what he was asking. 'How did he die?' Lucas asked abruptly. 'Your application form merely stated "deceased".'

'It was an accident.' She didn't want to continue this.

She was aware of the piercing eyes flashing over her face although she was looking straight ahead again, and his voice had the smoky quality that was so disturbing when he said, 'Car?'

'No.' They were in mainstream traffic now but, in spite of their conversation, the frantic rush hour busyness and the fact that it had begun to snow again making the difficult driving conditions even more treacherous, all Kim was conscious of was hard male thighs just on the perimeter of her visions and firm capable tanned hands on the leather steering wheel. And the smell of him. Whatever aftershave he was using it should be banned as downright dangerous to a woman's state of mind, she told herself silently. But perhaps it wouldn't smell the same on anyone else.

'Graham cut an artery when he fell through a shop window.' A full thirty seconds had crept by in screaming expectation and Kim couldn't take the pressure any more. 'He was drunk,' she finished flatly.

'Usual occurrence?' The silver light moved over her briefly.

For a man who used words so sparingly he certainly made every one count, Kim thought resentfully. 'Yes,' she said hollowly.

'And now you want to talk about something else.'

She had wanted to talk about something else from the moment she had got into the car! Kim sucked in a shaky breath and kept her trembling hands tightly clasped in her lap. 'If you don't mind,' she said numbly.

Lucas nodded slowly. 'Tell me about your daughter.' And his cool voice didn't betray he was as surprised by the request as Kim was.

'Melody?' Kim was startled into glancing at him and he met her big brown eyes for a second, his own thick black lashes hiding his expression in the next instant.

'Unusual name. Your choice?' he asked easily.

The scent of his male warmth was unnerving her more and more in the close confines of the powerfully virile car, forcing her to acknowledge her own awareness of him with a tenacity she couldn't escape. 'It was a long labour, difficult.' She didn't add that Graham had been out on a drinking binge and had only arrived at the hospital the following morning. 'One of the nurses was very sweet to me; she was Jamaican. Her name was—'

'Melody.' He finished the sentence for her.

Kim nodded. 'But it suits Melody,' she said quietly. 'She's a happy little girl, always singing and laughing.'

There was a warmth—a sweetness—to Kim's voice when she spoke of her daughter that Lucas hadn't heard before, and suddenly he was the one who wanted to change the subject.

'I'm sure she is,' he said evenly. 'Now, let me just run through the prime objective of this meeting before we meet Jim Clarkson and his son.'

Kim listened quietly as he expounded further, but inside she was so churned up half of what he said flowed straight over her head.

She wished she'd never taken this job. In spite of the fabulous salary, the car, everything, she did so wish she'd never set foot in Kane Electrical. She had known where she was with Bob Curtis. He had been a slave-driver, and quite shameless about using people to his own advantage, but he had been fat and balding and middle-aged and hadn't had the interest to ask her one personal question in the two years she had worked for him. And he'd driven a family saloon that was as exciting as a jam sandwich.

Lucas shifted slightly in the black leather seat and she felt her nerves tighten.

And Bob's suits had been off the peg and more often than not creased into the bargain, and he would no more have worn a silk shirt than the man in the moon. Whereas Lucas... Even in bathing trunks he would still have that air of unlimited wealth about him.

The thought of Lucas in bathing trunks was enough to cause her cheeks to flush hotly, and she hoped he would assume it was the warmth of the car after the bitter chill outside if he noticed.

Lucas did notice, and the feeling he had experienced in the lift swept over him again with renewed vigour before he forced himself to relax. Okay, so she was as nervous as a cat on a hot tin roof, he told himself with silent savagery, but the devil alone only knew what had gone on in her marriage. At least the creep was dead. He breathed out slowly, narrowing his eyes at the wintry vista ahead as he forced himself to concentrate on the road conditions. She was his secretary. That was all she was. Her past only affected him in as much as it might interfere with the job she did for him. *That was all.*

The rest of the journey to the restaurant was conducted in a silence that wasn't at all comfortable, and by the time the Aston Martin nosed into the immaculate car park at the rear of Fontella's, Kim's nerves were stretched to breaking point. Lucas was out of the car and opening her door before Kim had a chance to move, and as she swung her legs on to the gravelled drive she took a long, deep, silent breath.

She knew of Fontella's but had never ventured within its hallowed walls. The prices began at unaffordable and rose skywards.

'Chin up.'

She hadn't been aware of Lucas's eyes on her as they had begun to walk towards the gracious wooden doors leading into the building, but now as she glanced at him he continued, 'Jim is a wily old bird but as down-to-earth a guy as you could wish to meet and his son is from the same mould. You'll like them.'

Probably, but it wasn't the thought of meeting the king-pins of Clarkson International that was bothering her. It was the big dark man at the side of her. For some reason he caused a chemical reaction in her mind and body that she didn't seem able to control with logic or will-power, and it was getting worse as time progressed, not better.

Kim did like Jim Clarkson and his son, Robert. They were astute businessmen and as single-minded as Lucas when it came to any issues linked with commerce, but she sensed immediately the three men had had dealings in the past and liked each other.

To her surprise the conversation, although heated at times, was not without humour, and in spite of it being two against one Lucas more than held his own and manipulated events skilfully and quietly until he had obtained most of what he had been after.

That this wasn't lost on Jim Clarkson became evident as the four made their goodbyes in the car park. 'He's a wily operator, your Mr Kane,' Jim told her as he shook her hand in farewell. 'But of course you know that.'

'That was exactly what he said about you, Mr Clarkson.' Kim dimpled at the grey-haired, elderly man as she spoke and he laughed out loud, his blue eyes frankly appreciative of the beautiful woman in front of him.

'Flattery will get you everywhere, my dear.'

Lucas had been standing to one side, surveying them from eyes that reflected the winter sky overhead, and now he moved forward, cupping Kim's elbow as he said, 'I'll phone you tomorrow, Jim, once my accountant has looked into a couple of matters.'

'Goodbye, Mrs Allen.' Robert Clarkson had put out his hand as he spoke, forcing Lucas to delay his departure. 'It was nice meeting you,' he said softly, his eyes warm.

'Likewise.'

Robert opened his mouth to say more but Kim found herself whisked across the car park, which had been swept clean of even the faintest trace of snow, before the younger man could speak and then she was in the Aston Martin with the door firmly shut.

That had bordered on rudeness. She watched her boss walk round the bonnet of the car but could read nothing from the bland expression on the craggy face. But perhaps he was in a hurry to return to the office for some reason?

'That went well.'

They had just drawn out of the car park and she had acknowledged Robert's wave—the younger Clarkson standing by a superb dark-blue Mercedes—with a smile and an inclination of her head before she turned to answer Lucas. In spite of the positive content of his words, the tone had suggested something different.

'Yes, I thought so,' she agreed politely.

'You seemed to hit it off well with the Clarksons,' Lucas said expressionlessly.

'You were right—they're nice people.'

Lucas nodded sagely but made no comment.

Kim stared at the cool hard profile for a moment longer, feeling there was something here she had missed, but at a loss to know exactly what.

It was the same when they got back to the offices. Lucas disappeared into his after some curt instructions regarding the notes she had taken during lunch, but he seemed distracted somehow—irritated, even.

Kim found she didn't care. The roller-coaster of emotions she had been riding all day had taken its toll and she was physically and mentally exhausted, needing every scrap of concentration she had left to transcribe her notes into neatly printed pages. The excellent lunch didn't help the feeling of tiredness either; for the first time since she didn't know when she would have loved an afternoon nap, her stomach replete and her brain frazzled.

At half-past four she took a pile of paperwork into Lucas and placed it on his desk.

'Thank you.' He didn't look up.

'I'll come back in ten minutes when you've had a chance to sign the letters; they're on the top,' Kim said evenly.

'Fine.' His voice was distracted and he still didn't raise his head.

She was halfway to the door when she remembered she hadn't mentioned a report the financial director's secretary had just delivered and which she'd placed in the pile, and she turned swiftly, the words on her lips, only to have them freeze as she found him watching her.

Their eyes met and held for an eternity, glittering silver on dark brown, and then his gaze wandered to a tendril of hair which had escaped the neat braid at the back of her head. 'Your colouring is very unusual,' he said almost absently. 'Blonde hair with such dark eyes.'

'My hair is natural.' It was a touch defensive.

'I know; I can tell,' he said softly.

Of course he would be able to tell, with all the blondes—natural and otherwise—he must have known in his time. The fact that her mind had registered the thought, rather than the thought itself, disturbed Kim, and to cover her confusion she found herself babbling, 'Melody has the same blonde hair and dark eyes, actually.'

He nodded slowly. 'Genetic. Perhaps one of your parents had the same colouring?' His voice was very deep and very soft.

Kim wanted to gulp, her throat seemed to be closing up, but she breathed out through her nose and said calmly, 'My mother. I don't remember her but I have a photograph. My father was blonde too but he had blue eyes.'

'Right.'

He hadn't moved a muscle and there was no need to feel threatened but that was exactly what she did feel. Get a hold of yourself, she warned herself silently. This is a perfectly respectable conversation and you're acting like an idiot.

'I…I'll come back in a few minutes for the letters, then.'

'What?' Her ruthlessly focused, coldly intelligent boss stared at her vacantly for a moment and then nodded abruptly. 'Yes, do that, Kim.'

He lowered his head and she was off the hook, but it wasn't until she was in her own office again that Kim realised she hadn't told him about the financial report he had been waiting for. Well, she wasn't going in there again—he'd find it, she told herself shakily.

It was another ten minutes before he buzzed her, and as she took the papers he held out to her her eyes sprang to meet his as Lucas said quietly, 'Sit down a moment, Kim. There's something I need to say to you.'

What now? She sat demurely on the edge of the chair in front of the desk, her knees tightly together and her expression reserved.

'As my secretary you are privy to all sorts of confidential information that the rest of my employees are not.'

Lucas's voice was even and steady and Kim wasn't sure if he required an answer to what had seemed like a statement, but she said, 'Yes, of course.'

'You will find that people try to get to me through you for various reasons, some important and some not so important. There will also be instances when you will be approached on a personal level, but June found it was more circumspect to keep herself to herself at work and reserve her friendships for those individuals unconnected with Kane Electrical.'

What was he getting at? 'But I thought her future husband was a supplier for Kane Electrical?' Kim asked in surprise.

Granite eyes flickered briefly. 'The exception that proved the rule,' Lucas said crisply.

Right. Kim stared at him bewilderedly. Was that all?

'The thing is, Kim...' Lucas paused, his eyes tight on hers, and as she had many times before Kim felt as though his mind was looking straight into hers, probing, dissecting her secret thoughts and fears.

'Yes?' So what was the thing?

'I think you might be having a telephone call from Robert Clarkson,' Lucas said coolly.

'Robert Clarkson?' Kim stared at him as if he was mad. 'Why would Robert Clarkson call me?'

'Isn't it obvious?' His voice was harsher and he must have realised this because it was back to its normal even tone when he said, 'He likes you. When you were in the ladies' cloakroom at lunch he was asking about you.'

Kim was totally taken aback and her honest bewilderment was written all over her face. 'But…but I didn't… I mean…'

'You didn't notice.' It was a statement and spoken with mild exasperation.

'No, I didn't.' Kim sensed criticism and her hackles rose accordingly. 'I was there in the capacity of your secretary and doing a job, that's all.' And who would notice another man with Lucas Kane in the vicinity? The dangerousness of the thought shocked her and brought a flood of hot colour into her face.

'Very commendable.' It was dry and did nothing to soothe her ruffled feathers. 'Well, take it from me, Robert will contact you in the near future and suggest lunch or dinner—a date, anyway. Of course with Kane Electrical and Clarkson International being involved in delicate negotiations at the moment…'

'You think he would try and use me to gain an advantage?' she asked stiffly. More to the point, he thought she would be stupid enough to discuss confidential matters with every Tom, Dick and Harry! How dared he? How *dared* he treat her as though she had so little sense or respect for her position that she would allow herself to be so indiscreet?

'Not necessarily.'

'Then what?' Her voice had risen but she couldn't help it. She was so *mad*.

'I was merely pointing out certain factors, that's all.' His eyes were hard chips of narrowed ice now but Kim was too incensed to take heed.

'I work for you, and you have the right to demand my absolute loyalty and discretion with all matters connected to that work, but you do not have the right to tell me who

I can and can't date outside of these four walls,' Kim bit out tightly, her face chalk-white except for two red patches of colour on her cheekbones.

She had no intention of dating Robert Clarkson—she had no intention of dating anyone ever again—but if Lucas Kane thought he owned her, body and soul, he had another think coming. The arrogance—the sheer unadulterated *arrogance* of the man!

'Neither would I try,' he grated angrily.

'Oh, come on, that's exactly what you've just tried,' she flung back furiously.

There was an electric silence which vibrated the airwaves but for all his inward rage Lucas Kane's face was as unrevealing as a bare canvas. He had sat there all through that damned lunch and watched Rob fall over himself to impress her; it had been pathetic, he told himself savagely. And she'd smiled back at Rob in a way she had never looked at him; she hadn't flinched when Rob had touched her arm or helped her on with her coat, damn it.

He had battled with his feelings all afternoon, feelings new to him and acutely disturbing. He'd always prided himself on being a logical man first and foremost, a man who kept his life free and uncluttered and who liked his relationships to follow suit.

Human triangles, sentiment, jealousy—he had always found such matters irritating and non-productive and avoided them like the plague. He liked women who thought like men in the emotional sense—or like him, at least. Non-clinging, independent, able to let go when the affair ended with no tears and no messy entanglements.

And he still thought like that, damn it. Nothing had changed. *Nothing*.

'There's no need for hysterics.' His voice was as cold as ice and his arctic eyes drilled into her like unrelenting steel. 'I was simply putting you on your guard, that's all. You have worked for me for three months and nothing of this nature has cropped up before.'

He rose as he finished speaking, walking across to the door and opening it as he said, 'Perhaps you would make sure those letters are in the post tonight.'

He was dismissing her. Like a headmaster with an errant child! Kim rose to her feet, her clenched fists crumpling the papers in her grasp and forcing her to relax her fingers slightly.

She had intended to sail past him with haughty indifference, her head held high, but the anger that still had her in its grip made her careless. Whether it was the thin heel of her court shoes catching in the carpet or the fact that her legs were shaking so badly, she didn't know, but to her horror she found herself in danger of sprawling at his feet as she felt herself begin to fall just as she reached the doorway.

The letters flew out of her fingers in a whirling arc as she grappled vainly at thin air in an effort to right herself, and then strong arms caught her and brought her thudding against a muscled male chest.

Kim was so dazed and disorientated that she made no sort of move to free herself, and Lucas seemed to have frozen. And then he moved her an inch or so away in order to look down into her face. 'Have you hurt yourself?' His voice was deep and edged with huskiness.

Hurt herself? She didn't know what she had done, held in his arms like this. She could have a broken leg and it wouldn't register.

She knew she had to say something—she couldn't continue staring up into his dark face—but all the half-remembered, forbidden dreams that had haunted her sleep for the last months had come together and it was surreal.

Her hands had landed against the broad wall of his chest and she could feel the thud, thud of his heart beneath her fingertips, the smooth blue silk of his shirt not quite disguising the roughness of body hair beneath it.

Her own heart was pounding, racing the blood through her veins and echoing its thunder in her throat so that it stifled any words she needed to speak to finish this thing quickly and without further embarrassment. She was aware of his harnessed strength, of the power in the bunched muscles of his arms and the magnificent ribcage beneath her palms, but instead of driving her to jerk away—as it should have done—it increased the strange inability to move.

'Kim?' It was a soft murmur, almost a whisper, and then he bent his dark head and nuzzled the golden silk of her hair as he moved her into him again, his voice restrained as he said, 'It's all right; you're okay.'

He had known she was expecting him to kiss her, wanting him to kiss her. And he hadn't.

It was like a deluge of cold water and she pulled free in the next moment, utterly mortified as she bent and quickly gathered up the scattered papers, snapping—when Lucas made a move to help—'I can manage perfectly well, thank you.'

He froze immediately, his voice quiet but with a distinct edge to it when he said, 'Of course you can.'

She had never, not even when Graham had been at his worst, felt such burning humiliation as she was feeling now. The papers retrieved, Kim rose jerkily to her feet, her face flushed and her eyes brilliant with the shame that was making her rigid.

'I'll see that these go off tonight,' she muttered painfully, without looking at Lucas.

He had moved slightly away from the door and now she walked through it quickly, hearing it close behind her with a further stiffening of her already taut limbs.

All she wanted to do was to escape.

Kim stuffed the letters into their envelopes with a feverish haste that took no account of precise folding or anything else. Then, rather than following normal procedure and ringing through to Accounts to inform the junior there that Mr Kane's post was ready for collection, she took it down herself, lingering for a few moments to talk to the financial director's secretary before she returned to the top floor, although afterwards she had no recollection of what they had talked about.

Lucas was speaking on his private line when she walked into her office and she fairly flew round, collecting her coat and turning off the word processor, checking everything was in order, and then scurrying out to the lift as though the devil himself was at her heels.

She had never gone without saying goodnight before—neither had she left before five o'clock, and it was still only five to—but none of that mattered. If she had to face Lucas tonight, look into those mocking silver eyes and see the knowledge of her own weakness in his face, she would crumple. She knew it.

And it wasn't until she was safely in the blue BMW driving away from Kane Electrical that she allowed the first hot tears to fall.

CHAPTER FOUR

AFTER a riotous snowman-building exercise with Melody, followed by hot soup and crumpets smothered with butter and jam, Kim felt a little better.

Okay, so she had made the mother and father of a fool of herself, she admitted silently as she stood washing up the tea things, having sent Melody to tidy her room before her nightly bath. She had stood there like someone who had lost their wits staring up into his face, but perhaps he hadn't known what she was thinking? *She* hadn't realised what she was thinking until he *hadn't* kissed her.

She gave a small smothered sigh and gazed unseeingly over the back garden, the large snowman she and Melody had made gazing back at her unblinkingly from his vantage point in the middle of the lawn.

The crazy thing was she didn't want Lucas to kiss her, not in the cold light of day. It was the last thing she wanted, she told herself firmly. Even if Lucas Kane hadn't been her boss, she wouldn't have contemplated getting involved with him in a million years, or any man for that matter. But especially Lucas Kane.

He was too dominant a man, too strong physically and mentally and much too ruthless and cold and cynical. And too charismatic, too darkly sensual and magnetic, the little voice in her head jeered bluntly, prompted by her conscience and innate honesty.

'Oh, whatever!' She swished her hands irritably in the hot soapy water, angry with herself and Lucas Kane and the whole world. She didn't recognise herself any more; that was most of the problem. Or perhaps didn't trust herself was a better definition? He had made no move towards her—in fact, he had shown only too clearly that afternoon that she held as much attraction for him as a piece of wet lettuce—so she had to accept the problem was all hers. And it wasn't a problem, it really wasn't—not unless she made it one.

That reasoning helped, a little.

For some reason Lucas Kane affected her like no other man she had known. She had thought she was sexually attracted to Graham, but now she knew she hadn't even understood the first thing about such an emotion.

So... Her hands became still again and her eyes dark and unfocused. She either faced facts, got a hold on her ridiculous hormones and made sure an incident like this afternoon never happened again, or she left. It was as simple as that at root level. And if she left it was goodbye wonderful salary, goodbye car and very probably goodbye this house, because she wasn't at all sure she would ever get another job like her present one. Could she really justify robbing Melody of what promised to be a glowing future, simply because she found her boss the most sexy thing since Adam first walked the earth? No, she couldn't.

Her hands automatically found a teaplate and washed it.

She had to go into work tomorrow as though nothing had happened. She had worked for him for three months and she could continue to do so; it was mind over matter. And she wouldn't think about how she had told him one minute that she didn't like physical contact, and the next had been all over him. She groaned softly and then took herself to task again. No, keep it drama-free, Kim, she told herself tightly. You weren't all over him, you were just...willing. Oh, hell.

The ringing of the doorbell was a welcome relief to her thoughts, but Kim's brow wrinkled as she went to answer the door. It could only be Maggie, but her friend rarely came unannounced. Perhaps she had had a row with Pete again? Things seemed to be going from bad to worse in that direction and she knew Maggie was getting to the end of her tether with Pete's inability to make any real commitment. Men! Kim was frowning as she opened the door. They were nothing but trouble, the lot of them.

The source of her present and very real trouble was standing straight in front of her, and for a moment Kim could only stare up into Lucas's dark face as she did an imitation of a goldfish in a bowl, her mouth opening and then shutting without emitting a sound.

'I'm sorry to come to your home like this but I've been trying to call you since just before six,' Lucas said coolly. 'I understand that a combination of freezing fog and then this latest snow has brought some telephone lines down.'

'Oh.' Kim stared at him vacantly. The phone hadn't rung since she had been home, but then it rarely did.

'Can I come in?' Lucas asked patiently.

'What?' And then she caught herself, flushing hotly as she said, 'Oh, yes, of course. Come in.'

He looked incredibly big and dark in her little cream-painted hall, and as she indicated for him to walk through into the sitting room she kept a good three feet between them, moving hurriedly to the other side of the room away from his disturbing presence as soon as she could.

He was wearing a thick dark-charcoal overcoat over his suit and it increased the impression of brooding masculinity tenfold, freezing her thought process and making her all of a dither as she said, 'Sit…sit down, won't you?'

'Thanks.' He undid his overcoat before taking the seat she had offered with a wave of her hand, placing both hands on the arms of the easy chair and crossing one knee in a pose that was utter male.

She had thought she would at least have another fourteen hours or so before she had to face him again, and with the memory of the afternoon burning hotly and making her heart pound like a sledge-hammer further small talk was quite beyond Kim. Why was he here?

And then Lucas answered the unspoken question as he said coolly, his voice expressionless, 'I was looking for the financial report Clare sent through today. I'd attached a note to it asking you to confirm a couple of figures but I assume you left that for tomorrow? I couldn't find it when I looked on your desk, though, and I need it to work on tonight along with the Clarkson file.'

'Financial report?' Kim stared at him. 'It was in the papers I gave you this afternoon,' she said uncomprehendingly.

'I know.' His voice was still flat. 'I looked at it and made the notes and gave it back to you along with the correspondence to go out tonight,' he repeated evenly.

She continued to stare at him but now a terrible suspicion had rendered her dumb.

The silver eyes hadn't changed expression, neither had he spoken again, but somehow—in spite of Lucas's apparent calmness and immobility—Kim knew the same suspicion had occurred to him.

'You're sure you gave it back to me?' she asked faintly.

He nodded once.

'And...and you can't find it?'

He shook his head.

She felt sick, her stomach churning so much it threatened to let go of the soup and crumpets. 'I...I didn't see it,' she admitted miserably.

'Which means?'

The full enormity of the colossal mistake was sweeping over her. She hadn't been thinking straight when she had stuffed the letters into their envelopes that afternoon; she could easily have included the report with one of them. That was bad enough in itself, but it was a highly confidential breakdown of profit margins and sources to several suppliers, one or two of which Lucas had written to that day. If the report was in one of those envelopes...

Kim didn't prevaricate, taking a deep breath which didn't ease her thumping heart at all before she said, 'I must have sent it out with the letters. I'm terribly sorry, Lucas.'

'Any idea which one?' He hadn't raised his voice by so much as a decibel.

She wanted to shut her eyes and wring her hands, at the very least to groan out loud, but she shook her head, her eyes tragic as she said again, 'I'm so sorry, I really am. There's no excuse for such carelessness. I'll resign immediately, of course.'

'I don't want you to resign, Kim. I want you to think and tell me which letter the damn report is in.'

'I don't *know*.' It was in the form of a wail. 'It could be in any one of them.'

'Including Turners and Breedon?' In spite of all his efforts Lucas's voice was no longer expressionless.

'Yes.'

He looked down at his handmade shoes, the blue-black of his thick short hair adding to the overall dark maleness which seemed so alien in her little home, and Kim watched him helplessly. How could she have been so irresponsible, so criminally slipshod? This was the end; it had to be. Even if he didn't demand her resignation right away there was no chance of him ever trusting her again.

Useless to tell herself that she had been suffering the worst attack of panic she'd ever experienced in her life at the time of the blunder. That the feel of being in his arms, even for a few short moments, had caused emotions she'd never thought to feel again—never *had* felt, really, because certainly Graham, even in their carefree university days, hadn't inspired such overwhelming sexual awareness.

Lucas Kane didn't want to hear all that, even if she could

tell him—which of course was impossible. She would rather be hung, drawn and quartered!

'Mummy?'

As Kim's eyes focused on the tiny figure of her daughter standing in the doorway she was aware of Lucas's head snapping upwards, but she was already walking across the room, her voice soft as she said, 'It's all right, sweetheart. You finish clearing up your room and I'll be up in a minute.'

'I have finished.' Melody had sensed some kind of atmosphere and wasn't about to be ushered away without protest. 'Hello.' She cut through anything Kim might have said with the directness of childhood as she stared straight into the silver-grey eyes and added, 'I'm Melody Allen.'

'How do you do, Melody? I'm Lucas Kane,' Lucas said softly.

'My mummy works for you,' Melody said interestedly.

'That's right, darling.' It was Kim who answered and now her voice held a note Melody recognised when she added, 'Go and start getting ready for your bath *now*.' For some reason, and Kim couldn't have explained it even to herself, she didn't want her daughter to have anything to do with this man. Not even in the slightest way.

Melody nodded and even took one step backwards into the hall, but her innate friendliness added to healthy curiosity was too much, and her little voice piped up, again directed at Lucas when she said, 'We made a snowman and had crumpets for tea. Have you seen my snowman?'

'Not yet but I'd like to,' Lucas said quietly, smiling across at the small child who was a charming miniature of her beautiful mother. 'Perhaps you can show him to me after your bath?'

This was getting out of hand. 'I don't allow Melody to bathe herself,' Kim put in quickly, wishing he would go. The letters had gone and there was nothing she could do tonight to retrieve the situation. She would resign—eat humble pie, grovel, whatever he demanded—tomorrow, but she couldn't cope with seeing him in her home or talking to her daughter. It made him too...human.

'I can wait.' The silvery eyes challenged her to say more and Kim knew, she *knew* he had read her mind again.

'But you must be very busy—'

'I can wait,' he repeated smoothly.

'Do you like crumpets?' Melody had clearly decided this silly adult conversation had gone on long enough. 'We've got some left and you can have one if you like,' she offered magnanimously.

Lucas raised his gaze from Melody's sweet, dark-eyed face to her mother's horrified one, and Kim noticed his mouth was twitching and the silver eyes were bright with barely concealed amusement. 'I love crumpets,' he said very seriously, lowering his gaze to Melody's, 'and as I haven't had my tea yet that sounds great.'

'Great' wasn't quite the word she would have chosen. Kim stared helplessly, first at Melody and then at Lucas, who was returning her daughter's grin, and knew she had been outmanoeuvred by a pair of experts.

'You haven't eaten?' she murmured weakly.

'No, Kim, I haven't eaten,' he agreed quizzically.

She didn't believe this! How on earth had she found herself in this situation? she asked herself with silent despair. 'We...we had hot soup and rolls followed by crumpets with butter and jam,' she managed fairly distinctly, despite the choking feeling in her throat, 'but I can rustle up an omelette or a pizza if you'd prefer?'

'Soup and crumpets sound good to me.' He was speaking to her but smiling at Melody as he spoke, and again the panicky sensation took Kim's breath away.

It made sense to fix Lucas's meal before she took Melody up for her bath, but she didn't want to leave her daughter with her boss. She didn't want them to get on too well—for Melody to like him. Her brain was racing but the small-mindedness of her thoughts wasn't lost on Kim. But she *needed* to keep him absolutely separate in her head, she told herself frantically, isolated under the heading 'work' and totally detached from her personal life. She didn't dare question why; she just knew it was imperative.

'Do you want to come and help me fix a tray for Mr Kane?'

In spite of the gentleness of her mother's voice, Melody knew a rhetorical question when she heard one, and now the small blonde head nodded obediently.

A larger, dark head across the room registered the message in the 'Mr Kane', but the crystal-clear eyes continued to smile at the little girl as Lucas said softly, 'Thanks, Melody, and I look forward to seeing that snowman later.'

'Make yourself comfortable.' Kim couldn't get out of the room fast enough. 'I'll bring you a coffee in a moment, or perhaps you'd like a glass of wine?'

'I'm driving.' It was an answer in itself and Kim recalled he hadn't had anything stronger than mineral water at lunch, although the wine had been flowing freely and the other two men had imbibed.

A sudden memory—vivid in all its distasteful clarity—of Graham downing half a bottle of vodka before breakfast and then wondering why she had refused to let him take her and Melody to the shops in the car reared its head. It had resulted in a huge row; he had actually struck her that morning.

'Kim?'

Something of her thoughts must have shown on her face because Lucas's voice was sharply concerned, and now Kim realised she had been staring at him without seeing him. She murmured something about having remembered she'd left the gas on and stepped into the hall quickly, shutting the door behind her.

Brilliant. As Melody chattered away while they heated the soup and put the crumpets under the grill, Kim's mind was buzzing. Now not only would he think she was grossly inadequate at work he would think she was lackadaisical at home too. Left the gas on. Kim wrinkled her small straight nose. The cottage was all electric!

She sent Melody upstairs to begin undressing before she took the tray through to the sitting room. Ridiculous, maybe, she acknowledged silently as she turned the handle of the door—nearly upsetting the tray in the process—but the easy way Lucas had with the child had disturbed her. *He* disturbed her, always, but she hadn't expected him to know how to talk to children somehow. She would have thought he'd be even more cold and distant than he was with most adults, but he'd been warm, relaxed, his natural hardness quite gone. And she hadn't liked how it had made her feel.

Lucas had taken off his overcoat and his suit jacket and pulled his tie loose when she walked into the room, and as she glanced at him—sitting in apparent lazy relaxation in front of the flickering coal fire the sitting room boasted—Kim felt a bolt of electricity shoot right down to her toes.

'Nice, the real fire.' His voice was deep, low in his throat, and his eyes were unfathomable.

Kim nodded tensely, watching him straighten himself in the chair with something approaching panic as her gaze seemed to lock on hard male thighs. 'The previous owners had resisted the convenience of an artificial fire, so we followed suit,' she said tightly, her cheeks flushed as she handed him the tray. 'With central heating the cottage gets as warm as toast but a fire is so cosy on winter nights.'

Kim knew she was speaking too quickly, her words falling over themselves, but she was so flustered it was a miracle she could talk at all, she told herself desperately.

She smelt like apples and magnolia flowers and baby powder. Lucas felt his body respond to her closeness, the hungry stirring of hard male arousal, and kept his voice easy and cool when he said, 'This looks wonderful. Thank you.'

'It's the least I can do, in the circumstances.' It wasn't quite what she had intended to say, or rather his response to her innocent words—the faintly lifted sardonic eyebrow and devastatingly wry twist to his undeniably sexy mouth indicated he had put a different interpretation on her ingenuously polite reply—and Kim found herself scurrying out of the room like a frightened mouse.

Well, she'd handled that well! With the door safely closed behind her Kim sank against it in utter frustration and irritation at her inadequacy. This whole scenario was going from bad to worse.

Melody didn't help much, once she was in the bath and Kim was helping her wash her hair. 'I like Lucas.' It was a definite statement. Melody was one for definite statements and rarely changed her mind about anything.

'Mr Kane, sweetheart.' Kim kept her voice casual and very calm. 'You must call him Mr Kane.'

'Why?' A small nose wrinkled bewilderedly.

'Because…because it's polite, with him being Mummy's boss.'

'I like Mr Kane, then.' The little soapy body wriggled round so Melody could stare her straight in the eyes. 'Do you, Mummy? Do you like Mr Kane?'

'Of course I do,' Kim said briskly. 'Now, it's your night for clean pyjamas, young lady. Do you want your teddy bear ones or the ones with little flowers that Aunty Maggie bought you for Christmas?'

The distraction succeeded. It was an important decision and one which needed some consideration.

It was another ten minutes before Kim led Melody— impossibly angelic in forget-me-not-flowered pyjamas and Minnie Mouse slippers—into the sitting room for a cursory goodnight to Lucas. At least, that was what Kim had planned it would be. Lucas and her daughter had different ideas.

'I like your pyjamas.'

It was the first thing Lucas said and nothing could have guaranteed his esteem in Melody's eyes more.

'Aunty Maggie bought them for me.' Great dark eyes locked with silver. 'And Father Christmas brought my slippers. He brought me lots and lots of presents.'

'Lucky old you.' Lucas made a funny face. 'He didn't bring me anything.'

Melody giggled conspiratorially. 'That's because you're a grown-up, silly.'

'Oh, is that what it was? I did wonder.'

Melody giggled some more, moving to stand close to his chair with one tiny hand on his knee. 'You can have one of my chocolates if you like,' she offered solemnly. 'I had a big tin and Mummy only lets me have one every night because she wants me to have no fillings in my teeth.'

'Wise Mummy.'

There were all manner of alarm bells going off in Kim's mind but before she could say anything Lucas had bent down and lifted Melody onto his lap, his voice a stage whisper as he said, 'What I would really like is for you to show me that snowman. Would that be okay with you?'

'Uh-huh.' Melody had wound one arm round his neck, her small face close to his as she whispered back, 'His name is Mr Snow. I named him that.'

'I can't think of a better name.'

She didn't like this. She didn't like this at all. Kim had

combed out her severe office braid and changed into jeans and a sweatshirt before going into the garden with Melody, and now she flicked back her heavy fall of hair, her voice sharp as she said, 'Show Mr Kane the snowman and then it's bedtime, sweetheart.'

'Lucas.' It was quiet and even but something in his tone set Kim's heart hammering. 'You can call me Lucas, Melody.'

'But Mummy said…'

'Yes?' Melody had turned to look across at Kim confusedly. 'What did Mummy say?' Lucas asked softly.

'She said I had to call you Mr Kane because it's polite.'

'And Mummy is right,' Lucas said silkily. 'But now I've said I want you to call me Lucas it's polite to do that, okay?'

'Okay.' Melody wriggled happily, clearly captivated, and Kim silently ground her teeth in impotent rage. Who did he think he was, muscling in here, talking his way into a meal and then countermanding her instructions to her daughter? And then she remembered the reason for his call and the rage subsided as quickly as it had flared into life.

She had committed an unforgivable mistake and he would have had every right to storm in here tonight crying for blood. Instead he had been amazingly calm and reasonable. She didn't know what he was going to say to her once they were alone, but she couldn't fault his attitude in front of Melody. So…she owed him a little latitude.

She kept repeating that to herself when he stood to his feet in the next instant and wrapped Melody in his overcoat before the three of them paid brief homage to Mr Snow, Melody's stringy arms tight round Lucas's broad neck, but she drew the line at Melody's request that Lucas read her a bedtime story.

'No story tonight, sweetheart.' She took Melody from Lucas at the bottom of the stairs once they were inside the cottage again, handing him his coat with a tight smile. 'Mr Kane and I have some important work things to discuss, so you've got to promise Mummy you'll be a good girl and go straight to sleep tonight.'

'Aw…' Melody pouted, peering at Kim from under her eyelashes, but when she saw her mother's face was adamant she gave in with her usual good humour and Kim was downstairs again within two or three minutes.

She paused at the sitting room door before opening it, her stomach turning over, and then smoothed down her sweatshirt and wiped suddenly clammy hands on her jeans. If he was going to shout and scream he would have done so immediately, wouldn't he? But it wasn't just that possibility that was churning her insides and she knew it.

'You have a charming daughter.' Lucas was standing at the window as she entered the room and Kim's heart took a mighty jump as he turned to face her. 'She's a credit to you.'

'Thank you.' Kim stood just inside the door, uncertain of whether to sit or continue standing. This was *her* home, her little castle, but she felt as though she were the guest, she told herself crossly. How did he make her feel like that?

'Can she remember her father at all?'

It wasn't what she had expected him to say and he read the knowledge in the darkening of her velvet brown eyes. Perhaps he shouldn't bring the subject of her husband up again, Lucas acknowledged silently, but he needed to know much more about this reserved, honey-skinned, golden-haired woman and he had a distinct advantage tonight while she was feeling bad about the report. He felt no remorse in thinking this way; in the early days of his joining the family firm his father had taught him always to look for the weak spot in one's opponent and capitalise on it, and he'd found he had a natural aptitude for such ruthlessness.

And Kim was an opponent. He didn't know quite how

it had happened but he knew instinctively it was the case. For some reason she saw him as the enemy and it was grating more and more with every day that passed.

'Her father?' Kim thrust her hands deep into the pockets of her jeans, her face tense. 'No, she can't remember Graham.'

'Come and sit down, Kim.' Lucas indicated the sofa as he walked over to the chair he had vacated earlier, and again it was as if he were the host and she the guest.

She sat down on the very edge of the cushions but as he drew his chair at an angle to the sofa it brought him much too close and so she shifted back in the seat, moving slightly away as she did so. 'I'm very sorry about the report, Lucas.' Her voice was tight and formal. 'If it's in the wrong envelope I know what damage it might do, so the offer stands about my resignation.'

He stared at her for a moment, leaning forward with his elbows on his knees, although he was careful not to touch her. The warm fragrance of her nearness invaded his air space and his senses were registering how much younger she looked with her hair loose about her shoulders, uninhibited even. But looks were deceptive. He could feel the tension in her like a live thing, keeping him at bay.

'I joined Kane Electrical straight from university and I was as green as they come,' Lucas said quietly, his deep, slightly husky voice with its trace of an accent causing her nerve endings to quiver. 'But I was keen.'

He smiled at her, the silver-grey eyes wrinkling at the edges, and Kim forced herself to smile back although it was just a movement of her mouth. He had rolled up his sleeves while she had been out of the room and his muscled forearms were covered in a liberal dusting of black silky hair, and in the position in which he was sitting—with his dark head close to hers and the tanned jawline dark with a day's growth of stubble—it was impossible to ignore his flagrant masculinity.

'My father is a cautious Englishman and my mother a fiery and impetuous Colombian, so I've had to learn to temper my mother's explosive genes and perhaps take more risks on the paternal side. It works...mostly.'

Kim nodded. So that was where the echo of an accent came from. His mother.

'However...' Lucas paused, aware he had her interest. 'In my first year of working for my father, my mother's genes were rampant. I prefer that as an excuse than the foolishness of crass youth. I took a risk, a big risk, off my own back. There was no real need for it, I guess, but perhaps I felt the need to prove myself. I don't know. Anyway, it was a mistake, a huge one; it nearly broke us. It makes your slip-up very meagre in comparison. I never made that mistake again.'

He was looking at her very closely, his eyes intently searching her wide-eyed face. 'You will never make the same mistake again, Kim,' he said very softly, and somehow she got the impression he was talking about more than her blunder with the report.

Kim drew in a deep breath, fighting the sudden and unwelcome tears that were pricking at the back of her eyes. 'It's...it's very good of you to look at it like that,' she managed faintly, keeping strictly to the matter of the day and refusing to acknowledge any hidden connotations in what he was saying. 'But I'm aware it could be very embarrassing for you.'

'I'm not easily embarrassed.' He smiled, an unconsciously sexy quirk to his hard firm mouth, and the breath caught in her throat.

The flickering glow from the fire, the strength and warmth and irresistible drawing power of his dark magnetism were too seductive, too dangerous, and Kim surprised them both when she leapt to her feet, her voice high as she said, 'Coffee. I'll fetch some coffee.'

'Great.' His voice was casual and relaxed as he too stood to his feet, and as he reached out and took her hand his face didn't reveal the anger he felt as she stiffened against his touch. 'Just put it down to experience, Kim,' he said softly. 'Learn from it, take the positive and leave the negative on the side of the plate and don't let it cripple you.'

He *was* talking about more than work.

She hesitated and then raised her head to meet his eyes, her gaze wary. 'That's easier said than done.'

'Possibly.' He could feel her trembling slightly and it checked the crazy impulse he had to pull her into him and devour her mouth; the strength of his desire shocked him. He had never had any trouble in keeping work and play separate, in fact he would go so far as to say he had felt contempt in the past for any business associates who had been foolish enough to mix the two, but this was different. But perhaps that was what they all thought.

The heat from his fingers seemed to be flowing into her, trickling into every nerve and sinew and setting her body alive with a strange electric current. What would it be like to be kissed by a man like Lucas Kane? Kim gave up the fight to dismiss the thought that had been paramount for most of the evening. Thrilling, exciting, out of this world. He'd know how to kiss. Sexual expertise was there in his eyes, his body, even the way he walked and moved...

She jerked her hand free, disguising the gesture with a tight little laugh as she said, 'This won't get the coffee percolating.'

Damn the coffee. Lucas smiled blandly. 'Can I help?'

The thought of him in the close confines of her little kitchen was overwhelming. 'No, it's fine. I won't be a minute.'

Lucas's thick black lashes swept down, hiding his expression from her, and his voice was easy and controlled as he resumed his seat, saying, 'No hurry.'

No hurry? Once in the kitchen Kim leant her hot forehead against the cool impersonal surface of a cupboard and breathed deeply for several seconds. Her fingers were still tingling from his touch and her legs were actually shaking, she realised with a little dart of disbelief. It might be no hurry to him but she wanted him out of her house as soon as possible.

He was dangerous. She moved away from the cupboards and stared out of the window to where the snowman was still standing patiently in his white frozen world, and remembered how Melody had clung to Lucas as he had enthused over their handiwork.

Very, very dangerous. Kim's eyes narrowed and she felt something very cold douse the heat inside her as she switched on the coffee machine.

If Graham hadn't died when he had, she would have left him within weeks, if not days, anyway. The abuse when he was drunk had been becoming increasingly nasty, and the shopping incident had happened the day before his accident. She had known it was the end of the line for their marriage then; she wouldn't risk putting Melody in danger.

She hadn't loved him any more at that stage; she hadn't loved him for months, even though she had stayed because of his threats of what he would do to Melody and to her if she left him.

But that morning when he had struck her had cut the last tentative threads holding her to the marriage. It had happened to be her in the firing line then; it could have been Melody another time and the thought of that was insupportable.

But she hadn't had to leave. Graham had died, and in spite of all his death had uncovered she had felt a strengthening of her spirit, a determination that she would build a good life for her precious child. And a good life meant never putting Melody at risk again, never allowing a third party to come into their world. Friends were different, and Maggie had been wonderful, but a man…

She had made a terrible mistake in her choice of a partner and she couldn't trust it wouldn't happen again.

Melody liked Lucas. And perhaps he was only being friendly and supportive to her about the report incident, but she didn't dare allow the kind of matey relationship to grow between them she wouldn't have necessarily thought twice about with any other colleague.

She'd work her socks off for him, go the extra mile and beyond as far as her work was concerned—she owed him that at least—but she would keep him very firmly at arm's length. It might make things a little awkward at times but she'd have to cross that bridge when it came to it.

She nodded sharply to the golden-haired reflection in the window, lowered the blind abruptly and set about preparing the coffee tray, her mouth set in a grim determined line that wasn't at all like its normal soft self.

CHAPTER FIVE

CONTRARY to the fear which had gripped Kim when she'd watched the Aston Martin drive away that snowy night in January, Lucas didn't ask one personal question or do more than briefly enquire after Melody in the following few weeks, keeping their relationship focused and pleasant.

The report was returned within a couple of days from a somewhat bewildered friend of Lucas's to whom he had written regarding a forthcoming golf tournament, and was the best possible outcome Kim could have wished for.

February passed with more snow, rigid white frosts and a hectic time at the office as the Clarkson contract was finally settled to Lucas's satisfaction. March was a kinder month weather-wise, but by the end of that month Kim found herself wondering if her relationship with her dynamic boss was quite so cool and controlled as she had thought it was.

He had managed to get under her skin somehow, and not just in the sexual sense—that was something she'd accepted she would have to battle with daily; he was just one exceptional man—but in a hundred other, more subtle ways.

Lucas had a wickedly dry sense of humour for a start and he wasn't averse to laughing at himself, which was a revelation to Kim after Graham's self-important, pontifical attitude to life. She found herself laughing umpteen times a day, and often when she least expected it.

He had the habit of scattering numerous little personal facts about himself and his family into even the most businesslike of their days, and by now Kim knew that his parents had retired to a villa in the sun; that the prolific amount of aunts, uncles and cousins on his mother's side made for some crazy family parties when relations would fly the short journey from Colombia to his parents' home in Florida; that like himself his father had been an only child and his English relations were few and far between, and many other details besides.

Kim was aware that Lucas's large country residence situated well beyond the city limits was home to an elderly housekeeper as well as himself. Martha had been with the family since Lucas was a babe in arms, and besides the two human occupants the mansion housed an assortment of feline inhabitants—all belonging to Martha—and two Great Danes which were Lucas's.

This last had caused Kim one of many disturbed nights in relation to her boss.

She hadn't had him down as an animal-lover before he had mentioned his home situation, or the sort of man who could be altruistic to old ladies who hadn't wanted to leave the country of their birth for warmer climes.

The comfortably cold and detached picture of a cool stainless-steel, remotely controlled bachelor pad with all mod cons and the biggest bed money could buy had taken a knock, and when she had made the mistake of revealing her surprise and preconceptions and Lucas had admitted— charmingly—that a few years before she would have been spot-on, it had been scant comfort.

She wanted—*needed*—to keep him in a neatly labelled box in her mind and, annoying man that he was, he seemed determined to break out of it.

Somehow, and she didn't quite know how he had accomplished it, he had managed to paint a picture on her mind that was quite different from the one she wanted to see when she looked at him. If he had met her head-on in direct challenge she would have been able to cope with it and refuse to take on board Lucas the man, rather than Lucas the ruthless tycoon, but he had trickled himself into her psyche with the steady drip-drip of relentless running water.

He was a brilliant and inexorable strategist. She had seen him in action too many times in business now to doubt it, and had marvelled more than once that his adversaries hadn't seemed to be aware of what he was doing, not realising all the time he was applying an equally ruthless policy with her.

But perhaps she was imagining all this? Kim sat for a moment more in the BMW before squaring her shoulders and opening the car door. Whatever, she couldn't let her guard down with Lucas Kane, not for a moment. That, if nothing else in the whole tangled situation, was crystal-clear.

The March day was damp and mild but very blowy, and in spite of the fact that her parking space was only a few yards away from the main doors of Kane Electrical, the wind had tugged several golden tendrils of hair loose from its customary tight knot at the back of her head by the time she entered the building.

Charlie, the caretaker, was standing in a quiet and empty Reception—it being too early for the rest of the staff yet—and addressed her immediately, saying, 'Power cut, I'm afraid, Mrs Allen. All the lights are out and the lifts are down, but they assure me it won't be too long before we're back in operation.'

'Thanks, Charlie. Looks like it'll be Shanks' pony and the stairs, then.' Kim flashed the elderly man a grin before making for the stairs at the back of an unusually dark Reception and running up them lightly, her mind already grappling with the first few things she had to do that day.

She emerged from the fire door into the top floor corridor dimly lit by the emergency lighting, still concentrating on her imminent workload, and straight into the arms of her

esteemed boss with enough force to send them both against
the far wall.

She was pressed against the length of him, his arms holding her in instinctive protection against his muscled chest,
and as she raised a flushed and breathless face to him, her
wind-blown hair curling in shiny, silky strands about her
pink cheeks, he made no attempt to let her go.

The hushed dark corridor, the utter absence of all sound
or movement made the moment surreal, like a vaguely remembered chimerical dream, and it seemed part of the fantasy when his dark head bent and caught her mouth in a
deep languorous kiss that went on and on. His lips were
moving against hers slowly as he crushed her closer, his
hand cupping her head for deeper penetration as he urged
her into an increasingly intimate acceptance of his hungry
mouth, and it didn't occur to Kim to even struggle.

There was an insistence, a dominant mastery that demanded rather than asked for her consent and there was no
way she could refuse. She had lived this moment so many
times, tasted it, savoured it in her dreams, and now, in the
shadowy alien confines of the silent corridor, fantasy and
fact were combining in overwhelming ecstasy.

Heat was surging in the core of her, lighting flickers of
fire in every nerve and sinew, and as her lips parted to allow
his probing tongue access into the secret places her body
curved closer into him, the physical ache becoming
sweeter.

He made a small sound of pleasure deep in his throat
and Kim answered it with one of her own, faintly bewildered by her desire. She had lost all thought of where she
was, her mind and her emotions totally captive to the sensations he was evoking with such consummate ease. This
was the sort of kiss she had dreamt about as a young, romantic teenager before life had taught her such things only

existed in the land of make-believe, but this was *real*, this was now.

She was kissing him back in the way she had during her sleeping fantasies, without restraint, hungrily searching for she knew not what.

Graham had not been an adventurous or a thoughtful lover and she hadn't slept with anyone before her husband, therefore her sexual experience was limited to Graham's hasty couplings without much finesse. This was gloriously, frighteningly different.

The warmth and the slowly building ache in the core of her femininity, the spasmodic thrills circulating her bloodstream and causing her breath to shudder and gasp against his warm knowing mouth, were something outside her knowledge and desperately seductive. This was pleasure; this was the sort of pleasure she had read about but never imagined was so fiery, so consuming, so frightening. And she wanted more, much more.

Kim wasn't even aware of the sudden brightness of lights against her closed eyelids, but the whirr of the lift did cause her to open dazed eyes, or perhaps it was the fact that Lucas's mouth had left hers.

'The power's back on.' His voice was thick and husky and he still held her against him, his arousal hard against her softness.

She was trembling, she knew she was trembling, and now that his lips had stopped fuelling the fire that had eaten up all her inhibitions and common sense she felt a growing horror at her complete submission to his lovemaking. And bereft. Bereft at the feeling of loss now it had stopped.

'Let...let go of me.' It was a faint whisper but he didn't argue, his eyes a brilliant silver in the hard, ruthless lines of his face.

'That was unintentional, Kim.'

As she jerked back from him, her hands to her hot face,

the words caught at her. Was he saying he regretted it? She stared at him wildly, her eyes deep pools of black velvet in the flushed smoothness of her face. Probably. But then she had more or less offered herself on a plate and few men would resist such an opportunity. What would have happened if the power hadn't come back on when it did?

She clenched her shaking hands into tight fists at her side, noticing, with further shame, that Lucas was perfectly cool and relaxed. And it was her humiliation that made her say, her voice bitter and tight, 'You mean you just felt a sudden urge for a quickie?'

Immediately the ugly words left her lips she wished them back, the crudeness shocking her, but it was too late. She had said them. Out of pain and anguish, but she'd still said them.

And Lucas was furious. She knew it from the dark colour that flared across the hard cheekbones and the muscle working in his jaw, but his voice was at direct variance to his face when he said icily, 'You rate yourself very cheaply if you believe that.'

'I'd say it's you who rates me cheaply,' she hissed back sharply.

'Then you'd be wrong.' The words were like bullets. 'If you were anyone other than who you are I wouldn't have stopped at a kiss, believe me, Kim.'

What did that mean? That he had stopped because he didn't fancy her that much, or because she was his secretary and it would cause too many complications, or what? 'So you expect me to be grateful you didn't force me?' she snapped bitterly.

'I wasn't using any force.' His voice was soft now, soft and mocking, and his eyes dared her to deny what they both knew. 'You were with me every inch of the way from the second our lips touched.'

'I don't think so!' she flung sarcastically.

'I know so.' He paused, the glittering silver eyes like liquid steel as they held hers. 'But when I take you it won't be in a work situation and on the floor of a corridor, Kim. That's a promise.'

She stared at him, utterly taken aback and more frightened than she had ever been in her life. But not of Lucas. Of the feeling deep inside his softly growled words had evoked. She wanted to hate him or at least dislike him but she couldn't. Neither could she pretend that he was just someone she worked for and dismiss him the moment she left the building; he had woven himself too skilfully into her life for that.

'I resign.' She raised her chin defiantly, her back ramrod-straight. 'As of now.'

'Don't be childish,' he said cuttingly, and before she could say anything more he had stepped past her and opened the door onto the stairs, leaving her alone and shaking.

Childish? She stared at the door, nonplussed by the sudden end to what she had considered the most devastating experience of her entire life. *Childish?* How dared he?

She stood for a moment more and then forced her shaking legs to carry her into the office where she made straight for her little cloakroom.

The flushed, bright-eyed girl in the mirror, with the bruised mouth, was not someone she recognised, and she gazed at herself for a full minute before she could persuade her trembling hands to do something about her dishevelment.

Childish. The word had stung and she couldn't get it out of her mind. Possibly because she had to acknowledge, ruefully and only after another five minutes had ticked by in painful self-assessment, that there was more than grain of truth in it.

She had handled it all wrong from the moment his mouth

had touched hers. What she should have done—what any normal, level-headed, experienced woman would have done—was to accept the kiss lightly, move gracefully out of his arms after a moment or two and make some casual comment to defuse what had been—by his own admission—a momentary impulse on Lucas's part.

Instead she had nearly eaten him alive and then accused him of—she didn't like to think what she had accused him of. She gave a little groan, scraping every tendril of hair back so tightly into the knot that her scalp ached.

He must thing she had a screw loose. The mirror told her that she was once again transformed into the neatly tailored, cool and efficient Mrs Allen—on the outside, at least. Perhaps she did have a screw loose, she admitted weakly. In fact she suspected she had whole box of them jangling about with regard to Lucas Kane. Certainly he had the power to turn her into someone she didn't know, someone who was very different from the reserved, cool, careful person she had believed herself to be before she had worked for him.

She was typing away at her word processor, her mind ten per cent on her work and ninety per cent on Lucas's return, when she heard his voice in the corridor outside talking to someone. Her heart jumped up into her throat but she forced her hands to keep up a steady rhythm, even as every sense in her body tuned itself in to the moment when he would walk through the door.

She thought the other voice belonged to Lucas's general manager, who had his office at the other end of the corridor, but she couldn't be sure; most voices had a habit of lowering themselves deferentially in Lucas's presence.

And then the door opened and, although she kept her eyes on her work, she knew he was looking at her.

'Kim?'

She'd half hoped—coward that she was, she conceded

silently—that he would simply carry on as though nothing had happened, but she might have known Lucas wouldn't take the easy way out. She raised reluctant eyes to meet his piercing grey gaze and the butterflies in her stomach did a war dance.

'We have to discuss this properly. You know that.'

It was a statement, not a question, but she answered it as though it had been the latter when she said, her voice as cool and distant as she could make it, 'There's nothing to discuss.'

His compelling light eyes narrowed at the words. 'If you felt disturbed enough to make that ridiculous suggestion about resigning I'd say there's every need,' he said grimly. He perched on the edge of her desk—a habit of his and one which always sent her senses haywire—and continued to survey her unblinkingly.

Why did he have to be so attractive? she asked herself rawly. So incredibly, overwhelmingly attractive? She dared bet that there wasn't a female in the building, in the whole of Cambridge, who wouldn't jump at the chance of having an affair with Lucas Kane.

Was he seeing someone at the moment? The thought was entirely inappropriate in the circumstances but she couldn't help it.

'I've...I've change my mind about that,' she managed at last.

'Of course you have.' It was dismissive, as though the idea had been so ludicrous it wasn't worth mentioning. 'But nevertheless we need to discuss what happened.'

Her cheeks were scarlet again, she could feel them burning, and yet he was as cool and unfeeling as the polished granite his eyes seemed to have been fashioned from. But he hadn't been so unfathomable and cold when he'd been holding her in his arms. The thought made Kim's cheeks even hotter. He had been aroused then, hugely aroused, and it had been *her* body, her lips and mouth and tongue that had made him tremble with desire. She didn't know if she found the thought alarming or comforting but she did find it exciting, and that was more than dangerous enough to cope with.

'Look, Lucas, I'm prepared to look at it as a mistake, one of those things that happen now and again when people of the opposite sex work so closely together as we do,' Kim said with a steadiness she was proud of. 'It didn't mean anything—'

'The hell it didn't.'

It wasn't at all the response she'd expected and cut off all coherent reasoning. 'Wha...what did you say?'

'Kim, I don't know what sort of man you think I am,' Lucas said smoothly, his thick black lashes masking the flicker of anger her words had wrought, 'but when I kissed you it sure as hell meant something to both of us.'

'I didn't mean I didn't enjoy it,' she said quickly, without thinking. She heard him draw in a quick hard breath and realised her *faux pas*. 'I mean...' Her voice trailed away helplessly.

Lucas rescued her with his normal calm composure. 'You've worked for me for five months and I've wanted to see what you tasted like from day one,' he said as coolly as though he was asking her to type a letter. 'Why do you think I haven't dated anyone in all that time?'

'You haven't?' She checked herself quickly. Breathless murmuring was not the way to deal with this.

'And I've been patient,' he continued with silky quietness. More patient than she'd ever know.

'But...'

''Yes?'

'I work for you.'

Lucas ignored every principle he'd ever worked by and

said calmly, 'So? You're unattached and so am I. That's the only important thing, surely?'

Was he stark staring mad? Kim had spent five months fighting off the most devastating feeling of sexual attraction, which had frightened her far more than it thrilled her—at least, the potential power it gave to Lucas frightened her—and the only reason she was still working for Lucas Kane was because she had convinced herself the attraction was all on her side. To get involved, to have a *relationship* with a man like him, was too alarming, too utterly insane and impossible even to consider.

She stared at him, the breadth of his shoulders under the white silk shirt he was wearing suddenly oppressive, and wetted her dry lips. His eyes followed her tongue unblinkingly, his firm, cynical mouth slightly pursed, and her traitorous libido wanted to explode. It was further confirmation that an affair with Lucas was unthinkable. If he would affect her so badly without even touching her...

'It's out of the question, Lucas.'

'I don't accept that,' he said immediately in answer to her trembling voice. 'I'm not asking you to leap into bed with me—' Liar! his conscience screamed silently '—just for us to get to know each other without the pressure of a work environment.'

'I...I can't do that. There's Melody—'

'Melody isn't a problem.'

'It isn't just that.' She took a deep breath, her mind suddenly clear. 'I don't want to get involved with anyone, a man, ever again,' she stated firmly. 'I've been through all that and it didn't work.'

'With your husband, you mean?' he asked softly. And at her nod he shook his own head, his voice low and husky as he said, 'Don't let him spoil the rest of your life, Kim.'

'I'm not, but it *is* my life now and that's what I like.' Her dark-brown eyes held Lucas's gaze with an earnestness that was almost childlike. 'I...I don't think I'm the sort of person who should ever be with someone else, not really.' Graham had flung that at her once in a drunken rage but the barb had held and dug itself deep into her mind.

'What rubbish.' Kim lifted her chin in unconscious defiance and he added, 'Who told you that? Slimeball?'

'Slime... Oh, Graham?'

He could tell by the flush that rose in her cheeks he was on the right tack and anger thickened his voice as he said, 'Don't judge the whole male race by the lowest specimen, Kim, and sure as hell don't take on board anything he said. The guy was crazy not to appreciate what he had.'

'You don't know how it was,' she said defensively. 'It wasn't just Graham, it was... Oh, you don't know.'

Lucas expelled a silent breath. This was the first time she had talked to him, really talked to him, and he didn't want her to close up again. 'No, I don't know how it was,' he agreed quietly, 'so why don't you tell me?'

'I can't.' The colour had drained from her face, leaving it chalk-white. How could she make someone like Lucas understand what it had been like all those years in the children's home? Wanting, *aching* to belong to a family, to have people she could call her own? And then, as she had gone into her teens and realised it wasn't going to happen, she had purposely grown a protective shell, telling herself she didn't care, that she would make it on her own and blow the rest of the world.

And then Graham had happened in her first year at university. Handsome, charming Graham, sweeping her off her feet with all his attention. She had thought he loved her, believed everything he'd said, and it hadn't been until after they had been married that she had come to realise— through something he had yelled at her in one of their rows—that the main reason he had been interested in her was because several of his friends had wanted her. Graham always had to be the one who was admired and envied.

But Graham had given her Melody. By accident, admittedly, but Melody was worth a hundred times the heartache Graham had put her through. And now she had her family and she didn't need anyone else. She wouldn't let herself need anyone else. Needing Graham had made her vulnerable and exposed and weak and she would never give that power to a man again.

Lucas had watched the changing emotions wash over her white, fragile face and he knew she wasn't about to say any more—not here and now, anyway. She didn't trust him, he wasn't even sure if she liked him very much, but she couldn't deny the physical attraction between them. His bruised ego seized on the thought but it was scant comfort.

No woman had ever treated him as Kim had done. He had thought, at first, that the air of cool restraint would mellow as she settled into the job, but it had got stronger, if anything. That night at her home he had felt as though he was treading on eggshells, damn it, and all the ground he thought he'd gained over the last weeks now seemed to exist only in his imagination. She might look fragile and breakable but she was as hard as iron underneath.

So why didn't he cut his losses and congratulate himself on having an efficient and beautiful secretary who was clearly interested in her career and nothing else, and leave it at that? He had any number of women he could call who had made it clear in the past that they were available. Successful, confident, attractive career women. Women with no hang-ups, no inhibitions.

A loud knock at Kim's outer door, followed by the big, rotund figure of John Powell, Lucas's general manager, effectively finished the conversation. It brought Lucas to his feet; the other man was waving a file at his managing director as he said, 'Those subcontractors you wanted the low-down on? You were right, Lucas. We shouldn't touch them with a barge-pole.'

Perfect timing as always, John. Lucas kept his thoughts to himself, but his voice was curt when he said, 'Come into my office, John, and tell me what you've got.' He didn't alter the tone as he added, 'Coffee when you're ready, Mrs Allen.'

Coffee when you're ready, Mrs Allen.

Kim sat for some moments without moving after the door to Lucas's office had closed and she was alone.

The kiss, their conversation, all the emotion of the last half an hour or so hadn't meant a thing to him, not really. He looked on her as a challenge, if anything—that was it at base level. She hadn't fallen into his arms as women were prone to do with Lucas—she ignored the fact that that was exactly what she had done, both physically and metaphorically, that morning—or fluttered her eyelashes or given him the come-on over the coffee cups.

She rose slowly, angry with herself and Lucas. Did she believe he hadn't dated since she'd started at Kane Electrical? Kim considered the thought as she prepared the coffee tray, her slender hands moving mechanically as she frowned into space. Yes, she thought she did; Lucas wouldn't lie.

Lucas wouldn't lie? The moment it entered her mind, she attacked the thought like a terrier with a rabbit. Just because her boss was honest—brutally honest, on occasion—with regard to his business dealings, it certainly didn't mean he was equally honourable and veracious in his dealings with women, she told herself caustically.

Kim suddenly remembered Graham. She had believed him, trusted him, and look where it had got her. One mistake was understandable; a second would verge on stupidity. And she was not a stupid woman. He had called her that many times. She shut her eyes and could almost hear the echo of past fights. Graham had been cruel, spectacularly cruel when he'd been under the influence of alcohol. She had heard it said that an excess of alcohol revealed the real person beneath the social niceties civilisation imposed on the human race, and in Graham's case it hadn't been pleasant.

By the time she carried in the coffee tray Kim was the epitome of the cool blonde, her mouth set in a polite smile and her manner courteous.

'Thank you.' Lucas raised his dark head and looked straight into her eyes as she placed the tray on his desk, and in spite of her acute discomfort Kim felt there was some genuine concern as his narrowed eyes searched her face.

She berated herself for the weakness as soon as she was safely back in her office. June had said he was a Lothario, hadn't she? Well, Lucas's previous secretary hadn't actually said that *exactly*, she admitted in the next instant, but June had implied that Lucas was a love 'em and leave 'em type, and she ignored that at her peril.

She sipped her own coffee, her head whirling, and then contemplated the pile of work needing her attention with a rueful twist to her lips. Enough. She was here to do a job of work and that was exactly what she would do. This morning had been a regrettable hiccup but that was all it had been. She had to get a handle on this.

Lucas Kane was her boss *and that was all he was*. She would be doubly careful not to infringe on his privacy in any way from this day forth—although she didn't think she had done so before—in order not to give him the wrong impression.

And the things he had said? The little voice in her head was determined to be heard. About wanting to kiss her from day one? Wanting to get to know her better?

Kim breathed in and then out very slowly, flexing her

fingers on the keyboard and refusing to let the feeling of panic consume her. She wouldn't think about it. It might be the easy way out but it was necessary for her sanity!

She had made it perfectly clear to Lucas how she felt about any sort of personal relationship with him. And he was a proud man, arrogant even, and certainly egotistical. He would disregard all that had happened today, if she knew anything about it, pretend it hadn't happened and perhaps even concentrate his attention on some delectable female he could parade in front of her to make the point, that she—his secretary—was easily forgotten. Yes, that was what he'd do.

John Powell left Lucas's office ten minutes later and after a minute or two Lucas popped his head round the interconnecting door. 'I've reserved a table for two at a nice little place I know tonight,' he said expressionlessly. 'Be ready at eight.' And the door closed without further discussion.

CHAPTER SIX

RIGHT up until the moment Kim found herself on Maggie's doorstep, asking her friend if she could call round later to babysit, Kim would have sworn she had no intention of keeping her date with Lucas.

She had told him so several times throughout the course of what had been, for Kim, a particularly trying day, but it had been like talking to a brick wall. And she just didn't know how to deal with such intractability, Kim admitted silently to herself on the drive home from Maggie's.

In the two years since Graham had died she had had to freeze several advances from hopeful suitors, but it had been easy. A polite thank you but no thank you, a severe look if they'd needed further persuasion and that had been that. But what had worked admirably with the manager at the local supermarket, an old university friend of Graham's and one or two hopeful admirers from clients of Curtis & Brackley had not cut any ice with Lucas Kane.

She had tried to keep everything on a strictly businesslike basis that day, but Lucas had appeared to find her efforts amusing rather than anything else, Kim reflected irritably as she fixed Melody's tea.

But she would spell it out for him tonight, in letters a mile high if necessary, she told herself grimly. She was *not* going to start a relationship with anyone in the forseeable future, least of all Lucas Kane. Her priority in life was Melody—first and foremost. She didn't want or need anyone else.

Maggie arrived early but Kim had known she would. She hadn't been able to say anything more than that she needed her friend to babysit for eight o'clock when she had called by on her way home from collecting Melody, conscious of small ears twitching, but when Maggie had asked—naturally enough—where Kim was going and with whom, and she had mentioned Lucas Kane, Maggie's eyes had nearly popped out of her head.

Melody was tucked up in bed waiting for Maggie to arrive and read her a story, and after Maggie had called up to say she wouldn't be a minute or two, she had taken Kim's arm in a powerful grip and whisked her into the little sitting room.

'Well?' Maggie's nice homely face was agog. 'What gives with the tycoon?'

'Lucas, you mean?'

'You have more than one fabulously rich and gorgeous man asking you out?'

'He's not gorgeous.' It was too quick and they both knew it, and as Kim watched Maggie's eyes narrow speculatively she said more carefully, 'I mean he's just my boss, that's all.'

'And he's taking you out to dinner as what? A little treat for one of his employees?' Maggie asked a trifle sarcastically. 'Come on, Kim, this is Maggie, remember? So, I ask you again, what gives?'

'Oh, Maggie.' It was a hushed wail. 'It's all such a *mess*.' She told Maggie all of it and at the end Maggie nodded sagely, like a wise little ginger owl.

'I knew you'd been on edge these last months but I thought it was just worry about holding down the job,' she said quietly, her eyes sympathetic. 'Why didn't you tell me before, Kim? It might have helped. I don't pretend to have all the answers—look at me and Pete—but I'm always ready to listen.'

'I know.' Kim lifted tragic eyes. 'And perhaps I'm being ridiculous at panicking anyway. I'm only going out for dinner with him and any other girl would be only too pleased at the opportunity of an evening with Lucas Kane.'

'You're not any other girl, though,' Maggie said gently, 'and perhaps he has the good sense to realise it. Maybe he's serious about you, Kim.'

'I hope not.' Kim's voice was suddenly firmer. 'It's a terrific job and I'd hate to have to leave it.'

'You'd do that? Even fancying him the way you do?'

Kim dragged in a deep breath and expelled it quietly. 'I don't want a man in my life, Maggie,' she said grimly. 'Not now, not ever. I've done all that, I've got the T-shirt, and in my case it really is once bitten, twice shy.'

'But he wouldn't be like Graham,' Maggie said softly. 'You do see that, don't you? You can't let Graham ruin your life, Kim.'

'Funny, that's exactly what Lucas said.' Kim smiled at Maggie, a sad little bitter smile as she added, 'But I don't see it that way. Besides, how long do you think a man like Lucas would be interested in someone like me? A month— two, maybe? It might stretch to six at a pinch. I don't belong in his world, Maggie.'

'How do you know that unless you give it a try?' Maggie asked reasonably.

'I know, all right.' Kim suddenly wanted the conversation to end. 'Anyway, there's Melody to consider too, don't forget. I don't want her getting fond of someone only for them to disappear in a little while. There's one or two of her friends who have ''uncles'' who are here today and gone tomorrow, a new father-figure every time the wind changes. My child isn't going to have to go through that.'

'Okay, okay.' Maggie had the wisdom to know when to call a halt. 'Anyway, it's nearly half-past seven; you'd better go and get dressed.'

Kim had just walked out of the shower when Maggie had knocked, and was still wearing her bathrobe with her wet hair bundled in a handtowel turban-style, and now she glanced at the sitting room clock in horror before flying out of the room, calling over her shoulder as she made for the cottage's narrow stairs, 'Melody's milk and biscuits are ready on a tray in the kitchen. I said you'd read to her while she eats her supper.'

'No problem.' Maggie continued to stare after her friend for a moment or two before walking through into the neat and sparkling kitchen, and her broad freckled face was anxious. No problem, she had said, but unless she was very much mistaken there was a problem of momentous proportions brewing here.

Kim was lovely, exquisitely lovely to look at, but more than that she was lovely inside where it counts. But vulnerable, painfully vulnerable, and she hid that vulnerability behind an armour that somehow this Lucas Kane had managed to penetrate—whether Kim acknowledged it or not. And that wasn't good.

Maggie frowned to herself as she reached for the tray and made her way upstairs. She'd have a good look at this tycoon who was so apparently irresistible tonight, and if she thought he was the type to give Kim the run-around— well, she'd just have a good look at him tonight and take it from there, she told herself stoutly, but her mouth was set in an uncharacteristically grim line and her expression was formidable.

Kim wasn't downstairs when Lucas knocked at the front door just before eight, so after warning Melody to stay in bed Maggie made her somewhat ponderous way to the front door.

'Good evening.' Lucas smiled at the dour-faced woman in the doorway. 'You must be Maggie. I'm Lucas Kane.' He held out a huge bunch of flowers as he added, 'These are for you, to say thanks for babysitting at such short notice.'

Maggie smiled back as she took the flowers—she could hardly do anything else, she told herself silently, when she experienced a moment's contrition at her easy capitulation, besides which she had to admit Lucas had quite taken her breath away—and managed to say, a little breathlessly for her, 'Come in, won't you? Kim will be down in a moment.'

'She's trying to dry her nails but they're taking *ages*.'

This last was from Melody who, unbeknown to both her mother and Maggie, had slid out of bed and was now perched at the top of the stairs, staring through the banisters at Lucas with great brown eyes.

'Are they?' As Maggie and Lucas glanced upward, Lucas grinned at the tiny miniature of Kim. 'Mine took ages, too,' he assured her solemnly.

'Silly.' Melody giggled and wriggled her small body. 'It's only ladies who paint their nails.'

'You're supposed to be in bed, young lady.' Maggie was flustered and it was a new feeling for her, one she didn't care for. 'Back you go and I'll be up in a minute to finish that story.'

'Here, take this before you go.' Lucas reached into the pocket of his overcoat and drew out a small wrapped package which he threw up to Melody, who caught it deftly. 'That's for being a good girl for your Aunt Maggie. You are going to be a good girl, aren't you?'

'Melody's always a good girl.' Maggie felt she had lost control of the situation somehow and she wasn't quite sure how it had happened.

'I'm sure she is.' Lucas smiled down at Maggie again, his voice soothing, and then as Melody shrieked her delight with the beautifully dressed little teddy bear the parcel had contained, he added quietly, 'You go up and see to her, Maggie. I'm fine, really. I'll just sit and wait for Kim.'

'Right.' Maggie stared at him, nonplussed and out of her depth. 'I'll just put the flowers in the kitchen.' She looked down at the magnificent array of yellow roses, white carnations, baby's breath and freesias, and then, as she glanced at Lucas again, she saw his mouth was twitching.

'I admit it, I'm trying to win you over,' he said softly, reading her mind so aptly Maggie turned beetroot-red. 'I need all the help I can get with Kim.'

'I…I'll put the flowers in water.' Maggie berated herself as soon as she'd left the room for not seizing on such a *perfect* opportunity to ask Lucas how he felt about Kim, but somehow—now he was here in the flesh and a hundred times more daunting than ever Kim had described—she hadn't dared.

Which made her the wimp of the decade, she told herself irritably as she hurried upstairs to Melody's pretty pink and cream bedroom which she and Kim, along with Pete, had decorated the first weekend Kim had moved into her new house.

Just a few yards along the landing, Kim was surveying herself in the full-length mirror in her bedroom. She hadn't known what to wear—what did women wear for a date with a multi-millionaire anyway? she thought with wry humour—but had finally put on one of the two new evening outfits she had bought a couple of months before, courtesy of Kane Electrical's clothing allowance.

The sleeveless olive-green silk and cashmere dress had a matching waist-length cashmere jacket and had cost an arm and a leg, but when Kim had seen it in one of the more exclusive little shops in Cambridge she had known it was eminently suitable for any evening function she might attend as Lucas's secretary. It was chic without being ostentatious, elegant and stylish, and fitted her like a dream. The colour emphasised the striking contrast between her hair and her eyes and brought out the honey-gold tone of her skin to the extent she had gasped when she had first tried the outfit on.

What would Lucas think when he saw her? She caught at the thought, refusing to let it have head room, but nevertheless the thrill of excitement the beautiful clothes had induced lingered in spite of herself, and as Kim applied a dab of perfume to each wrist and small crystal studs to her ears her hands were trembling.

She popped in to kiss Melody goodnight before she nerved herself to go downstairs, and as she stepped into the room her daughter's eyes widened appreciatively. 'You look so pretty, Mummy, like the princess in Aunty Maggie's story.'

'Thank you, precious.' Kim sat down on the edge of the bed and gathered the small body close, careless of the new outfit. Melody smelt of baby powder and her soft blonde hair was still slightly damp from her bath and curling slightly round the elfin face. Kim felt such a surge of love well up in her as her daughter's arms wound round her neck and Melody's lips pressed against hers that she closed her eyes against it, holding Melody against her heart for some seconds before she settled her daughter back under the duvet.

'You look stunning.' Maggie had been with her when she had bought the outfit, and her voice was wry as she added, 'But you'd look great in sackcloth and ashes, like I told you before.'

Kim smiled at her friend; she knew Maggie found her lack of confidence in her looks amazing but she couldn't help it. The years in the children's home followed by her disastrous marriage and Graham's mental abuse had damaged something deep in her psyche, and although she had fought back—and would continue to fight—she wasn't quite there yet.

But she looked good tonight. She gave a mental nod to the declaration as she stood up, her voice low as she said to Maggie, 'Well? What do you think?', inclining her head towards the door.

Maggie answered the unspoken question about Lucas by shaking her fingers as though they'd been burnt. 'Wow.' One word but it covered everything.

And then both women turned to the small figure in the bed in consternation as Melody said, her piping voice very clear and direct, '*I* think Lucas is scrumptious.' One of Melody's Christmas presents had been a video of the film *Chitty Chitty Bang Bang*, and 'scrumptious' was her new word for the moment and used for all sorts of good things.

But Lucas? Kim glanced at Maggie anxiously and Maggie shrugged, her voice dry as she said, 'Bright as a button, and serves us right for being so arrogant to think we could talk in code with Miss Muffet around.'

'I do, I think he's scrumptious.' Melody had caught the vibes concerning her new hero and wasn't having any of it. 'Look what Lucas brought me, Mummy.' She held up the little bear for Kim's inspection.

'Lovely, darling.'

'He brought me flowers.' Maggie's voice was magnificently expressionless.

'He did?' Kim eyed her helplessly. 'But I hadn't told him you'd be babysitting.'

'You might not have told him but he knew anyway.'

The two women stared at each other for another long moment and then Kim said, her tone one of resignation, 'I'd better go down.'

The sitting room door was open, and as Kim came down the stairs and reached the threshold, Lucas turned from his quiet contemplation of the garden and Kim received a bolt of electricity as the thickly lashed, curiously silver eyes looked at her. He didn't say a word for what seemed like an eternity; he just stared at her, the most strange expression on his hard, attractive face.

'Hello.' Kim attempted a smile but it was more a quiver of her lips.

'Hello.' It was very soft and very deep and made every nerve in Kim's body twang. 'You look...exquisitely lovely.'

'Thank you.' The intensity of his gaze was making her skin tingle and to combat the feeling, and the warm seductive spell that had settled over the last minute or two, Kim said evenly, 'It was nice of you to bring Maggie the flowers and to think of Melody but it wasn't necessary.'

'Meaning you didn't like it,' Lucas challenged pleasantly.

'I didn't say that.'

'You didn't have to.'

He seemed quite unconcerned and it rankled, badly. She stared at him, totally unaware of how her face was betraying her, and was further taken aback when he strolled over to her with lazy assuredness, taking her arm as he said, 'So, my prickly little secretary, ready for an evening with the big bad wolf? Do you have a coat? It's chilly outside.'

'It's in the hall.' She had stiffened at his touch and had seen his mouth tighten but she just couldn't help it. He was so...big.

The Aston Martin was crouching on Kim's short drive, looking quite incongruous in such humble surroundings, and she found herself taking several deep silent breaths as she slid into the car and waited for Lucas to join her after he had shut the passenger door.

'Have you eaten since lunchtime?'

'What?' Kim turned startled eyes to his dark face.

'Food.' His voice was patient now, overly so, and made her want to kick him. 'Has any passed your lips lately?'

'I had a little of the spaghetti bolognese I made for Melody's tea,' Kim said a trifle defensively. 'Just the last bit in the pan. There was too much to put on her plate.'

'Dangerous habit, that.' He slanted a mocking glance at her from under hooded lids. 'You'll get fat if you eat Melody's leftovers.'

'It wasn't exactly her leftovers,' Kim returned tightly. 'Besides, I was hungry.'

In actual fact, she had thought eating something might calm the flutters in her stomach the thought of the evening ahead had produced, but it hadn't worked.

'All to the good anyway; we shan't be eating until later.'

He started the engine as he spoke, nosing the car out of the small driveway and on to the quiet residential road beyond Kim's front garden.

Kim forced herself to sit absolutely still although every sense in her body was screaming. He was wearing an intoxicatingly delicious aftershave that was subtly sensual and made her want to lean over for a good deep lungful as she nuzzled the harsh—and, she had noticed, recently shaved—jawline.

She lifted her chin in defiance against herself and said carefully, 'We're having that talk first?'

'We're going to the theatre first,' Lucas said mildly.

'The theatre?'

It was almost in the nature of a screech and Lucas narrowed his eyes against it as he repeated, 'The theatre.'

'But…but you didn't say anything about the theatre.' She felt somehow that this was turning into a proper date, with this new slant on the evening.

'Look on it as a nice surprise,' Lucas said smoothly at the side of her, his eyes on the road ahead.

'I don't like surprises.' It was a touch petulant but Kim was past caring. How on earth had she come to be sitting here like this with Lucas Kane driving her to goodness knew where? she asked herself feverishly. He was as male as males went, and everything which cold logical common sense told her was dangerous. Strong and aggressive, with a darn sight too much sexual charisma and pull in the male-female department, not to mention hugely experienced and wealthy to boot.

'Stop panicking, Kim. I'm taking you to the theatre and then to dinner, not to show you my etchings.'

Her eyes shot to the dark profile but Lucas's face was unreadable.

She opened her mouth to deny the accusation and then shut it again. She couldn't win in a war of words with Lucas. Every time she attempted it she seemed to get herself into a worse tangle and he won another battle. Besides which—she bit her lip hard and concentrated fiercely on the dark road ahead—he was right. As usual.

Okay, so she couldn't compete with him mentally, and neither could she deny the effect he had on her physically, she told herself silently, but what she could do was to conduct herself with cool dignity and reserve throughout the evening. The ice maiden approach. Say little, observe much and rise to nothing.

The more she had got to know him, the more she had realised why Lucas chose his lovers from women with careers as similarly high-powered to his own. He was an intimidatingly intelligent individual; he would require mental stimulation from any companion he invited into his bed as well as physical gratification. She wasn't dumb—even though Graham had tried to persuade her otherwise—but neither did she have what those sort of women had.

She had always liked the idea of a career, but she knew herself well enough to recognise that for her family and home would always come first. She didn't want to be up with the cream of the high-fliers—knowing all the latest deals, the latest gossip, having a finger on the pulse and acting ruthlessly and with absolute focus when she had to. And that was the sort of women Lucas gravitated towards.

She was just a change from his usual diet, a passing fancy; he'd find her infinitely boring after a time.

So... She narrowed dark eyes at the brightly lit streets as they reached the heart of the city. She would just be herself but with a great deal of reserve. And by the end of the evening he'd probably be champing at the bit to get her home.

Her soft mouth drooped unknowingly.

The theatre was splendid and their seats were in the stalls with an excellent view of the stage, but Kim was hardly conscious of her surroundings.

Like her, Lucas had dressed up—in his case, a black dinner-jacket and tie—and when he had removed his over-coat in the foyer she had had to force her eyes away with relentless determination when she realised she was ogling him, pretending to admire the elaborately decorated walls and ceiling instead, her cheeks burning.

Once in their seats she buried herself in the programme Lucas had bought her, steeling herself to show no reaction when his thigh briefly brushed hers as he adjusted his long limbs in the limited leg-room.

He leant over her slightly as the cast-list swam and moved before her eyes. 'Have you seen this particular company before?' he asked easily. His cool relaxed tone further evidence to Kim that she was the one with the problem.

'No—no, I haven't.'

'They're good.'

'Right.' As he settled back into his own seat Kim ex-pelled her breath in a silent relieved sigh and prayed for the performance to begin.

How could you be surrounded by people and yet feel as if the rest of the world wasn't there? she asked herself desperately. She didn't *want* to feel like this. It was too disturbing. She didn't want to be with Lucas Kane. *He* was too disturbing.

'Stop frowning; people will think we've had a fight.'

Her eyes snapped sideways and met the mocking silver gaze head on. 'You're my boss, I'm your secretary; having a fight isn't an option,' Kim said primly.

'Is that so?' Lucas contemplated the statement. 'Then what happened after I kissed you?' he asked interestedly. 'Correct me if I'm wrong, but if that wasn't a fight I wouldn't want to be around you when you're really mad.'

Kim eyed him severely. She didn't want to be reminded of that kiss and she suspected Lucas knew it. 'That was just setting the record straight.' And look where it had got her!

'The record being that you do not want a sexual relationship with any man ever again,' Lucas murmured softly. 'Which, of course, is too ridiculous to take seriously.'

'Ridiculous or not, that's the way I feel.' It was a sharp snap, all her earlier resolutions of keeping calm and distant blown to the wind.

'No, you don't.' There was triumph in the silver eyes. 'You want me, Kim. Your lips and your body told me that this morning.'

'*Lucas.*' Kim glanced round nervously.

'And sooner or later it will happen,' he continued silkily. 'You know that as well as I do; that's why you've been as jumpy as a cat on a hot tin roof from the first day you came to work for me.'

'It won't happen, Lucas.' Her eyes had darkened to ebony, and Lucas experienced a moment of intense irritation at the stubborn set of her soft mouth. 'I have Melody; she's the only person I need in my life.'

'Melody is a wonderful little girl but she's a child.' He was careful not to let any of his anger sound in his voice. 'I'm talking about a normal healthy relationship between two adults of the opposite sex.'

'If such a thing exists.' It was out before she even

thought about it, and she felt her heart thud with horror at what she had unwittingly revealed. How was it he made her say things like that? she asked herself feverishly. Made her face things she didn't even know she felt herself?

'Oh, it exists, all right.' His voice was very soft and his eyes piercing on her flushed unhappy face. 'And when it's good it's the greatest thing on earth.'

'I wouldn't know anything about that.' It was very stiff and cool. 'And frankly I don't want to.'

'Yes, you do.' He refused to accept her self-denial. 'But you're too scared, too locked up in yourself to admit it. You want me to hold you, Kim, to kiss you, taste you, ravish you. You want me to take you to heaven and back, to feel me inside you while you lie naked in my arms.'

'Lucas, stop it. You can't say things like that here.' She was shattered, but more by the dangerous desire his soft deep voice was invoking than anything else.

'Why? No one can hear us.' He was so close she felt enveloped in his maleness, his scent, his warmth, and she was trembling. She couldn't help it.

'Please, Lucas…'

'I want you, Kim. I want you more than I've ever wanted any woman in my life and after this morning I know you want me, too. I'm not going to let you deny us both.'

The arrival of further couples at the side of them, corresponding with the theatre lights fading and the start of the play, effectively finished any further conversation, but Kim continued to shake for the first ten minutes of Tennessee Williams's *Suddenly Last Summer*, and in spite of the potent and riveting nature of the play she couldn't seem to let her mind give it the attention it deserved.

The bar was crowded at the interval but Kim didn't mind that; it cut out the chance of any more intimate conversation.

She concentrated on sipping her glass of white wine with

what she hoped was seen as cool aplomb, but with Lucas's arm draped casually round her waist and his lean hard frame pressed against her in the crush of human bodies, the composure was only on the surface.

In just a few hours Lucas had managed to completely alter the tenor of their association from formal employer and employee to... Her mind jerked to a halt. To what, exactly? she asked herself silently. Well, whatever it was, it didn't matter. She had to get back to how it had been and as quickly as possible.

'You're frowning again.' His lips brushed her ear as he whispered against the silk of her hair and she felt the impact right down to her toes.

'Am I?' She looked at him out of the corner of her eye but refused to be drawn further.

'Uh-huh. And I dare bet you were thinking of me,' he drawled affably.

'Surprising though it may seem, I'm not always thinking of you.'

'Something I intend to rectify from now on,' said Lucas firmly.

Kim took another sip of her wine and prayed for the wit and courage to put him in his place. It didn't come. She adjusted her position slightly as a large plump woman on the other side of her who was drenched in a particularly sickly-sweet perfume trod on her left foot, but the manoeuvre only had the effect of emphasising that Lucas wasn't quite so cool and controlled as he looked as she came into contact with his thighs.

The betrayal of his body startled her into looking straight into his face and the silver eyes were waiting for her, his mouth twisted in a crooked grin that told her he was fully aware of her thoughts. 'I told you I wanted you, Kim,' he said gently against her ear again, his warm breath causing frissons of sensation in every part of her. 'And a cold shower isn't an option here.'

She knew her cheeks were burning and wished with all her heart that she was one of the sophisticated, blasé, worldly-wise women he was used to, women who would have a light amusing comment on their tongue to defuse such a situation without any awkwardness—but she wasn't. And then, as Lucas reached behind him and placed his empty glass on a shelf running along the length of the wall, he moved her into the circle of his arms, his hands resting possessively on her waist.

'Incredible woman,' he whispered softly against her forehead, his warm lips caressing her as he spoke. 'Defiant and angry one minute, shy and bewildered the next. I don't know one other woman who blushes like you do. Sensual and all woman in my arms and then as cold as a beautiful ice sculpture. You fascinate me, Kim. Do you know that?'

'I don't want to fascinate you,' she said desperately, whilst knowing—with a feeling of overwhelming panic—that that wasn't quite the truth. Which made her crazy, insane, because getting involved with Lucas would mean emotional suicide for sure.

'Perhaps that's part of what drew me at first,' Lucas murmured thoughtfully, almost to himself, as he leant back slightly in order to hold her drowning eyes. 'The world is full of gold-diggers, Kim, or men and women who chose their partners for the kudos reflected on them. Esteem, renown, furthering one's reputation or career—it's the name of the game.'

'Not my game.' She tried to extricate herself from his arms but he didn't seem to notice, and then, as she broke eye contact, she looked at his mouth and her heart seemed to stand still. It was a hard, faintly stern mouth—even when he was being gentle, the way he was now—and devastatingly sexy.

'No, I know that.' His brow creased in a quizzical ruffle. 'Sometimes you seem as young as Melody, and yet the very fact of her existence proves you are not what you seem. You've been married, borne a child. You're a mother, a single parent who provides for her family.' There was a faintly whimsical note to his voice, as though he couldn't believe what he was saying, and although she felt she should feel insulted Kim couldn't summon up the necessary anger.

'Lots of people are different underneath,' she managed evasively, vitally aware of his hands idly caressing her slender waist and the massiveness of his shoulders and broad chest. They were creating a whole host of feelings she could well have done without.

'Maybe, but usually for the worst,' Lucas responded drily.

'That might be the case with me.' She had spoken lightly but the root was in her fragile self-esteem, and instead of the witty or cynical answer she was expecting Lucas said nothing for a few moments, his eyes narrowing on her lovely face.

'If he wasn't dead, I'd want to kill him.'

It was like a punch in the chest and tension shot through every part of her body at the look in his eyes. She froze, becoming stiff and unyielding in his arms, and Lucas swore silently to himself for going too fast.

But then she slowly relaxed again, brushing a wisp of hair from her thick fringe out of her eyes as she said, very quietly, so quietly he had to lower his head slightly to hear her, 'He used to say that to me, that he wanted to kill me, towards the end. He knew I wanted to leave him and he used to threaten—'

'What?' Lucas was amazed she was talking like this and scared to say anything in case it drove her back in her shell.

'He used to say he would kill Melody first, then me. That

he would find me wherever I went, hunt us down. He…he was unbalanced when he was drinking, violent, capable of anything. And then other times, when he was sober, he would take Melody to the park and act like a normal father. But I could never relax. One time he went out sober and came back and I could smell the drink on his breath. He wasn't drunk, but he'd been drinking when he was supposed to be looking after her.'

She raised agonised eyes to his horrified face as he expelled a long hard breath.

'I wouldn't let him go out alone with her after that; I wouldn't let her out of my sight for a minute. He was becoming too unpredictable,' Kim said flatly.

'Did he go anywhere for help, professional help?' Lucas asked softly.

Kim shook her head, her eyes cloudy and dark. 'Graham wouldn't acknowledge he'd got a problem,' she said bitterly. 'It was me who was at fault, according to him. I was boring, a kill-joy; he used to—' She stopped abruptly, suddenly aware she was saying too much. There were some things, secret things, she had sworn she would never tell a living soul.

'He used to?'

'It doesn't matter.' She was retreating from him but there was nothing he could do about it in the middle of a theatre bar, Lucas told himself silently.

'Could I have another glass of wine?' Kim finished the last of the clear white liquid in one gulp and held the glass out to him with a brittle smile. She didn't really want another drink but she had to do something to break the curiously intimate bubble his arms had woven round her, a bubble that had made her reveal far more than she had intended.

In the last few minutes before the bell rang for the second half Lucas kept the conversation light and amusing, and

Kim tried to respond in kind, but inwardly she was as tight as a coiled spring.

Now that the spell his nearness had evoked was broken she couldn't believe how she had spoken to him—*him*, Lucas, the one person in all the world she needed to keep at a distance. She didn't want him to know anything about her life—past or present—she told herself feverishly. He had power enough over her as it was.

In spite of all her misgivings and self-recrimination, Kim found herself enjoying the second half. And then the lights rose and they were making their way out to the car, the damp chilly air after the hot-house warmth of the theatre making Kim shiver on the steps of the building.

'Cold?' Lucas didn't wait for an answer, drawing her into his side with a practised ease that seemed perfectly natural and which made Kim feel she would be overly crass if she objected to the arm round her shoulders. But it was too cosy, too 'coupleish' to be anything but acutely disturbing.

The meal, at a wonderful little Italian restaurant a short drive from the theatre, was delicious, and contrary to all her expectations Kim found herself relaxing enough to enjoy the excellent food.

Lucas seemed to have metamorphosed into yet another of his many selves and this one, a convivial and charming dinner companion, was sufficiently non-threatening to be, if not quite comfortable, then certainly agreeable.

He didn't mention her disclosure from their talk at the theatre during the meal, nor yet on the drive home, and Kim felt too emotionally drained to bring up the original purpose of their dinner date. Anxious as she was to set their relationship on the right footing again, any further discussion about it was beyond her for the moment.

She stared out into the dark night as the Aston Martin purred through misty, deserted streets.

Lucas was the most confusing, exasperating, arrogant, authoritarian man she'd ever met, she told herself crossly, painfully conscious of every tiny movement from the hard male body at her side.

Since they had started the drive home he hadn't said more than a word or two, his attention seemingly concentrated on his driving, but the silence was neither quiet or restful—as far as Kim was concerned. In fact the car seemed to vibrate with a throbbing current which was setting Kim's teeth on edge, as though fingernails were rasping down a slate blackboard.

She was feeling horribly vulnerable for a whole host of reasons: all she had revealed about her past, the fact that she had—despite all her efforts to the contrary—enjoyed being with him, but most of all the knowledge that soon—very soon—he would kiss her again. But she could control the kiss this time, she assured herself vehemently. Of course she could. Whatever Lucas expected, she would make sure it was a polite thank you type of embrace, a brief touching of their lips before she got out of the car and she was not—*she was not*—going to ask him in for coffee.

With each mile that passed Kim could feel herself getting tenser and tenser, and then they were cruising down her street and the Aston Martin nosed its way across the crossover and into the short pebbled drive in front of the cottage.

She was home. Kim took a deep breath, the courteous little speech she had rehearsed for the last ten minutes hovering on her tongue, and then she found the wind completely taken out of her sails when Lucas said, his tone even and pleasant, 'That was a great evening, Kim. Thank Maggie again for me, would you, for helping out with Melody?'

'Yes, yes, I will.' Was that it? That couldn't be it, *surely*?

She watched in something approaching disbelief as Lucas opened his door and walked round the wetly gleaming bonnet, and then her door was open and his hand was helping her to alight.

'Good night, Kim.' The brushing of her lips was as brief as ever she had determined earlier, but it was *Lucas* calling the tune and controlling events.

'Good night.'

The word was still on her lips when he turned and walked back to the car, opening his door and sliding into the leather interior with a cool smile.

How dared he? After all he had said, how *dared* he not kiss her? she raged silently. Not that she would have allowed the sort of kiss they had shared earlier, not for a minute, but how dared he not try?

She was still standing there, seething with hurt pride and sheer astonishment, when the car backed out of the drive and on to the road beyond. And then it was gone, in a flash of sleek metal and bright lights, and the damp, chilly night enfolded her in its shadowy darkness.

Why hadn't he kissed her? She touched her mouth with a bemused hand. *Really* kissed her? She glanced up into the night sky but the dense thick rainclouds held no answers. Didn't he like her any more? Perhaps he had been bored tonight, the way she'd wished earlier; they said you should be careful what you wished for.

Of course, it was all to the good. She drew in a lungful of cold air that smelt of wet earth and vegetation, and bit her lip against the urge to cry. It really was. This way she was saved the embarrassing necessity of having to rebuff his advances, to fight him off.

Fight him off! She smiled bitterly. He hadn't been able to get away quickly enough. Well, that was the end of that. She nodded to the thought and then said it out loud, her breath a white cloud in the cold air. And she was glad. She was really, really glad. She only felt this sick churning in her stomach because of the rich food, that was all.

She stood for a few moments more until she became aware her coat was enshrouded with tiny droplets from the misty rain and turned abruptly, squaring her shoulders as she walked over to the front door and searched her small handbag for her key.

It would be work tomorrow as usual.

CHAPTER SEVEN

KIM spent a wretched night tossing and turning and finally gave up all hope of sleep at four in the morning, padding quietly down to the kitchen and making herself a steaming cup of hot chocolate.

She drank it curled up in one of the armchairs with just the dim light from a table lamp lighting the sitting room, and the dying glow from the embers of the fire providing a little warmth.

She didn't want to feel like this. It was a silent wail but none the less anguished for it. She didn't want to let any man under her skin ever again. But somehow…somehow Lucas had managed to turn her world upside down in the five months in which she'd worked for him. She had been fighting this strange attraction, this almost consuming fascination from day one, if she was being truthful.

She should never have accepted the post as secretary to Lucas, it had been foolhardy—madness. But then she wouldn't have had this lovely home, had a chance to clear her debts once and for all and to take charge of her life, and Melody's, again, would she? she argued back.

And she could get a handle on this; it just needed discipline, and of course it would be a whole lot easier now if he had decided she wasn't worth the effort.

The thought hit her hard in the chest and she bowed her head over the mug, her eyes desolate. She was going crazy, here, she told herself miserably. She had to pull herself together. She would never contemplate exposing herself and Melody to the risk of another disastrous relationship, she knew that deep inside, so whether Lucas wanted her or not was immaterial.

After another cup of chocolate Kim decided she had moped enough. She set her face resolutely, pulled out the ironing board and tackled the pile of ironing she had been trying to ignore for days. That finished, she fetched out her baking tins and set about making one of the rich chocolate cakes Melody loved so much, followed by a cheese and bacon flan for their tea later that day.

It was light outside by the time she had finished, and after clearing up the kitchen she ran herself a hot bath and luxuriated in the warm bubbles for over half an hour, relishing that she had plenty of time for once.

After washing her hair and applying a rich conditioner she let it dry naturally whilst she creamed every inch of her skin, pampering herself in a way she hadn't done for ages.

She wanted to look her absolute best today. She didn't question why it was so important, it just was.

Once in her cream and pine bedroom, Kim contemplated the contents of her wardrobe thoughtfully. She needed to radiate cool control and efficiency. Never mind she didn't feel it, she told herself bracingly, half the population got through on a wing and a prayer at some point in their lives, and this was her point. She was not going to creep into the office this morning like a small whipped puppy—she was going to be the dignified, mature, capable woman she really was. Simple.

By the time every item of clothing was strewn over the bed, Kim was panicking. It was time to get Melody up for school and normally by now she was dressed, perfectly groomed and had prepared their breakfast.

'Calm, girl. Calm.' She spoke out loud before shutting her eyes and breathing in and out deeply a few times. 'This is just a normal working day. That's all it is.'

'Who are you talking to, Mummy?' Melody had poked her head round the half-open bedroom door and now Kim saw great liquid brown eyes surveying her unblinkingly. 'And why is that big heap of clothes on your bed?'

'Mummy's having a sort-out.'

'Can I take Edward to school to show Kerry and Susan?' Kim saw the small bear Lucas had bought her was tucked under one pyjama-clad arm where no doubt he'd spent the night. It did not help Kim's current state of mind an iota.

'I don't think so, darling. What if he got lost or dirty?' Kim said as calmly as she could. 'Why don't you put him with all your other cuddly toys and then he'll be here when you get home tonight?'

Melody considered the suggestion with a tilt of her blonde head. 'I'll put him on my pillow,' she decided firmly, 'and then all the others will know he's the boss.'

Kim smiled weakly. It seemed to sum everything up somehow.

Once she had chivvied Melody to have a quick wash and get dressed, Kim nipped downstairs and prepared their breakfast of cereal and toast, before flying upstairs again and reaching for the nearest item of clothing on top of the pile.

She would clear everything away when she got home, she decided feverishly, dressing hastily before brushing her hair through. The conditioner had done its work, and her golden blonde locks hung like a shining silk curtain to her shoulders, her fringe almost shimmering in the artificial light over the mirror.

She could wear her hair loose today. It was a full ten seconds before she realised she was seriously considering the thought, and for all the wrong reasons. She didn't *want* Lucas to be attracted to her, she told herself vehemently, or consider what he had missed by not attempting to take things further last night. She didn't want him in her life, not in a personal sense. He was too manipulative by half, and far too charismatic—he had already won Melody over, hook, line and sinker, and Maggie had been distinctly mellowed by that outrageously extravagant gesture with the flowers.

She glared at the reflection in the mirror before pulling her hair back so ferociously not a wisp dared escape, and once it was secure she applied her usual light make-up and stood back to survey the result.

Her neatly tailored suit in a sedate navy blue was smart and practical, and the cream blouse underneath buttoned right up to the neck with a demure stand-up collar. She looked every inch the executive secretary, and that was *all* she wanted to look like.

She would go into work as normal this morning, perform her duties to the best of her ability and return home satisfied in the knowledge she had earnt every penny of the excellent salary.

And if—and, going by Lucas's departure last night, the if was huge—he should ask her for another date she would refuse, politely and firmly, and stand her ground this time, come hell or high water.

Kim drove into the large car park of Kane Electrical at her usual time and then stared in surprise at the empty space next to her reserved spot. No Aston Martin meant no Lucas.

The reason for this became clear when she reached her office. There was a cream envelope on her desk with her name written on it in Lucas's unmistakable bold black script. The note the envelope contained was brief and to the point:

Kim, my father contacted me just before midnight from the hospital in Florida where they'd taken him and my mother after the car he was driving burst a tyre at high speed. They have a few broken bones between them but I understand the tree that was foolish enough to get in the way fared worse. I'm flying over to check how things are but hope to return tomorrow. Their telephone number is in the address book in the left-hand drawer of my desk if you need me.

There followed a list of instructions about the pile of work under the envelope, followed by his name. And that was all.

Kim stared at the writing for some time, her mind swirling and her conscience telling her she was dreadful, *awful*, to think about the formal tenor of the letter at a time like this.

His parents were in hospital and he was obviously worried enough to go shooting off halfway across the world; he probably hadn't had any sleep or food or anything else, and here was she worrying that the letter seemed…cold, off-hand. And why shouldn't it be, anyway? she reprimanded herself in the next instant. She was his secretary, that was all. *That was all she was.*

The day dragged interminably, and whether it was due to the sleepless night she had endured or the amount of correspondence she doggedly worked through Kim wasn't sure, but by the time she left the building her head was thumping and she was so exhausted she went straight to bed as soon as Melody had gone to sleep.

The next morning she tried to ignore the anticipation that was sending little frissons of sensation down her spine on the drive to Kane Electrical, but as the day progressed and there was no word from Lucas Kim found herself leaping to answer the phone each time it rang, and holding her breath every time she heard voices in the corridor outside.

Five o'clock did eventually make its appearance. Kim

slid the cover over her word processor and refused to let the cloud made up of hurt and disappointment and a hundred other confused emotions besides settle over her.

She was glad all this had happened right now, she told herself firmly, as she took the lift down to reception. She might, she just *might* have been foolish enough to take on board some of the things Lucas had said and done if this hadn't showed her it was all surface level. The wanting her, his quiet gentleness and compassion when she'd revealed a little of how it had been with Graham, the way he'd set out to charm her and make her laugh during their meal— oh, a million things!

She sighed irritably. She still had a whole truckload of ghosts to lay before she could consider herself free from the past, and confronting some of those personal demons was going to be hard enough as it was.

Yes, this was definitely all for the best. When Lucas arrived back in the office no doubt he would resume the easy working relationship he had adopted before that disastrous kiss, and everything would be back to normal. Whatever that was.

When she and Melody got out of the car a little while later, Kim stood for a moment or two on the drive just looking about her.

It was the first day of April, and the spring evening was cool and mellow with a hint of woodsmoke wafting in the lazy breeze that ruffled the branches of the silver birch at the corner of the front garden.

Underneath the tree a host of sweetly coloured crocuses and primroses were in full bloom, and although the pebbled drive made up the rest of the garden the whole effect was pretty and pleasing. And it was hers, all hers, Kim thought soberly. And she had a great job, and she and Melody were healthy and financially secure for the first time in years— everything was terrific.

So why, in view of all that, did she have such a feeling of heaviness on her? Kim asked herself silently. There was a lead weight on her heart and an underlying feeling of restlessness she could well do without.

This was further enhanced when the telephone rang just after she and Melody had finished tea. It was Maggie, and from the tone of her friend's voice Kim knew immediately something was wrong.

'I'm taking that job in America for six months, Kim.' Maggie had told her a few weeks before about the wonderful offer from a wealthy businessman who wanted Maggie to design and oversee the interiors of both his new apartment in New York and a sumptuous beach house in California. But Maggie had been unsure about leaving England—and more particularly Pete—for such a long stretch, and had been dithering as to whether to take the commission. 'I leave after the weekend.'

'It's a brilliant opportunity, Maggie.' Kim repeated the words she had used when Maggie had first told her about the venture. 'What made up your mind to accept?'

'Pete,' said Maggie flatly. 'I've had enough, Kim. I've told him he's a free agent while I'm gone but if he wants me when I come back it means the whole hog—full commitment, and that includes marriage. I want children, Kim, and soon. We've been together long enough for him to make up his mind one way or the other, and this seems like the perfect time for him to sort himself out. If he can't do without me, great. If it's all over when I come home, so be it. This is the short, sharp shock treatment you suggested once.'

'Are you sure?' Kim asked anxiously. Maggie worshipped the ground Pete walked on.

'No, I'm frightened to death he'll pull the plug, if you want to know,' Maggie said dejectedly, 'but I can't carry on the way we are, either. It's killing me, Kim. We've agreed no contact, no letters or phone calls for the whole of the six months, so it's really make or break.'

They talked some more and after Kim had replaced the receiver she continued sitting at the foot of the stairs, staring into space.

She'd miss Maggie, and so would Melody, but she felt in her spirit Maggie was doing the right thing. It was a gamble, but then everything in life carried some sort of risk.

She frowned suddenly, aware her mind was trying to tell her something she couldn't grasp. And then the doorbell rang.

Kim glanced at her watch. Seven o'clock. Who on earth was calling at seven o'clock? she asked herself wearily. It had to be a salesman of some kind or other—the only other person who would pop round was Maggie and she'd only just got off the phone to her. She hoped it wasn't one of the more persistent individuals, that was all. She didn't feel like doing battle tonight.

She pulled herself up from the bottom stair and walked across the hall, opening the door with a polite refusal already hovering on her lips. *'Lucas!'* She could feel the colour pouring into her cheeks but she couldn't help it.

'Hello, Kim.'

'But you're in America,' she said stupidly.

'Am I?' He smiled. A tired smile. 'Clever me.'

'I mean, I thought you were in America,' she corrected quickly, suddenly hotly aware of the old jeans and skinny-rib jumper she had pulled on before making tea.

'Can I come in?'

She could feel the intensity of his gaze on her hair, which she had brushed out when she'd changed and was wearing loose on her shoulders, and her blush deepened. 'Oh, yes. I'm sorry. Of course, come in.' She was so flustered she nearly fell over her own feet as she backed away from the door, and then Melody emerged from the sitting room like a small bullet, her tiny face all lit up.

'Lucas!' With a total lack of inhibition Melody ran over to him and smiled up into the hard rugged face. 'Have you come to see me?' she asked trustingly.

'That I have.'

With his gaze now on the small figure of her daughter Kim was able to really look at him, and she saw the harsh face had a grey tinge of exhaustion and he looked utterly done in.

'Good,' Melody declared happily. 'Mummy and me are doing a jigsaw I had for Christmas. You can help if you like. It's *very* hard,' she added with a small frown.

'Darling, Mr Kane—Lucas—is tired,' Kim said quickly.

'But not too tired to try my hand at the jigsaw,' Lucas put in swiftly, holding out his arm to Melody, who took his hand immediately and dragged him off to the sitting room.

The jigsaw was lying on a big tray on the rug in front of the fire, and Kim watched with something approaching disbelief as her dignified and illustrious boss shrugged off his suit jacket and loosened his tie before squatting down next to Melody on the floor.

The light caught the shining blue-black jet of his hair and the fragile fairness of Melody's waves, emphasising the contrast between them, and for a moment Kim felt such a sense of panic she wanted to run across the room and snatch Melody up in her arms.

'Would...would you like a drink?' she asked helplessly from the doorway.

'I'd love one. Black coffee, please.' Lucas turned round and looked at her as he spoke, and the flickering glow from the fire picked out the lines of strain round his mouth and eyes.

He was dead beat. Kim stared at him for a second more

and then heard her voice asking, 'Have you eaten? I can rustle up something, if you like?'

He looked at her quietly for a moment. 'That would be great, Kim. Thank you.'

'Are your parents all right?' Too late she remembered she hadn't asked after them, but that was the trouble with Lucas, she told herself crossly. All coherent thought seemed to fly out of the window when he was around.

'They'll live.' It was dry. 'Dad is suffering more from the tongue-lashing Mum gave him than his broken leg and torn muscles. He always tends to drive too fast and she's sure that contributed to the accident.'

It seemed strange hearing him refer to his parents as Mum and Dad, somehow, and Kim didn't like the feeling the warmth in his voice engendered either. She didn't want to think of him as a loving son; it made him that touch more human and that was dangerous.

As Melody claimed Lucas's attention by tugging on his sleeve Kim said hastily, 'I'll get that coffee,' and shut the sitting room door quickly.

She stood still for a moment in the kitchen, aware her heart was pounding. He was here, he'd come. What did that mean? Her heart gave a mighty kick and she shut her eyes tightly, but that only painted the picture of Lucas—his shirt taut across muscled shoulders and his long legs crossed Buddha-fashion as he sat next to the tiny figure of Melody—more vividly across the screen of her mind.

Food. With unconscious drama she raised her hands and opened her fingers wide. Concentrate on the food, Kim, she told herself silently. She knew where she was with that.

At half-past seven Kim served up pork chops with lemon and herbs, and new potatoes and baby carrots and peas for Lucas, whisking Melody out of the room at the same time so Lucas could eat his food in peace whilst Melody had her bath and got into her pyjamas.

'This looks delicious. Thank you.'

The soft deep voice stopped Kim just as she was about to shut the sitting room door again and she turned, indicating for Melody to continue up the stairs, before she glanced back at Lucas and said, her smile brittle, 'There's either spicy apple, date and sesame loaf to follow or a piece of the chocolate cake Melody likes if you'd prefer.'

'Home-made chocolate cake?' It was almost winsome.

Kim nodded carefully.

'It's been years since I had home-made chocolate cake,' Lucas murmured appreciatively.

'Chocolate cake it is, then.'

After she shut the door Kim found she had to lean against it for a full thirty seconds. He was too sexy, she told herself despairingly. Too sexy by half. How did he manage to look so broodingly tough and little boy lost at the same time?

And she hadn't asked why he was here. She hadn't even acted as though a boss appearing on his secretary's doorstep at seven in the evening was unusual. She'd just simply offered him coffee and then proceeded to cook him a meal. Barmy. This man was sending her stark-staring barmy.

Once Melody was bathed and in bed Kim left her drawing a picture with her new set of pencils, after promising her she'd return and read her a story in a few minutes after she had fixed Lucas's dessert.

She heated the large slice of chocolate fudge cake just the slightest in the microwave, the way she did for Melody, and served it with a generous dollop of fresh cream, carrying it through to the sitting room quickly.

Lucas was sitting staring into the fire as she opened the door, his elbows on his knees and the empty plate at his side, and she noticed immediately he had taken his tie off and rolled up his shirt sleeves. The aura of masculinity was overwhelming, and Kim felt her stomach tighten.

'I should have rung before I came round,' he said

abruptly, rising to his feet at her entry into the dimly lit room.

What did he expect her to say to that? They looked at each other for a second, and then Kim said quietly, 'Why didn't you?'

'Because you would have put me off coming, said you'd see me tomorrow at the office, and I couldn't wait that long.'

He had moved closer to her as he had spoken, taking the plate from her suddenly nerveless fingers and placing it on a chair before straightening again and towering over her, his tall lean body hard and uncompromising and his silver-grey eyes registering the shocked surprise on her face.

'Lucas—'

'For the last forty-eight hours all I've done is to tell myself what a damn fool I was not to kiss you when I had the chance,' he growled softly. 'To hell with doing the honourable thing and giving you time. I need you, Kim.'

'Lucas, please—'

He caught the last breathless word with his lips, his mouth taking hers in a kiss that was all fire and passion, a kiss which rocked Kim to the core. But then almost immediately the ruthless control he exerted in every other area of his life slotted into place, and he was caressing her lips with small, sweet kisses as he moulded her against him.

His tongue rippled along her teeth and Kim shivered her response, barely aware that her hands had lifted to his muscular shoulders where her fingers rose further to tangle in the short, spiky black hair above his shirt collar.

His hands moved in slow exploration down the length of her trembling body with exquisitely controlled sensuality, and Kim found herself kissing him back with a hunger that matched his. She could hear little guttural moans but at first she didn't realise they were coming from deep in her throat, and even when the knowledge dawned she couldn't do anything about it.

She could feel the play of muscles beneath the silk of his shirt when she let her hands roam over the hard expanse of his powerful back, and the scent of him—that delicious, intoxicating mixture of expensive aftershave and pure male—was adding to the wild pleasure sweeping her senses.

His body was magnificent. The height and breadth of him was all around her, consuming in its maleness. *He* was magnificent. And the primitive raw excitement he induced when he so much as touched her was magnificent too. She had never imagined human beings could feel something as elemental as this.

'You're so beautiful,' he murmured huskily against her hungry mouth. 'Incredibly, fantastically beautiful.'

His lips moved to the silky hollow of her throat and she arched back her head, the thick fall of her hair like a shimmering curtain. She could feel the hot hardness of his erection against the softness of her belly and knew he was hugely aroused, but her emotion was one of fierce pride and power that she could make this man, this hard, ruthless, cold man, shake with passion.

And then they both heard it from the bedroom upstairs; a small but determined voice calling, 'Mummy, Mummy. I want you to read my story *now*.'

He raised his head very slowly and only after a trail of kisses ending at her half-open mouth. 'Saved by the bell?' he murmured quizzically against the smooth flushed skin of her cheek.

She stared at him, her eyes huge and seemingly unable to tear themselves away from the carved lines of his mouth and the dark stubble of beard on his chin. 'Your...your dessert,' she managed faintly. 'I came to give you your dessert.'

'It looks good enough to eat,' he said softly, and they both knew he wasn't talking about the cake.

'I need to go.' She gestured vaguely with one hand but still without taking her eyes off his hard, handsome face. 'Melody is waiting for me.'

He smiled, dropping a warm, featherlike kiss on the tip of her nose but without loosening his hold of her by the slightest. 'I know how she feels,' he said huskily. 'I feel like I've been waiting for you all of my life. I came straight from the airport tonight and if you hadn't been here I'd have camped outside until you came back. How come you've done that to me, woman?'

There was a note of real bewilderment in his throaty voice that almost made Kim smile. Almost. But now his mouth had left hers reality was rushing in, and with it the knowledge of how close she had been to losing control. Who was she kidding? she chided herself savagely in the next instant. Her control had been nonexistent. If it hadn't been for Melody calling...

'Lucas, you don't know me.' She tried to prise herself out of his arms as she spoke.

'The hell I don't.' It was soft and intent. 'What do you think the last five months have been all about? I know you and you know me, Kim. Don't try and kid yourself. We've spent most of the last one hundred and fifty-odd days together, damn it.'

'But not intimately,' she blurted out confusedly.

'I'm more than willing to rectify that at the earliest opportunity.'

'You know how I feel,' she muttered weakly, managing to move away from him as Melody's voice called again.

'Yes, I do,' he said with deadly certainty. 'And it's quite different to what you're *telling* me, isn't it, Kim?'

'No.' The protest was weak and the silver-grey eyes reflected their recognition of it.

'You want me, Kim, and I want you. It's as simple as that.'

'Nothing is as simple as that,' she shot back shakily. 'You've got no idea, have you? You think falling in and out of bed is just a grown-up game but it's not. It's not! I'm not like that.'

'Like what?' he bit back angrily, his face straightening and becoming as severe as the wintry hue of his eyes. 'I'm not suggesting a one-night stand, for crying out loud. And while we're on the subject, promiscuity has never been a habit of mine, in case you're wondering—neither have I ever fallen in or out of anywhere, to my knowledge!'

'I didn't mean…' Her voice trailed away as he surveyed her from narrowed unblinking eyes. 'Look, I have to go up to Melody.' She pointed to the cake with a trembling hand. 'Eat your cake.'

She heard him mutter something very rude as she turned and escaped from the room, but she didn't stop in her head-long flight.

Melody was all pouts and frowns when Kim entered her daughter's bedroom, but after establishing that no, Lucas could not come and read her story, and yes, Kim would stay with her until she was asleep, Melody snuggled down in bed and was asleep before the story was finished.

What had she done? Kim sat in the shadowed bedroom watching Melody as she slept, her eyes lingering on the small rosebud mouth and the thick lashes on the porcelain skin, the way Melody's fine silky hair tumbled over the pillow like spun gold.

She had to tell him, as soon as she went downstairs, that she wanted him to leave. Moreover, that if their relationship couldn't be constrained to a purely platonic working association, then she would have to leave Kane Electrical.

Her heart gave a massive thud and then raced for a few seconds, reminding her—as if she needed it—that the thought made her feel sick. But she would do it, she told herself firmly. This was survival. He'd got too close.

She wasn't quite sure when and how it had happened but it didn't really matter now. The end result was the same. She had let him work himself into her life and that meant the potential of pain and misery. It was a road she just wasn't prepared to walk down.

She sat for another five minutes in the quiet room, listening to Melody's steady regular breathing and watching the peaceful baby face. Lucas's bear was tucked under her daughter's arm and the toy confirmed every fear she had, somehow. This had to end, now, tonight. Never mind it had never really started.

Her step was purposeful as she walked downstairs and she had the words trembling on her tongue as she opened the sitting room door.

Lucas was lying slumped on her two-seater sofa, one arm dangling on the floor by his empty plate and the other flung across the cushions in unconscious abandonment. He was fast asleep. Kim stopped just inside the room, her stance like that of a doe before a hunter, and then walked carefully to his side.

Now those riveting eyes were closed and his face was in repose she could see just how exhausted he was. She stared down at him, her eyes drinking in every line and contour of the hard male face. The authoritative sweep of his black brows, the uncompromising cheekbones and determined mouth all spoke of power and hard virility.

It was a face that told the onlooker that subjugation was not an option, that defeat was an unknown and unacceptable concept, and the big lean body and muscled strength evident in every inch of the honed frame was daunting. And sexy. Indescribably sexy.

He was dead to the world. A little shiver ran down her spine and she ached to put her lips against the sleeping

mouth, to trace the faint indentation in the stubbly masculine chin. She should wake him up and tell him to go,
especially in view of what had occurred before she'd gone
upstairs to Melody. He might look curiously vulnerable and
exposed at this moment, but it was an illusion. There wasn't
a vulnerable bone in Lucas's body.

Her eyes lowered to the strong male throat and the beginnings of dark body hair just visible below his open collar, to powerful masculine thighs against which the material
of his trousers were straining.

Was he hairy all over? Her breath caught in her throat
and she suddenly felt as guilty as if she were a peeping
Tom, but she still couldn't seem to tear her eyes away from
the sleeping giant in front of her.

What would it be like to wake up beside him in the
morning after a night of making love? She found she had
no defence against the erotic thoughts crowding her mind.
To taste him, please him, to have him taste and please her?
But she was talking about a lover, here, about giving someone the rights to her body and her life.

Suddenly all the horror connected with the days of her
marriage flooded in and she felt smothered with the weight
of the memories. She took several long deep breaths, pulling at the air as though she were drowning, but still the
feeling of being trapped and desperately frightened was
overwhelming.

She couldn't talk to Lucas now, not now. She needed
time to come to terms with what her head was telling her.
She stood for a moment more and then crept out of the
room to fetch the spare quilt, draping it over the sleeping
form when she returned to the sitting room and turning off
the lights before she closed the door again.

Once in the sanctuary of her bedroom Kim sat on the
edge of the bed and stared vacantly into space.

Lucas Kane was stretched out on her sofa and it looked

as though he was there until morning. She shook her head bewilderedly. Somehow the impossible, the unimaginable had happened. Maggie just wouldn't believe this!

She got ready for bed with both ears straining for the slightest sound from the sitting room, but there was nothing.

Once in bed Kim tried to read for a while but although she dutifully turned the pages she couldn't remember a word she'd read when she thought about it.

Eleven o'clock came and went, then half-past, and finally it was midnight. Lucas was definitely here for the night. Kim put down the book, drank a glass of water and slid down under the covers with a sudden feeling of *que sera sera*.

Short of marching downstairs and throwing him out she could do nothing, she told herself silently, so she might as well try and get some sleep herself. It had been a long day, and an even longer evening, and she had the feeling the next day wasn't going to be any better.

CHAPTER EIGHT

WHEN Kim awoke to the smell of frying bacon she thought for a moment she was still dreaming.

It had been almost light before she had fallen into a fitful doze followed by an hour or two of deep, exhausted slumber, and now, as she glanced at her tiny alarm clock, she saw she had overslept by nearly an hour.

In all the confusion and heart searching of the night before she must have forgotten to set her alarm, she thought feverishly, flinging back the covers as she swung her feet to the floor.

It was unfortunate that Lucas chose that precise moment to enter with a cup of tea. Unfortunate for Kim that was. For Lucas the sight of Kim in a sheer, whisper-thin nightie with her blonde hair tousled and tumbled and her eyes wide with shock was the best start to a day he could remember for a long time.

'Lucas!' Kim shot back in the bed and pulled the covers up to her chin, but not before she had seen the spark of something hot in the silvery eyes.

'I should hope so,' he said calmly. 'Who else were you expecting?'

'I wasn't *expecting* you,' she reminded him severely, her colour high. 'And I'm late; I forgot to set my alarm.'

'Relax.' He strolled over to the bed and her hormones went into hyperdrive. The designer stubble was dynamite. 'You've plenty of time to get Melody to school—and if you're late for work the boss will understand.'

Kim slid a tentative arm from under the covers, the other

141

still holding the duvet tight round her neck, and took the cup of tea he was offering with a nod of thanks.

'One sugar, I understand?' Lucas said lazily. 'Melody's helping me cook breakfast and is a mine of information as to your likes and dislikes. That's a very intelligent little daughter you've got there.'

'I know.' Just go. *Go.*

'You look gorgeous to wake up to.' Lucas seemed in no hurry to leave, his eyes stroking over her flushed face and his stern mouth uncharacteristically tender.

'You didn't wake up to me,' Kim protested quickly.

'I've recently woken up, you're here…' His words faded as his mouth covered her own and the teacup wobbled alarmingly. The kiss was brief and incredibly sweet, and he studied her face for a moment when he straightened again. 'Gorgeous,' he said softly.

'Lucas, you shouldn't be in here. Melody will think—'

'Absolutely nothing,' he finished for her smoothly. 'There's always a dozen or so small people running about when my family gets together, so I know how children's minds work at Melody's age.'

So that was why he was so comfortable around young children. Kim stared at him, realising—with a touch of exasperation—that everything she learnt about him dispelled the image of a hard-hitting automaton a little more. She wanted to find out he was mean to old ladies, that he didn't like children, that he kicked the cat and beat the dog— anything!

'Do you like children?' It was out before she had time to think.

He didn't seem to consider the question strange. 'When they're like the ones in my family, or Melody,' he said calmly. 'Brats I can do without.' And then he smiled mockingly. 'Not what you wanted to hear?'

'I don't know what you mean.' The colour which had

just begun to diminish returned in a fresh surge of scarlet. Impossible man!

'Of course you don't,' he taunted softly.

She wasn't going to win this one. Kim tried to look stern and assertive. 'Where's Melody?' she asked pointedly.

'Sitting at the breakfast bar, eating a bowl of Frosties,' Lucas returned easily, 'before her bacon and egg. Speaking of which—' he dropped another kiss on her nose before turning and walking out of the room, saying over his shoulder '—you can be first in the shower but you'd better be quick. Breakfast will be ready in five minutes.'

First in the shower, for goodness' sake! As the door closed behind Lucas's big frame, Kim found herself glaring across the room. Anyone would think he lived here the way he was carrying on.

And then, before she had time to school her features into anything resembling sweetness, the door opened again and Lucas popped his head round. 'I forgot to say thanks for the bed and board,' he said softly, his eyes amused as they took in her expression. 'I appreciate it more than I can say, Kim.'

She managed a creditably gracious smile. 'That's okay; you were obviously out on your feet. I'd have done the same for anybody.'

'Now don't spoil it. And you're down to four minutes, thirty seconds, by the way.'

Kim had time to do no more than shower and slip into her bathrobe before breakfast, piling her hair into a towel turban-style before running downstairs to the kitchen.

Lucas and Melody were perched on the two high stools the small kitchen boasted in front of the minuscule breakfast bar, and they looked comfortable together. Too comfortable. Melody was in the middle of one of her long and involved stories about a happening at school to which Lucas was giving his full attention, and as Kim surveyed

Melody's animated face and Lucas's patient one she felt a dart of pure panic.

'Mummy!' Melody saw her first. 'Lucas has cooked bacon and eggs and he says I can have mine in a bun. Can I, Mummy?'

'If you eat it all up,' said Kim mechanically, walking across and kissing the top of Melody's fair head as Lucas slid off his stool and waved for her to be seated.

They ate with Lucas propping up the sink unit as he devoured three buns bursting with bacon and egg whilst Melody looked on with unconcealed admiration.

Her daughter clearly thought he was the best thing since sliced bread, Kim told herself crossly, and Lucas was playing up to his role of man of the hour with gusto. Immediately as the thought hit she acknowledged its unfairness. Lucas was just being Lucas, she admitted miserably, which made everything a thousand times worse and a million times more dangerous.

'Can I ask a favour?'

As Melody danced off upstairs to change from her pyjamas into her school clothes Lucas perched himself on the stool she had vacated. It brought him close, much, much too close, and Kim's voice was something of a snap as she said, 'Yes?'

'Do you have a razor I can use?'

It wasn't what she had expected and of course he knew that only too well, Kim thought nastily, but although she knew she was blushing she kept her voice very even when she said, 'I've only light duty disposables that I use for my legs, I'm afraid. I'm not sure they'll cope with a man's beard.'

'I'll manage.'

And then, before she was aware of what he was doing, he had moved his stool in front of hers so that his long legs were either side of her.

'You've a crumb on your chin.' His voice was soft as he reached out and stroked her skin, and she felt terribly aware that she only had her bra and panties on beneath her towelling robe.

She knew what he wanted—it was written all over his dark face—but the shiver that slithered down her spine was more of anticipation than apprehension as his mouth lowered to hers and his whole body seemed to enclose her.

He kissed her slowly and thoroughly, taking his time, savouring her lips with a pleasure that was visible. His tongue nuzzled her teeth and as her mouth opened to accommodate him he plunged immediately into the secret territory, fuelling her desire with a heady rush of sensation that made her gasp out loud.

When he pulled her off the stool to stand in front of him she was powerless to resist, even when his hands slid beneath the folds of the robe to the warm silky flesh beneath. His fingers were possessively skilful as he brought her breasts to tingling life through the lace of her bra, and the sharp little needles of pleasure grew and grew in time with her pounding heartbeat.

His thighs were hard against hers, the image of his sexuality stamped forcefully on her soft belly, and Kim could feel his heart slamming against his ribcage like a sledgehammer as he allowed the kiss to deepen into an intimate assault on her senses that was almost like a consummation in itself.

And then, slowly, she felt the embrace change, his hands continuing to stroke and pet her as they moved to the small of her back but with a control that restrained even as it pleasured.

She raised dazed eyes to his and the silver gaze was waiting for her, his voice rough and not quite steady as he said, 'Melody is upstairs,' and then, when he could see she was still too bemused and disorientated to understand,

'Another minute and I wouldn't be able to stop. Okay? You do something to me, Kim. Something mind-blowing.'

'Do I?' she asked faintly, aware the towel had fallen as her hair tumbled free.

She raised a trembling hand to push back the heavy fall of silk from her face as she spoke, and as she flung back the shining, thick curtain the robe fell fully open, revealing her slender, honey-tinted, rounded curves to Lucas's hungry eyes.

With a wordless exclamation Lucas pulled her to his chest again and kissed her hard on the lips, his mouth urgent and expressing the desire that still had Kim weak and shaky. 'It'd be good between us—you know that, don't you?' he whispered huskily. 'Say it, tell me you know it too.'

Yes, it would be good, incredible, but what about when it ended? Kim asked herself silently. How did one cope in the aftermath of a nuclear missile exploding everything that was safe and familiar to smithereens?

She had never wanted this. She had never wanted to fall in love again. And then she froze, her face turning as white as a sheet as the truth she had been trying to fight for weeks refused to be ignored any longer. She loved Lucas. She *loved* him.

'Kim?' He had been watching her closely and his voice was terse. 'What's the matter?'

'Nothing.' All the desire and excitement his love-making had induced was gone and she felt as cold as ice.

'You look like someone has just kicked you in the teeth so don't tell me nothing,' Lucas said as evenly as he could, struggling for calmness.

'I said nothing is the matter, so nothing is the matter,' she said numbly, struggling out of his arms with a strength that took him by surprise. 'Just leave me alone, Lucas.'

'Leave you alone?' he said incredulously.

'Yes.' She was crying and screaming inside but her voice was actually cool, she thought amazedly. 'I want you to leave, *now*.'

'Oh, no—oh, no, sugar.' There was a raw determination in his voice that was even stronger than the anger. 'No way. We've come a long way since October and I'm sure as hell not going backwards. You talk to me.'

'You can't make me do anything.' Her chin was sticking right out but the fear and defiance in her face was all at odds with what he was asking. Lucas stared at her, recognising that this opposition had its roots in something much more deep than their conversation that morning. And, for all her aggression, she looked about as old as Melody right at this moment.

His anger collapsed. 'No, you're right,' he said quietly, 'but only because I don't and wouldn't operate like that. Brute force or any sort of blackmail is not my style, Kim. But nevertheless we *are* going to talk. And do you know why?'

She stared at him, her eyes wide and enormous in the lint paleness of her face.

'Because I love you,' he said softly.

'No!' It brought a response but not the one he had hoped for. Lucas felt as though ice-cold water had been thrown at him but he didn't betray it by the flicker of an eyelash.

'Yes,' he said coolly. 'I've been around enough to know the real thing when it happens, Kim. And just for the record I've never said that to another woman, not even in the most…intimate times.'

She jerked her head, her eyes wild as she went for the jugular in an effort to make him leave. 'And there have been plenty of those,' she flung at him tightly.

'I've not been celibate,' he agreed with silky smoothness, 'but licentiousness has never held any appeal.'

'I don't want a relationship with you.' She said it slowly,

with a sharp little pause in between each word, and Lucas felt his anger mounting again at the sheer intractability in her face.

'Then you'll spell out why,' he ground out equally slowly. 'You owe me that at least and I'm not budging until we have that talk, Kim. Take Melody to school and then come back here. I mean it.'

She had heard that particular note in his voice too many times over the last months to doubt it, normally when he was digging his heels in over a business situation that seemed impossible and which he was determined to change. But he couldn't change her. Not now, not ever. But she would talk to him. Perhaps when he heard it all he would realise she was serious? And she was. Oh, she was, she told herself desperately. But how was she going to tell him about the humiliations, the awfulness of it all? But she'd have to; it was the only way.

'All right.' It was dull, lifeless, and took away any triumph Lucas might have felt.

Melody was all skips and smiles and giggles when Kim came downstairs from getting dressed a little later, and once her daughter had said goodbye to Lucas—insisting on being lifted up into his arms so she could kiss his cheek—she gambolled out to the car like a spring lamb.

The reason for her exuberance became apparent once they were on their way to school.

'Is Lucas going to be my new daddy?' Melody asked interestedly, almost causing Kim to swerve into the kerb.

'What?' Her voice was too shrill and she tried to moderate it a little as she said, 'What do you mean, sweetheart? Of course not.'

'Aw.' Melody grimaced at her like a dissatisfied elf. 'Susan has got a new daddy and so has Kerry, and Kerry's daddy makes her breakfast. She told me. And he brings her presents sometimes.'

The penny dropped. Kim took a long silent breath as she searched for the right words and then said carefully, 'People often bring other people presents, chicken, just to be nice, especially grown-ups for children.'

'And do people stay and cook breakfast too?'

'Sometimes.'

'I *like* Lucas.' It was defiant and hopeful and bewildered all in one, and Kim's heart went out to the small scrap of humanity at the side of her.

'And he likes you too, darling,' she assured Melody quickly.

'But not enough to be my new daddy?'

This child of her heart had a way of going straight for the kernel in the nut. Kim glanced at her helplessly. 'There's more to being a daddy than that,' she managed softly. 'Adult things, and very complicated. But Lucas likes you every bit as much as you like him, I promise you.'

She could feel Melody gazing at her and prepared herself for what might come next, but in the mercurial way of children Melody suddenly tired of that avenue of thought and said instead, 'I got all my letters right yesterday, Mummy. Even the hard ones.'

'Well done, darling.'

'Kerry didn't. And she can't hop, either.'

So a new daddy didn't provide the answer to everything. Kim's hand reached out and squeezed one of Melody's for a moment. They would get through this. Somehow.

On the way back to the house Kim found she was shaking, and she stopped the car in a quiet lay-by for a few minutes to give herself the chance to calm down and prepare for what lay ahead.

Somehow, and she still wasn't quite sure how or when the situation had escalated so alarmingly, she was going to have to convince Lucas she wasn't in the market for an affair, albeit a potentially serious one from his comment about loving her. Did he? Did he love her? Kim considered the possibility with tightly shut eyes, her hands resting limply on the steering wheel.

How could you want something and yet fear it so much it made you nauseous at the same time? she asked herself silently, dragging in the air through lips that trembled.

Love meant disappointment and betrayal and bitter hurt. She knew that; she *knew* it. It meant a transference of power from one person to another with terrifying consequences. It meant subjugation and a bondage that was worse than anything in the physical realm because it involved the heart, the emotions, the very essence of who you were.

She couldn't really remember her parents beyond a deep male voice mixed with the faint odour of cigar smoke, and the feel of her mother's softness enveloping her in a warm, secure, satisfying embrace in the middle of the night when—presumably—she had woken from some bad dream or other. But she could remember her Aunt Mabel. Remember the promises that she was safe now, that everything would be all right, that she would be loved and looked after like Mummy and Daddy would have wanted.

And then her aunt had gone, and she had found herself in an alien environment. She had cried and screamed, she could recall that as though it were yesterday, and someone—a trained child counsellor, probably—had explained everything to her.

It hadn't been until much later that she had realised her Aunt Mabel, who for two years had been her security and base, hadn't made any provision for her. Had left her at the mercy of those relatives who had descended like vultures on her aunt's estate.

Kim opened her eyes wide and stared straight ahead. And then there had been Graham... Her face set in rigid control and she turned the ignition key with a sharp movement of her hand.

Lucas was waiting for her when she drew up outside the cottage. He looked tough, remote, but she now knew that remoteness of his was a devastating weapon which he used with expert finesse, lulling one into a false security that was deadly.

'The coffee's ready.' His voice was gentle—deliberately so, Kim warned herself silently.

'Lucas, this is pointless, us talking like this,' Kim nerved herself to say quickly.

'I disagree.' He smiled blandly.

Kim tried a different approach. 'The Marsden contract is hanging on a thread,' she reminded him evenly. 'You were supposed to call Miles Marsden at nine this morning.'

Lucas suggested somewhere that Miles Marsden could go before narrowing his eyes and staring at her fixedly. She stared back for a moment before the silver gaze became unbearable.

'Coffee,' he reaffirmed smoothly, his voice firm but expressionless. 'I've got used to my daily quota and I can't do without it, or perhaps I should say I don't intend to do without it.'

They weren't talking about coffee. Kim walked past him into the hall as he waved her over the threshold of the house, and again she had the feeling that she was the guest and Lucas the host. It rankled but she welcomed the shot of adrenalin; she would take any Dutch courage she could get to see her through the next little while.

Kim continued through to the kitchen and she saw immediately that Lucas had restored the place to its usual gleaming brightness. The only hint of their earlier breakfast was the faint smell of bacon.

'You shouldn't have cleared up,' she said stiffly. 'There was no need.'

He ignored the comment as though she hadn't spoken, following her into the limited space and leaning against the wall, his hands thrust deep into his trouser pockets and his eyes broodingly intent.

He had shaved whilst she'd been gone. Kim found her gaze drawn to the hard square jaw and her heart gave a little kick. And showered too by the look of his still-damp hair.

Kim found she was moving jerkily as she poured the two cups of coffee; the liquid steel gaze was far too intense to be comfortable. She swallowed hard as she handed Lucas his coffee, keeping her gaze fixed on a spot over his left shoulder.

'Thanks.' He straightened as he took the cup and she felt her senses respond with humiliating swiftness. 'So...' He made no effort to stand aside and unless she literally barged past him she was effectively trapped in her little part of the kitchen. 'I told you I loved you and you reacted by telling me to get the hell out. Care to explain why?' he asked with a cool lack of expression.

'Would you listen if I said no, I wouldn't?' Kim responded painfully.

'No.'

'I thought not.'

Where could she start? She took a hefty gulp of the scalding hot coffee and then winced as it burnt her throat, her eyes smarting. 'Do you want me to resign?' she asked quietly, knowing she was prevaricating.

'No, Kim, I do not want you to resign,' Lucas said with formidable control. 'I want you to talk to me.'

He was asking for the hardest thing in the world, as though it was as easy as falling off a log. She stared at him, her face tight with tension, and then looked down into the rich warmth of the fragrant coffee as she said very softly, 'It's a long story and it won't change anything.'

'I'll be the judge of that.'

She looked up at him then, searching her mind for an

escape route, but there wasn't one. She had known all along there wouldn't be. He had made up his mind he wanted the 't's crossed and the 'i's dotted and, Lucas being Lucas, that was exactly what he would get. Never mind about her pain, her humiliation, her excruciating shame...

She took a deep breath and began talking. It wasn't so bad at first; she began with the agony of her aunt dying and the way she had been whisked into care, detailing the fight to rise above the loneliness and isolation she had felt in a steady quiet voice. And then she paused, her voice very low as she said, 'And then I went to university and met Graham.'

'Did you love him?' Lucas asked softly.

'I thought I did.' She smiled bitterly. 'It was so amazing to have someone need me so badly, to want to be with me every minute, to love me so much. I'd never had that before and it quite literally bowled me off my feet. *Graham* bowled me off my feet. And then we got married.' She stopped abruptly, feeling horribly trapped and moving restlessly in the tiny space. 'Can we go through to the sitting room?'

'Sure.' He gently touched her cheek with one large hand before standing aside to let her pass. His fingers were cool, steady, and the tingling sensation in her flesh made her suddenly short of breath. It made her scurry through to the sitting room with more haste than dignity, and as she turned to face him again he raised his eyebrows at her.

'I wasn't going to ravish you on the kitchen floor.'

'I know that.'

'You don't lie very well, Kim,' said Lucas matter-of-factly. 'Continue with the story. You're now married.'

It sounded simple when it was said like that.

'Graham didn't love me,' Kim said mechanically, forcing herself to go into automatic to get through the next minutes. 'I don't actually think he was capable of the emotion. He'd put on a good show at university and we always seemed to be with a load of people there, the life was so gregarious. His drinking didn't stand out there, either; everyone in Graham's set drank too much.'

Lucas nodded. 'I too was young once,' he said drily.

'His parents financed a little business for him and he was pleased with that at first, acting the big I am among his friends and cronies. But the drinking was getting worse. I tried to help him but he'd turn everything round on me, saying he had to drink because I was a useless wife, hopeless in bed, that sort of thing.'

She had tried to continue in the flat even tone but the pain of Graham's rejection, the incredibly cruel things he had used to throw at her, was still a raw wound.

'We'd been married eighteen months when he suggested…' Kim sat down on one of the easy chairs, her head lowered and her hair covering her face like a veil. She had felt too weary that morning to fiddle with it before taking Melody to school, but she was glad now of the slight protection it gave from those piercing eyes.

'What did he suggest, Kim?' Lucas said tensely.

'He asked…he wanted me to sleep with one of his prospective clients,' Kim said numbly. 'He'd been furious when I got pregnant with Melody so quickly after we'd got married, and when I wouldn't have an abortion like he wanted he blamed that—the added responsibility of a family—on the business failing. He said I owed him.'

Lucas swore softly but the sound was none the less ugly for its quietness. He knew this slimeball's type; unfortunately there were several spawned in each generation. Men without conscience, men who would use vulnerability and gentleness in another person to bring them under their domination. Kim had been a sitting target for him with her background, and with her looks he must have thought he'd won the jackpot.

'Melody was five months old,' Kim continued quietly, 'and right up to that point I'd tried to convince myself that I could turn the marriage around, for our child's sake if nothing else. I'd done everything I could to make him love me, tried to please him in every way I knew how.' She stopped again, the memory of her abasement from those days horribly vivid. How often, in the weeks and months following Graham's vile request, had she told herself she must have been mad, insane, not to see what he was really like? But she hadn't. She just hadn't.

'But that day I went berserk.' Her voice was shaking now in spite of her efforts to control it. 'Really berserk. I flew at him, hitting him, punching him, and he struck me back so hard I lost consciousness for a time.'

'Hell, Kim.' He knew she probably didn't want to be touched, not in view of what she was reliving, but Lucas couldn't see her sitting there, so small and slender and broken, and not hold her. He lifted her up to him, and as she stiffened, her body tensing, he said softly, 'It's all right, it's all right; I just want to hold you as one human being comforting another, that's all. Nothing more, Kim. I swear it.'

He would have given the world for five minutes alone with Graham Allen if the dirty swine hadn't been dead. And he would have made him suffer. An artery pumping out his life blood had been too quick an end for the so-and-so.

'When I came to he was sitting in front of me with Melody on his knee,' Kim whispered against his shirt, her head still hanging limply. 'He told me if I ever confided in a living soul, told them anything of what had gone on, he would kill her, and then me. I believed him, Lucas. He was actually capable of that when the mood took him. He said it was important for the business he was seen as an established family man and that if I tried to leave him he would find us. He did promise he'd never hit me again, though.'

'You should have left him. There are places—'

'No. He'd have found us.' Kim raised desolate eyes, her lashes starred with tears. 'But from that day I moved into Melody's room on a camp bed. I couldn't bear for him to touch me. Something died for ever that day, Lucas. I know it. I could never trust any man again.'

'I'm not any man,' he said grimly, seating himself on the sofa with Kim on his knee and holding her when she would have struggled away.

'Things got worse and worse,' Kim continued, her body tight and rigid. 'He…he became like a devil. And then, the night after the shopping incident, when he'd broken his word and hit me again, he found me looking at flats in the paper. He attacked me, said I was withholding his conjugal rights so he'd take what was rightfully his by force if he had to. But I fought back, hit him over the head with a saucepan in the end and locked myself in Melody's room. I thought he might try to break the door down but in the event he went off on a drinking binge, and the rest you know.'

She took a deep breath. 'Except that he left debts, huge debts—for me, that is—and I was stupid enough to have signed documents that made me as responsible as Graham.'

'Hence you jumping at the job at Kane Electrical,' Lucas said softly, his voice shaking a little with what he was feeling. 'And here was me thinking you had fallen for my irresistible charm.'

He was trying to lighten things, Kim knew that, but his closeness was too much to cope with. 'Please let me go, Lucas,' she said tremblingly. 'And don't feel sorry for me. I didn't tell you about Graham for that.'

'Listen to me, Kim.' He lifted her chin so that she had to look into his face, and she saw fierce anger was battling with a tenderness that made her want to howl like a baby. 'I can't deny I want him to suffer the torments of the damned for what he's put you through, and if he were alive I'd find him and teach him a lesson that would mark him until his dying day. That's the way I'm made, I'm afraid. But you've got to put that maniac behind you. He's history, dead, gone—and I don't mean in just the physical sense.'

She was dazed and shaking, as much by their intimacy as the terror she had relived.

'If you let him shape your future he's really won, don't you see that?' Lucas urged huskily. 'And you're worth more than the dregs he's left you, and so is Melody.'

'Melody is one reason I don't want a relationship with anyone, ever,' Kim said tightly, afraid the pull of his magnetism was going to convince her black was white. 'We're safe as we are, Melody and I, and that's all I ask of the future, Lucas. To be safe.'

'The hell it is.' It was a growl, and immediately he added, 'I'm sorry. Don't look like that; I'm not going to hurt you, for crying out loud. But, like I said before, I'm not anyone, and what's between us is something outside the normal realm of things. Of course you want to be safe, but there's more to life than just that, my love. Don't throw all your hopes and dreams and aspirations on the funeral pyre of that rat. I can make you alive in a way you've never dreamt of.'

My love. Kim couldn't speak at all, she could only look at him, but her eyes were huge with distrust and fear and he read the panic and denial in her face with deep and silent frustration.

'I want you, Kim, but not for a night or a week or a month,' he said very softly.

'No.' Before he could say any more she jerked herself away from him, sliding to her feet and shaking uncontrollably as she said, 'You have to understand, Lucas, please. I can't... I don't want commitment.'

How many times had he said exactly that to some beauty or other he was inviting into his bed? Lucas's thoughts were self-derisory and caustic. And now he was being hoist with his own petard. But he was damned if he was going to let her go. She was his, in her heart. He just had to convince her of it. But she had had enough brute force and manipulation to last her a lifetime and he wasn't about to indulge in more of the same. If he took her she would capitulate in seconds; he had no doubt about that. But he wanted more than her body and a momentary acceptance in her emotions. Much more.

'Okay.' He stood up slowly to face her, thrusting his hands into his pockets to remind himself not to touch her. How he wanted to touch her...

'Okay?' The tears were still sparkling on her white cheeks and Kim took a shaky breath. 'What do you mean okay?'

'I accept your proviso that we're just friends,' Lucas said evenly, 'and I appreciate that you trusted me enough to tell me about your past. That's the first requisite of friends, trust.'

Kim stared at him, feeling she was entering an Alice in Wonderland experience. She hadn't mentioned anything about being friends, had she? she asked herself bewilderedly. And where had he got this idea about her trusting him?

'So, we'll go on from here with no bad blood between us, yes?' Lucas's tone was soothing. He had noted the brittle stance of her body, her chalk-white face and agonised eyes, and it had warned him she was at the limit of her endurance for one day. He also knew he wanted her more than ever.

'I...I don't know,' Kim stammered defensively, suddenly unsure of exactly what was being said.

'Kim, you've told me you need to work to pay off Graham's debts,' Lucas said calmly, 'and surely you want to provide Melody with the best standard of living in the meantime? That taken as read, you working as my secretary is a good deal for both of us. I get someone who is completely trustworthy and willing to give the job her all; you get an excellent salary with no strings attached.'

'But...but what you said...'

'About loving you, wanting you?' Lucas expelled a quite breath. 'That still stands, I'm afraid, but I'm no callow youth in the grip of adolescent urgings he can't control. And life goes on, even in the midst of my bruised ego. I'm a businessman first and foremost, Kim. You should know everything comes second to that.' And the funny thing was, he would have meant that last sentence at one time, Lucas admitted with bitter self-mockery.

'The last few months have been somewhat...strained at times, haven't they?' Lucas raised dark sardonic eyebrows, and at Kim's faint nod inclined his own head in agreement. 'But now we both know exactly where we stand and with no hard feelings. Okay?'

'Okay.'

He smiled as she spoke but Kim was beyond smiling back. Her eyes opened wide as he placed his hands on her slender shoulders but she stood quietly before him, forcing herself not to shrink away. And when the dark head bent and he lightly brushed the top of her head with his lips she still remained motionless, wondering—with a bewilderment that was stronger than anything she'd felt before—why she felt her heart was breaking.

CHAPTER NINE

KIM didn't go into work that day although Lucas left immediately after their 'clearing of the air', as he referred to their talk.

He had ordered her to go back to bed and get some sleep before she had to collect Melody again, but she found sleep was the last thing on her mind in the hours that followed. After an hour or so of tossing and turning she threw back the covers irritably and got dressed again, giving the house an impromptu spring-clean that took all the rest of the day and most of the evening.

The hard physical work helped; at least she fell asleep as soon as her head touched the pillow that night, and her dreams—if she had any—must have been non-threatening because she couldn't remember them in the morning, which was a Saturday.

She found her heart was beating so hard it was suffocating the first time she met Lucas after the morning at the cottage, but he had retreated into the hard, attractive, distant tycoon of earlier days and within an hour or two—amazingly to Kim—she found herself relaxing, and by the end of Monday she was sufficiently loosened up to laugh at one of his wickedly amusing observations on life.

The next morning she experienced the same hot shivers and thudding of the heart as the day before, but when Lucas made no attempt to be close or anything but her boss, their old working relationship gradually settled into place.

The silver-grey eyes still pinned her on occasion but that was Lucas, she assured herself each time she caught him looking at her in a certain way. And the habit he had of almost reading her mind was peculiar to him too. It didn't make her comfortable, but cosiness or serenity had never been an option around Lucas anyway.

Kim found she was missing Maggie more than she would have thought possible as the days and weeks crept by, especially after one of her friend's phone calls or letters which were all determinedly cheerful and which never mentioned Pete.

She had mentioned Maggie's situation to Lucas whilst assuring him she would make alternative arrangements for Melody, should the need arise, but it was four weeks before this happened and then the late meeting just necessitated Janie—the mother of Melody's schoolfriend—walking across the road to the school and keeping Melody until seven, when Kim collected her.

By the time the May blossom had fallen and June had arrived, and Melody was well underway with her herb and vegetable patch, Kim was forced to acknowledge to herself that she was lonely. She adored Melody, worshipped her, but the lack of adult stimulation was getting to her, she told herself crossly one Saturday morning after a particularly vivid and erotic dream concerning Lucas.

She missed Maggie's easy, funny companionship, that was all it was. She narrowed her eyes against the hot June sunlight streaming in through the kitchen window. But it wasn't, was it? her innate honesty forced her to recognise in the next moment.

It wasn't so much that she was lonely as lonely for Lucas, and there was a subtle difference there. Since she had accepted that she loved him there was barely a minute or two that ticked by that he wasn't on her mind. It wasn't so bad when she was at work—at least she could see him there, hear him talk, laugh at his jokes and exist on the perimeter of his busy life.

Sad girl. The thought was immediate and extremely annoying, but truthful. She hunched her shoulders against it and frowned at the sunlight.

And all the long work lunches they shared didn't help. She was forced to see him in a different light when he took her to one of the little restaurants he favoured, or to the pub, and although he assured her he'd treated June exactly the same and it was the way he liked to relate to his secretaries, it nevertheless caused Kim untold painful heart-searchings.

As had the couple of times she had found herself at his home. She'd met Martha, his housekeeper, and the animal occupants of the beautiful mansion. Again, good reasons for her being there—the first time he had called in on his way back to the office after lunch for a file he'd forgotten, and the next he had asked her to bring some papers to him one morning when he had been working at home, but each time Martha had insisted Kim partake of coffee and home-made shortbread before she had left, and treated her as—what, exactly? Kim asked herself silently. A buddy, a friend? Certainly not as one of Lucas's employees.

And Lucas's relationship with his housekeeper she'd found particularly unsettling. His gentle teasing of the little old grey-haired woman, the warmth and tenderness in Lucas's voice, and the blatant devotion in Martha's when she spoke of the man she called 'my wee lad' had all been disconcerting. Unnerving even.

Not that Lucas had stepped out of line for a minute. Oh, no, not ice-man. 'Oh, stop it.' Kim acknowledged she was being spectacularly unfair. It was just that she hadn't expected her 'just friends' decision to be quite so hard, or so apparently easy for him! Sour grapes. Kim nodded to the accusation. Probably. Which made her really mean.

Enough. Get your mind off Lucas and on to something else, she told herself sternly, and with that in mind she walked out of the kitchen door into the spangled sunlight of the garden. 'Fancy the paddling pool out, sweetheart?' she called to Melody, who was busily engaged in looking for weeds in her little plot of ground.

A whoop of delight was the answer, and within half an hour the paddling pool was full and they were both in their bikinis, Melody splashing about in the tepid water and Kim sitting in a deckchair under the shade of a copper beech with a mug of coffee in her hand.

An abundance of wisteria had gracefully draped itself over the adjoining garden wall during May, and this was now giving way to a cascade of rambling roses, their delicious scent wafting gently on the still air.

It was a world away from the nightmare of the little bedsit they had endured for two long years. Hot tears pricked at Kim's eyes—which was ridiculous, she told herself firmly, when she ought to be smiling if anything. But Lucas had made all this possible—given her back her independence, her chance of carving a good life for herself and Melody, of living somewhere like this. And she was grateful, incredibly so, but she'd never really told him.

She blinked very hard. And sooner or later some woman, a little more beautiful or talented or charismatic than the rest, would snare him. She wasn't aware he was dating again but he could be, for all she knew, and she couldn't blame him if he was. As he'd said, celibacy wasn't his style.

And it would be her fault. Her fault she had missed a chance of heaven. But… Kim stared straight ahead but the garden had vanished into the black abyss of her thoughts. If she had her chance over again she would do exactly the same. She might be throwing away her chance of heaven but the hell she had endured with Graham precluded stepping into a relationship again. With Graham she'd had the excuse she hadn't known what she was doing, but there would be no justification for willingly putting herself and Melody at risk again.

The same old arguments and counter-arguments she had mentally indulged in for the last two months raged in her mind, and when Melody tapped her arm impatiently, saying, 'Mummy, *Mummy*. I said I can hear the doorbell,' it took Kim a few seconds to bring herself back to the real world.

'I'm sorry, sweetheart. Mummy was daydreaming.' Kim smiled into the little face frowning up at her, hastily reaching for the cloudy blue sarong that matched the bikini as she rose.

She wrapped the delicately patterned cloth round her waist as she entered the house and padded through the hall to the front door, and it was only as she opened it she realised she hadn't given a thought to who might be calling at ten o'clock on a sunny June morning.

'Lucas!' For a moment she stared blankly at the tall, lean figure in front of her dressed casually in a charcoal shirt and black jeans, but as the silver eyes narrowed slightly and showed their appreciation of her clothes—or lack of them—reality surged in in an overwhelmingly hot flood that started at her toes and worked upwards.

Kim resisted the impulse to cross her arms over her breasts and said instead, her voice as cool as she could make it, considering she was giving a first-rate impression of a furnace at full tilt, 'What's the matter? Is anything wrong?'

'Plenty,' he drawled lazily, 'the first thing being that I'm kicking myself for not calling round before, this summer.'

She tried for a smile, which was a mistake because it turned into more of a nervous twitch, and then, as she heard Melody's excited voice just behind her calling Lucas's name, Kim groaned inwardly. If she knew anything about her hospitable little daughter, Lucas was going to be invited to come and see Melody's new paddling pool, which of course was fine, great—or would have been if her mother wasn't half-naked!

'Lucas!' Melody skidded along the hall on small bare wet feet and with an abandonment Kim envied, and as Lucas bent down and held out his arms Melody jumped right into them. 'I kept asking Mummy when you'd come and she said she didn't know,' Melody told him as she put small hands on his shoulders and looked into the dark rugged face. 'She said you were busy.'

'Not too busy to call and see you,' Lucas said easily, straightening with Melody still perched in his arms and standing to look at Kim. Two pairs of eyes, one glittering metallic silver and the other deep liquid brown, surveyed her unblinkingly, and Kim sighed her acquiescence to the unspoken request.

'You'd better come in,' she said a touch ungraciously to Lucas. She couldn't fight them both.

'Thank you,' he said with mocking gratefulness, and the colour which had just begun to die down returned with new ferocity.

Irritating, impossible man! All the warmer feelings she'd indulged in earlier went right out of the window.

'Coffee?' She led the way down the hall, painfully aware of the transparency of the sarong and the revealing nature of the bikini. The purchase of the bikini had been in the nature of a statement one Saturday a few weeks before.

Lucas had taken her out to lunch the previous day, and as they'd been leaving the restaurant there had been a low and discreet call from a table across the room, and a woman had made her way to their side. An exquisitely dressed and equally exquisitely beautiful woman.

Lucas had introduced them, and Kim had been very conscious of a pair of green feline eyes looking her over from head to toe. Perfectly painted, glossy lips had managed a half-smile before the woman had gone on to ask if Lucas was coming to some party or other that weekend. 'It will be such fun, darling,' the carefully modulated voice had urged seductively. 'Clarice's little get-togethers always are. Remember the last time when we finished up in the pool and I lost my bikini top? A designer one, too, darling,' she added in an aside to Kim. 'Although Lucas found it for me.'

She just bet Lucas had. Kim's face must have spoken volumes because she remembered Lucas's mockingly cynical smile as he had made their goodbyes, and led her out of the restaurant with a light hand at her elbow.

'An old friend?' She'd resisted asking until they were nearly back at the office.

Lucas had shrugged easily. 'In a manner of speaking.'

'The party sounded as though it was a bit wild,' Kim had said brightly, hating him.

'Not really.' Amused eyes had rested on her flushed face for a moment. 'Felicity could make a wake sound like a riot. Clarice and her husband recently spent a fortune on an indoor pool that could house the Olympics, so now every invitation comes in an evening dress and swimwear form. Clarice just likes to be different.'

'Evening dress *and* designer swimwear,' Kim had said tartly. 'The competition must be fierce.'

'I wouldn't know.' They'd arrived back at Kane Electrical and Lucas had driven smoothly into his parking space before turning to her, resting his arm casually on the back of her seat. 'I prefer *au naturel*, myself, but if I have to wear something a pair of old jeans will do.'

The mental pictures that had flashed on to the screen of her mind had taken some working through, but by the time Kim had left the building later that day she'd managed to get her errant thoughts under control. Just.

However, the image of a green-eyed, red-haired beauty

had stayed with her, along with the uncomfortable knowledge that the only item of swimwear *she* possessed was a very functional one-piece that had seen better days. She had bought the bikini and matching sarong the next day.

'If you go out into the garden with Melody I'll bring the coffee in a minute,' Kim offered coolly once they were in the kitchen and Lucas was standing by the open back door.

He looked very dark and masculine in her little limed-oak kitchen and every bit as disturbing as the most erotic of her dreams.

'No hurry.' Melody had nestled herself comfortably in his arms, half-turned so that her fair head was resting against his collarbone and her face was turned towards Kim. 'We're fine.'

He was making no secret of the fact that he was enjoying looking at her, and Kim was distinctly conscious of the briefness of the bikini and the deep V between her tingling breasts. And of Melody next to his heart. The pose was relaxed and Lucas looked natural, like a father. It sent such whirling panic through her she almost dropped the coffee pot.

Once in the garden Lucas refused Kim's offer of the deck-chair and lay sprawled out at her feet after insisting she be seated. It caused her equilibrium untold problems to see his dark head at a level with her thighs, his long, lean muscled body propped on one elbow as he surveyed Melody splashing in the sunlit water.

'A water baby.' His deep voice was lazy and amused and Kim bitterly resented his imperturbability when she hardly knew where to put herself.

'She's always loved the water.' It was tight and stiff but the best she could do. She paused a moment, trying to make her voice normal before she asked, 'Why are you here, Lucas?'

'Because it's a beautiful day, Maggie is in America and

I thought you might be able to use a friend's company,' he said quietly, still with his gaze directed at the small figure in front of them.

He'd done it again, read her mind. Kim didn't know whether to be angry or thrilled, but in view of all the complications that went hand in hand with this man she decided on the former.

'That's very kind of you,' she began tersely, 'but—'

'No, it's not kind, Kim.' He looked up at her then, and she felt her breath leave her body at the intensity in the beautiful silver eyes. 'It's selfish, if you really want to know. I want to be here with you, and with Melody. I've wanted to be with you every damn weekend for months and this morning I decided enough was enough.'

'Oh.' She stared at him, totally taken aback and with all coherent thought clean gone.

'So what do you say to a day together?' he asked slowly.

He wasn't touching her, not in any physical way, but Kim could feel the power of his magnetic personality reaching out and enclosing her. He looked hard and dark and sexy, and she found herself beginning to tremble.

'I thought perhaps lunch at a little place I know,' he continued quietly, 'and then an afternoon on the river, followed by dinner at my place. Martha is standing by for Melody's likes and dislikes.'

'Lucas—'

'Just friends, Kim, if that's what you want.' He surveyed her with unfathomable eyes. 'You can't deny you could use a friend right now.'

A friend was one thing; Lucas Kane was quite another. Nevertheless the thought of a day with him was like Christmas and New Year rolled into one and magnified a million times, and Kim felt her resolve wavering. And then Melody took the decision right out of her hands when her daughter came to stand in front of them, small hands on tiny hips, as she said, 'Can Lucas stay for lunch, Mummy? *Please?*'

Kim hesitated for a moment, but it was long enough for Lucas to sense her indecisiveness and capitalise on it with the ruthlessness that was an integral part of him. 'Better than that,' he said lightly. 'We're going out to lunch and then you can have a ride in a boat on the river—would you like that? And if you're *very* good...'

'What? What?' As Lucas let his voice die away mysteriously, Melody jumped up and down in her excitement.

'If you're very good you can come and see where I live,' Lucas said softly, 'and meet Jasper and Sultan.'

'Who are Jasper and Sultan?'

'My dogs—very big dogs.'

'Do they bite?'

'They don't know how to bite,' Lucas assured her seriously, 'only how to lick.'

Melody nodded, believing him utterly. 'I like dogs like that,' she stated firmly.

Kim looked at them helplessly, and then, as Lucas raised his eyes to hers, the crystal gaze pinned her. 'Go and get changed,' he said very quietly, 'while I wait for you.'

They continued looking at each other for a second, and Kim's pulse leapt at the tone of the last words. He was an enigma, this man. Every time she thought she had got him worked out he did something to amaze her, the way he had today. But whereas all Graham's surprises had been nasty ones, everything she learnt about Lucas just made her love him more.

It was too dangerous a line to pursue, and Kim held out her hand to Melody. 'Let's make ourselves pretty,' she said as lightly as she could.

It was an enchanted day, the first of many in the weekends that followed. Lucas seemed to hit just the right note with

Melody, being neither too indulgent or too strict, and Melody took to Greenacres—Lucas's fabulous home with its several acres of grounds—like a duckling to water.

She took huge delight in bossing Lucas's enormous hounds around and fell in love with each one of Martha's cats, as well as Martha herself. And the old woman fully reciprocated the feeling, taking on the role of fussy grandma as though she had been born to it.

Lucas was always the perfect host—relaxed, urbane, amusing and thoughtful, and his kisses—social kisses, Kim assured herself, and not to be confused with anything else—were gentle, warm and totally non-threatening. The kisses of a friend.

After that first Saturday, Kim had tried to refuse further outings but Lucas had simply ignored her protestations with an arrogance that was pure Kane, although she had stuck to her guns about never staying the night at Greenacres. She felt uncomfortable at the thought of waking up in Lucas's home; she felt uncomfortable about a lot of things that were happening. But she kept reassuring herself that Lucas knew exactly where he stood—she couldn't have been more specific.

So all in all it was a magical summer, partly, but with dark surreal undercurrents that sometimes brought Kim wide awake and sweating in the middle of the night.

And then, at the beginning of September, two things happened within a few hours of each other which ripped Kim's fragilely built world apart, and were all the more unexpected for the great weekend she'd just had.

The weekend had started with Maggie phoning her from America on Friday evening to say that Pete had turned up on her doorstep with an engagement ring.

'He can't do without me, Kim.' Maggie had been on such a high the receiver had fairly vibrated. 'Apparently when I left England it prompted him to do some serious thinking and he's been having counselling for his fear of commitment. It brought up all sorts of things, issues he's been burying for years all relating back to his childhood and so on, but he knew he'd lose me if he didn't persevere—so he did!'

'I'm so glad, Maggie.' And she had been.

'He wants us to get married as soon as possible and get a place together. He's so *different*. He's talking about the future, children; I can hardly believe it's Pete.'

'If anyone deserves a happy ending it's you, Maggie,' Kim had said warmly.

'I think he half expected me to contact him in spite of all I said before I left, and when I didn't it convinced him this was make or break time. He'll never know how near I came, time after time, to picking up the phone, though,' Maggie added ruefully. 'He's staying out here with me for a short holiday and then we're flying home together the third week of September, so I'll see you then.'

'What's the ring like?'

'Oh, Kim, it's gorgeous! Three emeralds enclosed by a border of diamonds.'

There was more of the same, and the two women chatted for another two or three minutes before they finished the call. The news gave Kim a warm glow all through the following Saturday, spent at Lucas's home with Melody, and the Sunday when Lucas took them out for Sunday lunch before they visited an antique fair in the afternoon, returning home early because Melody had a headache.

But Monday morning started badly. One of Melody's school shoes disappeared off the face of the earth, a full glass of milk hopped off the breakfast bar and hurled itself on to the floor—according to a tearful Melody—and then Kim couldn't find her car keys. By the time they turned up under a cushion Kim was running half an hour behind schedule, which wouldn't have mattered so much normally but in view of the important meeting due to start promptly at nine in Lucas's office mattered *immensely*.

Since their weekend jaunts, Kim had become almost obsessive about fulfilling all of her responsibilities at the office. The last thing—the very last thing—she wanted was for Lucas to think she was presuming on their relationship; she still hesitated to call it friendship, even in her mind. Friendship should be a pleasantly relaxing, easy, agreeable type of thing, predictable and harmless. Lucas didn't fit one of those criteria.

Kim was constantly on tenterhooks around him, vitally and exhaustingly alive. She was exhilaratingly aware of every little thing about him—the slightest inflexion of his voice which told her the sort of mood he was in, the way his intimidatingly intelligent mind never stopped selecting and storing data, the way he could strike with deadly intent and accuracy. And yet he'd allowed her to see his private side too, that seductive and fascinating part of him that was much more dangerous than anything he displayed in his working life.

On arriving in Kane Electrical's car park, the heavy driving rain exploded into a cloudburst as soon as Kim opened the car door, and in spite of the doors to Reception only being a few yards away her light summer coat was soaked through after her breathless dash.

Great. Raindrops were trickling down her neck and dripping off her fringe as the lift whisked her up to the top floor. Ten minutes past nine and she looked like a drowned rat.

Once in her office she could hear voices from the other room, and after switching on her desk lamp—the morning had turned as dark as night—she hurried into her private cloakroom and stripped off her wet coat, quickly dabbing her fringe and the rest of her hair before peering in the mirror at her damp face.

'Kim?' The knock on the cloakroom door corresponded with Lucas's voice. 'Are you okay?'

Whether it was the irritations and panic of the morning, or the fact that she felt she had been living on a knife-edge ever since she had first come to work for Lucas, or simply that her period was due soon and she was ready to argue with the bricks in the wall, Kim didn't know, but suddenly she felt angry.

She wrenched open the door and glared up into Lucas's face as she said, 'Of course I'm okay. You haven't left them all in there to come and ask me that, have you? What will they think?'

'Think?' He hadn't liked her tone and the chiselled face told her so. 'What on earth are you talking about?'

'I'm talking about you nipping out here,' she snapped back testily, aware she was being horrendously unfair but unable to stop herself. 'They'll either think you're checking up on me or that we're having an affair.'

He stared at her as though she had gone mad. 'In the first place I have never "nipped" anywhere in my life,' he said icily, 'and in the second this is the first time you have been later than half past eight in all the time you've worked for me. When I saw a light go on and you still didn't make an appearance, I wondered if you'd had a bump on the way to work in view of the atrocious weather conditions.'

'Well, I haven't.'

'So it appears.' The silver eyes narrowed into slits of light. 'And as for anyone making a judgement on what I do and don't do as far as my secretary is concerned, it's none of their damn business.'

'In other words, you don't care what assumption they might make,' she said frostily, as an errant raindrop trickled down her forehead.

'Don't be ridiculous.' He was really furious now; the grey eyes were positively shimmering with white heat.

'I'm not being ridiculous.' She knew she ought to stop, she knew it but her tongue seemed to have a life of its own. 'You might think it's okay for people to think we're having an affair but I don't! Word has probably already got around that we've been seeing each other out of work; what do you think that looks like to everyone?'

'That we like each other?' Lucas suggested with a silky smoothness that spoke of controlled rage.

'You know what they'll think, especially with your reputation,' she shot back tightly.

'That enough, Kim.' He looked as if he was about to shake her.

'No it's not. Not nearly enough.' She couldn't remember how all this had stared but suddenly she knew this moment had been brewing for weeks, if not months, perhaps from the first days of their relationship when he had started to inveigle himself into her life and into her heart.

She couldn't be what Lucas wanted her to be. She didn't have the will-power or the strength to try, or the courage to face the pain and rejection if he decided she wasn't good enough. Graham had told her she was an empty shell— beautiful packaging with no present inside was how he had described it, once. Useless in bed, frigid, cold—he'd thrown accusation after accusation at her until, in spite of herself, she had begun to believe them. She didn't dare sleep with Lucas and see the disappointment in his eyes...

'Come into my office when you've calmed down and are ready to begin work,' Lucas said with cold emphasis. 'We'll discuss this later.'

'I'm giving you my notice.' Her face was as white as a sheet but her voice was steady. 'And I am calm.'

'You're giving in your notice because I asked you if you were all right?' Lucas bit out incredulously.

'No. Yes. I mean...' She willed herself not to cry, forcing

back the tears with superhuman effort. 'I don't want to work here any more.'

'You don't want to work for *me*,' he said grimly. 'What about Melody?'

'What about her?' she said, sticking her chin out. 'I've paid off the last of the debts—' thanks to his generosity '—and we're solvent again. I can find a job that covers the mortgage and our bills and that's all I want.'

'I meant, what about *me* and Melody?' he rasped tersely. 'It might have escaped your notice but your daughter's got pretty fond of me over the last little while. How is it going to affect her if I disappear out of her life without so much as a by your leave?'

She jerked her head back, her face blazing with a mixture of hot defiance and panic, and it was the panic that made her say the words that cut like a jagged blade. Cruel words, words she didn't mean even as she voiced them. 'So all this has been a ploy to get me into your bed through Melody, has it?' she said in a stony voice that was a cover for the desperate wailing inside. 'You would actually sink so low to use a child to get what you wanted?'

For a moment he stared at her in blank disbelief, and then she saw a rage such as she'd never seen on any human being's face darken his countenance like a terrifying winter storm. He stepped into the small cloakroom, slamming the door behind him as his eyes shot white fire into her frightened face.

'I've taken things from you I've never taken from any woman,' he said with deadly intent, 'and look where it's got me. I thought you needed time, gentleness, like a highly strung thoroughbred that's been abused by a moron in an effort to break its will when what it really needed was careful handling and tender persuasion. I've tried to show you who and what I am—I've bared my soul to you, Kim, and

I've never done that to another woman. What a damn stupid fool I've been.'

'Lucas, please.' She was frightened, terrified. There was such revulsion in his eyes she thought she would die from it.

'And all the time you've had me down as the type of sick individual who manipulates a kid in order to get her mother to service him,' he growled furiously. 'Because that's how you think I view it, isn't it? No finer feelings, no affair of the heart—just bodily needs that require dealing with.'

'I didn't say that,' Kim whispered desperately.

'That's exactly what you said. Well, maybe I'll revert to type, then, eh? Give you the satisfaction of telling yourself you were right all along?'

He pulled her against him without any warning and with such savagery that her head snapped back, exposing the pure line of her neck as her face lifted to his.

The cool restraint that had always been a part of his dealings with her was gone, burnt away by the force of the grenade she had thrown at him, and as she began to struggle in his arms his dark head bent and took her mouth in a fiery kiss.

The memory of that last searing time with Graham was suddenly acutely real, but instead of a wet slimy mouth smothering her face, hard, cruel hands ravaging her body voraciously, this was Lucas. His mouth was dominant and determined but it was lighting a fire that was made up of desire, not fear or revulsion, and his mastery of her body, his strength and virility as he crushed her against him, was sending the fire flickering into every nerve and sinew.

She continued to struggle for a few moments more, confusion and whirling distress at his easy command of her senses, his conquest of her mind and body causing her to try and fight when all real protest was gone, swallowed up in the pleasure that was taking hold.

'You want me, Kim,' he ground out between increasingly intimate kisses. 'You might not like that, you might not like *me*, but you want me nevertheless.'

His hand was cupping her head as he moulded her against him, and she could feel he was already hot and hard and brutally challenging.

'No...' It was feeble, humiliatingly so, and he recognised her weakness, his voice holding a quieter, almost gloating note as he said, 'Yes, oh, yes, my cool little secretary, my elusive ice-queen.'

His hands were ruthlessly exploiting her need of him and she couldn't resist what his hands and mouth were doing to her, arching against him as she finally gave up all efforts to lie to herself and Lucas, her fingers exploring his hard lean body as intimately as his were doing to her.

It was wild and savage and primitive, a delirious longing to get closer and closer to the man she loved and satisfy their mutual need. There was no past and no future, just the close, desperate exploiting of their shared passion, and with every moment that passed, every delicious sensation that was taking her further and further away from anything she had ever known or imagined, she wanted him more.

She was vaguely aware of where she was but somehow it didn't matter, it wasn't real; reality was Lucas's mouth and hands and the things he was doing to her. And then, as she felt him move her back a pace and position her against the wall, she opened her eyes wide. He was going to take her, right now, with a meeting going on next door and anyone liable to come looking for them.

The same thought must have occurred to Lucas.

The hands that were preparing to hoist her skirt upward froze, his breath laboured and ragged as he fought for control. Kim found herself looking straight into his face and the silver-grey eyes were brilliantly clear, their light burning into her brain as she watched him take raw gulps of air.

When he eased himself away from her it was slowly, giving her time to persuade her trembling legs to take her weight without the support of his arms.

He took a step backwards, raking his hair through a couple of times before adjusting the collar of his shirt and then his tie, and all the time Kim watched him with huge disbelieving eyes.

Her body was burning, aching for an assuagement only he could give, and she couldn't believe, she just couldn't take on board that he had stopped.

She saw his hand reach out behind him and open the cloakroom door as he turned, but even when the door began to close again and she was alone she still continued to stand in an attitude of frozen disbelief. And then she began to shake, not so much with the growing feeling of shame that was dawning as the liquid ice of her numbed emotions began to melt and trickle into her bloodstream, but with the knowledge that he was gone, that in the last resort he hadn't wanted her, *he had been able to walk away and leave her*.

CHAPTER TEN

AFTER she had transformed herself into the cool, collected Mrs Allen again Kim walked straight out of the cloakroom and continued out of the building.

It was probably the coward's way out, she told herself, as she drove along the route she had driven just an hour before, but the thought of facing Lucas again was impossible. She would write her formal resignation tonight and for the sake of propriety make the excuse of domestic difficulties making it necessary she leave immediately.

She thought, later, that it was ironic how lies could come back to haunt you.

She took the phone off the hook as soon as she got home, sitting in numb misery for an hour or more before she found the release of tears, and then after a storm of weeping that left her pale-faced and red-eyed she made herself a strong cup of black coffee and took stock.

She had burnt her boats with Lucas. It was consuming, overwhelming and she was frightened at how much it mattered. He had shown her all too succinctly that he could take her or leave her, and he'd decided to leave her. And she couldn't blame him. She really couldn't. When she thought of what she'd said…

She moaned softly, the sound echoing round the sitting room like the cry of a small bewildered hurt animal.

Lucas wasn't like Graham. She stood up quickly, finishing the coffee in a few hard gulps before going upstairs and running a bath. She felt dirty; not because of what she had allowed with Lucas, funnily enough, but because of her accusations. And she hadn't meant them—even as she'd said them she had known she hadn't meant them. But Lucas didn't know that, and he wouldn't believe her now, whatever she said. He must hate her. She moaned again, hot tears coursing down her cheeks.

She continued to cry all the time she lay in the bath, but by the time she was dressed again in jeans and a long loose jumper she had told herself she had to get herself under control.

In the mercurial way of British weather, the fierce storm of the morning had given way to a mild tranquil September day that even promised sunshine for the afternoon, and Kim glanced at her watch as she came downstairs again. Half-past eleven. Six hours to go before she was due to pick up Melody and she would go mad if she spent them brooding in the house.

She glanced at the telephone and as her hand went out to replace the receiver she stopped herself.

She'd write her resignation now and then post it when she went for a walk; Lucas would receive it tomorrow morning. If he was trying to contact her now she didn't want to know; the last thing she could do was to talk to him. She would break down and humiliate herself further, beg him to forgive her or something similar, and he had shown her—in words and action—that he was finished with her.

How come it had taken losing him irrevocably to tell her she was the biggest fool in the world? But then perhaps she had never really had him in the first place? Why would a man like Lucas Kane want her? All the old insecurities and doubts flooded in, but although they tried to convince her she had done the right thing, that finishing this affair that wasn't an affair was the safe and right thing to do, they didn't hold their normal power.

She should have given him—and herself—a chance. The tumult in her breast was sickening as she realised the enormity of her mistake. He had done everything right, everything, and she had thrown it all back in his face.

And Lucas was right. Graham had won. Even from the grave he was still winning. And she had let him, she had aided and abetted him.

Lucas had said he loved her. Whether that would have led to more, to marriage even, she didn't know, but now she never would.

She pulled out her notepaper and envelopes, and before she had time to lose her nerve she wrote Lucas a letter telling him exactly how she felt. She wrenched all the barriers down and bared her soul, exposed herself so completely that she felt she'd become a little child again, vulnerable and unprotected. She didn't beg or plead, she didn't ask to be taken back either in his heart or as his secretary, she just told him how she felt about him. And she finished by saying she was enclosing her letter of resignation. If he wanted to accept it she understood. If he was willing to give her a second chance he could tear it up and let her know accordingly.

Once she had written her notice and sealed the two pieces of paper in the envelope she felt slightly better.

She would go for a walk. It had been ages since she had walked alone in the fresh air, and she would post the envelope while she was out.

She'd made a mess of everything, a terrible, unforgivable mess, and it had separated her—and Melody—from the one man in all the world she would ever love. If Lucas didn't love her enough to forgive her she only had herself to blame; she had given him very little in their one-sided relationship. Her one hope was Lucas himself, because he wasn't like other men. He was head and shoulders above even the best of them.

She left the house quickly, tears trickling down her cheeks again, but once she was walking in the mild

September afternoon the tears dried up, although the sick churning in her stomach didn't get any better.

After posting the letter she went for a walk on nearby woodland that housed an adventure playground, sitting for some time on one of the wooden benches overlooking the children's playing area with the weak sun warming her face and the musky smell of wet vegetation wafting on the autumn breeze.

It was nearly four o'clock when she ventured home, and as she turned the corner of the street and saw a car parked outside her house she only gave it a cursory glance. The red Cavalier was not a car she recognised.

It was only as she turned on to her drive that the car door opened and Charlie, Lucas's caretaker at the plant, called her name.

'Charlie?' Kim stared at him in absolute amazement. 'What on earth are you doing here?' she asked, walking over to the car and peering in at his hoary face. 'How did you know where I live?'

'The boss told me.' It was the way Charlie always referred to Lucas. 'He was looking for you earlier. He's been ringing you all day, from what I can make out, and after he'd come here and you weren't in, I said I'd come and wait outside.'

'You did?' Kim was completely lost but there was something in the old man's face that was alarming her. 'I don't understand.'

'He'd have come back himself but he thought he'd be more use at the hospital,' Charlie said disjointedly. 'And he didn't want everyone sticking their oar in, nosy lot some of 'em, but you know how he talks to me. Go back a long way, me and the boss. Known him since he was a nipper.' And then, as though that had reminded him, he said quietly, 'It's your little 'un, love. Don't get yourself in a panic, but she was a bit poorly at school.'

'Melody?' Kim's face drained of colour. 'Where is she?'

'At the hospital—that's where I'm to take you, the boss says.'

'Oh, Charlie.' Kim found she was gripping the top of the car door like a lifeline.

Charlie drove to the hospital as though he was competing in Formula One, and once there Kim was whisked away by a sympathetic-faced nurse and led through a bewildering maze of corridors to the children's wards. The nurse would say nothing beyond Melody had been taken ill at school and they were doing some tests, but the sister who met her at the entrance to the unit was more forthcoming.

'Suspected meningitis,' she said very softly after she'd told Kim Melody was in an isolation room. 'Another child from Melody's class was brought in with the same thing during the night and the school was informed first thing, fortunately. Has Melody been poorly at all over the last day or two? A little off-colour or feverish?'

'She's been a little tired, headachey,' Kim said numbly, feeling like the worst mother in the world. 'I wanted to keep her off school this morning, actually, but there were tears and she insisted she wanted to go. They were choosing children for the country dancing display at the summer fête next week.'

The sister nodded understandingly. She'd had children herself. 'It was only at midday she was taken really poorly,' she said quietly, 'but with the school having been informed about the other child they decided not to take any chances, so when they couldn't contact you she was admitted. Wise decision, in the event, but she's now on antibiotics and she'll be fine so try not to worry. This is easy to treat if it's caught early enough, but in some cases it worsens very rapidly, especially in babies and children as young as Melody.'

'Can….can I see her?' Kim asked faintly.

'Of course. Your fiancé has been with her almost from when she was brought in, so she hasn't been alone for the tests, Mrs Allen. I think it would have been easier to prise a bear cub away from its mother than Melody from Mr Kane,' she added a trifle drily.

Her fiancé? Kim gazed at the small brisk woman bewilderedly but said nothing.

When Kim entered the small, white sterile room, Lucas rose immediately from the chair at the side of the bed, but not before Kim saw he had been holding one small dimpled hand between his own.

Melody was fast asleep, her fair hair spread out over the regulation hospital pillow and her thick eyelashes resting on flushed cheeks. She didn't actually look ill at all, Kim thought faintly, as she walked over and stood looking down at the small figure, tears streaming down her pale cheeks.

'It's okay; they've told you it's okay?' Lucas said softly as he came and stood beside her, his arm round her shoulders.

'Oh, Lucas.' She turned into his arms, sobbing uncontrollably, and he held her very tightly until she calmed down, by which time the sister had left and they were alone. He put her from him a little, looking down at her with intent compelling eyes as he said, 'She's *really* going to be all right, Kim. It's not a sop, okay? I've checked with everyone in authority and they've caught it in the early stages, due to the warning of the other child.'

There was another silence but still she couldn't speak, the tears sparkling on her cheeks like tiny diamonds. 'I'm sorry.' It was a faint whisper but he still heard it.

'This is not your fault, Kim. You weren't to know.'

'I mean…I mean about us, this morning, everything. I…I can't believe I said all that.'

'You're sorry? When I practically raped you,' he said with a rough softness that spoke of inner torment. 'When

I sent you racing off to goodness knows where? I'll never forgive myself—'

'It wasn't like that.' She felt paralysed by all the emotion of the day, utterly spent, but she couldn't let him take any blame for something that had been all her fault. 'It was me. I was horrible,' she said brokenly. 'I said horrible things.'

'Because I made you,' he said gruffly, his voice shaking. 'You never lied to me, Kim. You were totally honest from day one, making it quite clear you didn't want to get involved with any man. But in my arrogance I thought because I loved you so much I could make you love me. I couldn't believe I could feel the way I did and it wouldn't affect you. I used the physical attraction between us to try and make you look at me as a man rather than just your employer.'

'I...I do.'

'As a friend, I know.' He took a deep hard breath and then they both stilled as the tiny figure in the bed sighed softly, before falling back into a deeper sleep.

'Not as a friend,' said Kim in a shaky whisper. He had said he loved her. Did he still love her? 'I...I love you, Lucas. I have done almost from when we met but I was too scared and hung up on everything that's happened in the past to believe it could work. Graham...some of the things he said and did—I couldn't believe any man would want me if they knew what I was really like. He said I was frigid, a pretty parcel with nothing inside.'

He was looking at her with incredulity stamped all over his hard, handsome face, and that, more than the words that followed, convinced Kim how wrong, how terribly misguided, she had been to ever link Graham and Lucas in her mind for one moment.

Lucas was the sort of man who loved for ever. She had trampled his male pride into the ground this morning and made him hate himself in the process, and yet—believing it was all over between them and that she loathed him—he had come to Melody's side to be with her because he knew Kim couldn't. He could be a hard man, and ruthless, but with her and with Melody he had been wonderful.

'Kim, I love you more than I can ever say and I always will,' Lucas said with quiet emphasis. 'I want to marry you and have children with you and grow old with you. I want to know you are my wife and I have the right to cherish and protect you and take care of you and our family. I love you more than life, Kim. It kills me that you've had to go through what you have, but I'll spend the rest of my life making it up to you, if you'll let me.'

'I...I thought you wouldn't want me any more, after this morning. You stopped—' She couldn't go on but she didn't have to.

'I stopped because I suddenly realised what I was doing,' he said softly, his voice husky and the faint accent that occasionally flavoured his words giving a smoky undertone to what he was saying. 'I didn't want our first time to be like that, Kim, even if it was going to be our only time,' he added with faint ruefulness. 'I'd lost control. I was angry; it made me no better than Graham—'

'No, don't say that, not ever.' She placed a finger on his lips, her voice breaking. 'You're the best there is, Lucas.'

His mouth sought hers and he kissed her with gentle reassurance at first, holding her close as he whispered his love against her lips, and then more passionately as she melted against him. 'Earth and heaven might disappear, my love, the moon might stop shining and the sun might fall into the ocean, but I'll never stop loving you,' he murmured after a time as they drew away to look into each other's faces.

They talked and kissed some more before Lucas brought another chair close to the bed, so they could sit together. 'I feel like she's my child, too,' Lucas whispered softly, turning away from the little figure in the bed as he lifted Kim's chin and met her eyes. 'Right from the first time I saw her, and I could swear she feels the same. I nearly went crazy when I first got here before they said everything was going to be okay.'

'You said you were my fiancé?' Kim murmured quietly.

'I hadn't got time to worry about red tape or any rules about only family. Melody needed one of us,' Lucas said with Kane disregard for convention.

'Oh, Lucas.'

'I'd like to adopt her legally, Kim, so she takes my name after we're married.'

'Oh, *Lucas*.' Kim smiled tremulously.

It was much, much later when Melody awoke properly, but Kim and Lucas were still sitting by the bed, Lucas's arm holding Kim tight and her blonde head resting against his shoulder as she slept. His other hand was clasped tight in Kim's.

Melody surveyed them sleepily and Lucas smiled at her, saying, 'Hi, sweetheart. You feeling better now?'

'Uh-huh.' Melody nodded drowsily, her brown eyes going again to their clasped hands and her mother's sleeping face. Kerry's mummy and daddy held hands. 'Lucas?'

'Yes, sweetheart?'

'Are you going to be my new daddy?'

'You bet your sweet life I am, sweetheart.'

'Scrumptious!'

A PROFESSIONAL
MARRIAGE

by

Jessica Steele

Jessica Steele lives in the county of Worcestershire with her super husband, Peter, and their gorgeous Staffordshire bull terrier, Florence.

Any spare time is spent enjoying her three main hobbies: reading espionage novels, gardening (she has a great love of flowers) and playing golf. Any time left over is celebrated with her fourth hobby, shopping.

Jessica has a sister and two brothers and they all, with their spouses, often go on golfing holidays together.

Having travelled to various places on the globe researching background for her stories, there are many countries that she would like to revisit. Her most recent trip abroad was to Portugal, where she stayed in a lovely hotel, close to her all-time favourite golf course.

Jessica had no idea of being a writer until one day Peter suggested she write a book. So she did. She has now written over eighty novels.

CHAPTER ONE

'MR DAVENPORT will see you now.'

Chesnie's insides had been on the fidget for the last half-hour and now renewed their churning. But she rose elegantly to her feet and maintained her cool exterior and followed Barbara Platt—the woman whose job she was hoping to secure for herself—into the adjoining office.

'Chesnie Cosgrove.' Barbara Platt introduced her to the tall, dark-blond-haired man who was rising from his chair.

'Thank you, Barbara.' He had a pleasant, well-modulated voice, but as his present PA went out and closed the door Chesnie noted that there was something about the thirty-six or thirty-seven-year-old man who turned his blue gaze on her that said he could be exceedingly tough if the occasion demanded it. 'Take a seat, Miss Cosgrove,' he invited, in one sweeping glance taking in her slim five feet nine inches of height, her immaculate business suit, her red-blonde hair, green eyes and what one of her sisters had called her 'pale, flawless complexion to die for'. 'You found us without any trouble?' Joel Davenport opened pleasantly.

The vast offices of Yeatman Trading would be hard to miss. 'Yes,' she replied evenly, and that was all the time he had available for pleasantries, it seemed, for in the next split second her job interview with him was underway.

'So—tell me about yourself,' he opened.

'My qualifications are—'

'Were I unaware of your three years' experience as a senior secretary, your excellent typing speeds, and—according to your previous employer—your outstanding or-

5

ganising and communication skills, you wouldn't be sitting here,' he cut her off.

Did she really want this job? He *was* tough! She'd had a couple of interviews with Human Resources before she'd got this far; clearly there was nothing about her business background that hadn't been passed on to this man. She wondered about going back to Cambridge to work—but hadn't she made up her mind to make a complete break? She decided to give Joel Davenport another chance.

'I'm twenty-five,' she informed him, and managed to stay outwardly cool when she realised that if he'd seen her application—and he seemed the kind of man who left nothing to chance—then he already knew that. 'I've been working in Cambridge.' He already knew that too. Stay cool, Chesnie, stay cool. The fact was, though, that she didn't know what she could add to what he already knew; her second interview had been thorough in the extreme. She stared at him, this man she was hoping to work for, green eyes staring frankly into blue, and, feeling defeated, asked the only question possible. 'What would you like to know?'

He studied her, not a smile in sight. She'd had more appreciative glances. 'You're well qualified. Your reference from your last employer is little short of glowing. Lionel Browning obviously thought the world of you.'

'And I him,' she answered. Lionel Browning had been an absolute darling to work for. A touch muddle-headed, true, which was why he had left so much to her—and which would all stand her in very good stead were she lucky enough to land this job.

'Why then leave?'

Chesnie opened her mouth to trot out the same reason she had given Human Resources: advancement in her career. To a certain extent that was true. But, had matters not come to a head when Lionel's son, Hector, had decided to come into the business she didn't know if she would ever have been able to leave muddle-headed Lionel to run things on his own. But suddenly she found she did not want to lie to this direct-looking man. 'I'd been thinking for some time that I wouldn't mind something more challenging to get my teeth into,' she began truthfully.

'But...?'

She looked back at Joel Davenport. He was cool, cooler than she. And he was sharp—my word, he was sharp. He *knew*, for all she was sure she hadn't slipped up anywhere, that there was more to it than that.

'But I probably wouldn't have been able to leave Lionel had it not been for his son coming into the business.' She halted, too late regretting she had let this tough-looking man see she had a softer side when it came to her ex-employer. 'Hector Browning's own firm went bust. So he decided he'd come and give his father a hand.'

'You didn't get on?'

'It was part of my job to get on with everyone,' Chesnie answered, not taking kindly to having her professionalism questioned.

'So what went wrong?'

She had an idea this interview was going very badly, and decided she'd got nothing to lose by telling that which, hurt and humiliated, she had not told another living soul. 'Everything!' she answered evenly, adjusting her position on her chair, catching the flick of his glance to her long slender and shapely legs now neatly crossed at the ankles. 'On the same day I heard from my landlord that he'd decided to sell the property—and, no desperate rush, but would I care to look for a flat elsewhere?—I had a row with Hector Browning.'

'You usually row with the people you work with?'

'Lionel and I never had a cross word!' Chesnie retorted—and inwardly groaned. She'd be having a row with Joel Davenport any minute! And she wasn't working with him, or for him—or ever!

He was unperturbed. 'Hector Browning rubbed you up the wrong way?'

'That I could, and did, cope with. What I was not pre-

pared to stay and put up with was that—was that...' Joel
Davenport waited, saying not one word, which left her
forced to continue. 'From the various snide remarks Hector
Browning had made I knew he resented my closeness to
his father, my affection for him and his affection for me.
He—Hector...' Again she hesitated, but the fact that she
knew herself innocent made her tilt her chin a fraction.
'When he that day accused me of having an affair with his
father,' she made herself go on, 'I knew that one of us
would have to go. Blood being thicker than water, I also
knew it would be me.'

'You handed in your resignation.'

'I left last week—the end of the month.'

'And were you?' Joel Davenport asked.

'Was I what?'

'Having an affair with his father?'

Her eyes widened in surprise and annoyance that anyone
could ask such a thing. Somehow, though, she was able to
maintain the outer cool she showed to the world. 'No, I
was not!' she stated clearly, and, not wishing to say any
more on the subject, she left it there.

To his credit, Joel Davenport allowed her to do so. He
nodded, at any rate—she took it that he believed her. 'Human Resources will have explained the package that goes
with the position.' He took the interview into another area.
'Obviously the salary, pension and holiday entitlement are
acceptable to you or you wouldn't have proceeded with
your application.'

'It's a very generous package,' Chesnie stated calmly.
Generous! It was a sensational salary!

'The successful candidate will earn every part of it,' he
replied, which she felt hinted that she was not the successful candidate. Though when he continued she began to
wonder... 'The job as my PA demands one hundred per
cent commitment,' he advised her, and surprised her by
adding, 'Your qualifications aside, you're a beautiful

woman, Miss Cosgrove—' he did not seem personally impressed '—and no doubt have many admirers.'

About to deny she had any, Chesnie, who just wasn't interested in relationships, suddenly felt feminine enough to want to go along with his view that she had a constant stream of admirers at her door. 'They wouldn't interfere with my work,' she replied.

'I may need you to work away with me on occasion,' he went on. She knew from the job description that there were times when Joel Davenport required his PA to accompany him on overnight stays when he visited their Glasgow offices, and had no problem whatsoever with that. 'Supposing such an occasion arose at short notice—say, half an hour before a theatre date with your favourite man?'

'I'd hope my favourite man would enjoy the theatre just as much without me,' she replied promptly, and thought she caught a momentary twitch of her serious interviewer's mouth—quite a nice-shaped mouth, she suddenly realised—but it was come and gone in an instant.

'There's no one man in particular in your life?'

'No,' she replied. Who had the time? Or the inclination, for that matter?

'No marriage plans?' he asked sternly, her one-syllable answer insufficient, apparently. But she resented his question. She hadn't asked him if he was married or about to be! She studied him for a moment. Good-looking, a director of the expanded and still expanding multi-national Yeatman Trading—he had it all, which no doubt included some lovely wife somewhere.

Suddenly she became aware that as she was studying him, so keen blue eyes were studying her. 'I'm not remotely interested in marriage,' she stated bluntly, belatedly realising his question, in light of his statement that the job as his PA demanded one hundred per cent commitment, was perhaps a valid one.

'You sound as if you've something against marriage,' he commented.

With her parents and her sisters as fine examples, who wouldn't have? Chesnie kept her thoughts to herself. 'I believe the latest statistics show that forty per cent of marriages end in divorce. Personally, I'm more career-oriented than marriage-minded.'

He nodded, but when she was expecting some comment on her reply, he instead enquired, 'You're still living in Cambridge?'

'For the moment. Though at present I'm staying with my sister, here in London, for a few days.'

'You're obviously prepared to move here. Have you found anywhere to live yet?'

'I thought I'd better sort out a job first,' she answered, and was surprised when, without a response, he got to his feet.

'Perhaps you should set about finding your accommodation without delay,' he suggested pleasantly.

Chesnie looked at him. Clearly the interview was over. She stood up as he came round his desk. She was wearing two and a half inch heels and still had to look up at him. 'I'm not sure...' she faltered, not at all sure she should believe what she thought he was saying.

He held out his right hand, and automatically her right hand met his warm, firm clasp. 'I should like you to start on Monday, Chesnie,' he confirmed, and for the first time he smiled.

Chesnie managed to keep her face straight while she was in the Yeatman Trading building, but once she had left the building so too did she leave her cool, sophisticated image, her lovely face splitting into an equally lovely grin. She'd got it! She'd jolly well got it! Only then did she acknowledge how very much she had wanted this job as PA to Joel Davenport.

It sounded hard work—she thrived on hard work. To be constantly busy had been her lifeline. She hadn't been sure what sort of work she wanted to do when she had left school, but with her studies finished and no need to spend time at her desk in her room she had spent more time with her parents. Their constant sniping at each other had driven her to take various courses at evening classes, all to do with business management.

It seemed to her she had been brought up in a house full of strife. The youngest of four sisters, with a two-year gap separating each of them, she had been twelve when her eldest sister, Nerissa, had married—for the first time. Nerissa was now on her second marriage, but that didn't appear to be any happier than her first. Chesnie's second sister, Robina, had married next—she was always leaving her husband and returning for weeks on end to the home she had confided she had only married young to get away from.

When her sister Tonia married, Chesnie had thought surely it must be third time lucky for one of her sisters. But, no. Tonia had produced two babies in quick succession and seemed to have quickly developed the same love-hate relationship with her husband that her parents shared.

With one or other of her sisters forever returning in tears to the family home, to rail against the man she had married, Chesnie had soon known that she wanted no part in marriage. She had attended college most evenings, doing most of her studying at the weekends. She had not lacked for potential boyfriends, however, and occasionally had gone out on a date with either someone she had known previously or had met at college. On occasions, too, she had experimented with a little kissing, but as soon as things had looked like getting serious she'd put up barriers.

She'd become aware she had started to get a reputation for being aloof. It had not bothered her—nor had it seemed to stop men asking her for a date.

Chesnie had been working in an office for two years when her studies came to an end. She'd taken more courses, and done more study, and two years later had been ready to take a better-paid job. She'd changed firms and begun work as a secretary and she'd been good at it.

What she had not been so good at was handling the traumatic friction that seemed to be a constant feature in her family home. She'd told herself she was being oversensitive and that everyone had their ups and downs. The only trouble was that in her fraught home, the animosity was permanent.

Having been brought up to be self-sufficient, she had thought often of leaving and had soon felt she could just about afford a bedsit somewhere. Only the knowledge that her mother would be furious should she leave her commodious and graceful home for some lowly bedsit had stopped her.

Matters had come to a head one weekend, however, when all three weeping sisters, and crying babies, had descended. From where Chesnie had viewed it, each sister had been trying to outdo the other with reports of what a rotten husband her spouse was.

When Chesnie had felt her sympathy for the trio turning into a feeling of weariness with all three of them, she'd gone out into the garden and found her father inspecting his roses.

'You came to escape the bedlam too?' he asked wryly.

'Dad, I'm thinking of moving out.' The words she hadn't rehearsed came blurting from her.

'I think I'll come with you,' he replied. But, glancing at her to see if she was smiling at his quip, he saw that she wasn't. 'You're serious, aren't you?' he asked.

The words were out; she couldn't retract them. 'I've been thinking of it for some while. I'm sure I could manage a small bedsit, and...'

'You'd better make that a small flat, and in a good area, if you want me to have any peace.'

Two days later her mother sought her out. 'Your father tells me your home isn't good enough for you any more.'

Chesnie knew that she loved her mother—just as she knew the futility of arguing with her. 'I'd like to be—more—independent,' she replied quietly.

Ten days after that, and much to her astonishment, her mother told her she had found somewhere for her. Chesnie was so overjoyed that her mother, having slept on it, had decided to aid her rather than make life difficult, that she closed her eyes to the fact that the rent of the flat was far more than she could afford.

Furnishing the flat was no problem. What with bits and pieces from her parents and her grandparents, and with her restless sister Nerissa always changing her home around and getting rid of some item of furniture or other, Chesnie soon made her small flat very comfortable.

She had been resident for two months, though, when she had to face up to the reality that she just couldn't afford to be that independent. Her mother would be horrified if she went downmarket and found herself a bedsit. And from Chesnie's point of view she would be horrified herself if she had to give up the peace and quiet she had found to return to her old home.

When Browning Enterprises advertised for a senior secretary she applied for the job, and got it. It paid more, and she earned it when she started taking on more and more responsibility. The only fly in the ointment was Lionel Browning's son. But Hector Browing had his own business, and apart from visits to his father, usually when Hector's finances needed a cash injection, Chesnie saw little of him. She was aware that he resented her, but could think of no reason for his dislike other than the fact that he knew that *she* knew he was as near broke as made no difference.

She was happy living in a place of her own, but since she lived in the same town as her parents she popped in to see them every two or three weeks—and always came away glad she had made the decision to leave.

Then, a year later, her paternal grandmother died, and after months of living in a kind of vacuum her grandfather sold his home in Herefordshire and, with her parents having ample room, moved in with them.

Chesnie adored her grandfather. She seemed to have a

special affinity with him, and had feared from the beginning that life with her bickering parents would not suit her peace-loving Gramps. She took to 'popping in' to her old home more frequently.

She knew he looked forward to her visits, and knew when he suggested he teach her to drive that he was looking for excuses to get out of the house.

She and her grandfather spent many pleasant Saturday afternoons together, and when she passed her driving test she took to taking him for a drive somewhere. Three months ago she had driven him across country to Herefordshire, and to the village where he had lived prior to moving in with her parents.

Six days later she had arrived home from her office to find her grandfather sitting outside her flat in his car. 'I'm not such a good cook as my mother, but you're welcome to come to dinner,' she invited lightly, watching him, knowing from the fact of him being there as much from the excited light in his eyes that something a touch monumental was going on.

Over macaroni cheese and salad he told her he had noticed a 'To Let' sign in the garden of a small cottage on their visit to his home village last Saturday. He hadn't phoned the agent because, knowing the owner, he had phoned him instead. The result being the tenancy was his straight away on a temporary let while he waited for something in the village to come up for sale.

What could she say? 'It's what you want, Gramps?' she asked quietly.

'I should never have left,' he answered simply, and she could only think, since he had never parted with his furniture but had put it in store, that perhaps without knowing it he had always meant to return.

'What do my parents think?'

A wicked light she hadn't seen in a long while entered his eyes. 'Your father's all right about it—er—your mother's taken it personally.'

Chesnie knew all about her mother taking it 'personally'—she would go on and on about it, and Chesnie suspected he would want to move out sooner rather than later. 'When are you leaving?' she asked.

'I was wondering if you're free to drive me there tomorrow?' he asked, looking positively cheeky.

He had got everything arranged so quickly! She had to grin. 'I'd love to,' she answered, and was thinking in terms of availability of trains for the return trip when her grandfather seemed to read her mind.

'You wouldn't care to look after my car for me, would you? I'll seldom need it, and it will only be until I can find a property in the village with a garage. There isn't one at the cottage.'

That had been three months ago. Chesnie missed her grandfather but had driven to see him several times. When, six weeks ago, Hector Browning had accused her of having an affair with his father she had known she couldn't possibly work at Browning Enterprises any longer.

Knowing she was going to part company with Lionel Browning, and having just received a letter asking her to vacate her flat, it had been decision time. She needed somewhere new to live and work; she could do both anywhere.

When Chesnie had seen the advert for the PA's job at Yeatman Trading, and subsequently passed the first and second interviews, she'd crossed her fingers and hoped...

She still had a wide grin on her face when she drove up to the smart appartment block where her sister lived. She had a new job now, PA to none other than Mr Joel Davenport himself.

Nerissa was in, took one look at her beaming face, and squealed, 'You got it!'

Later she calmed down enough to say that she had known she would get it. 'The rest of us had to get married to afford to leave home. But not you, clever girl, you inherited the family brain.' From Chesnie's viewpoint it hadn't been that easy. She had worked hard, but Nerissa was going blithely on, 'Now to sort you out with a flat. Stephen was having a word with someone last night who may have something—' She broke off waspishly. 'He does have his uses.'

From that moment on everything seemed to move at lightning pace. Chesnie was not a partying person, but Nerissa made her promise to return for a party she and Stephen were holding on Saturday evening, and Chesnie returned to Cambridge and packed up her belongings ready for her move.

The party was a success; Nerissa wouldn't have had it any other way. But, although Chesnie found the function enjoyable, she had other things on her mind—she had only two weeks to work alongside Joel Davenport's present PA and get up to speed. It wasn't very long—would she cope?

Chesnie arrived back at her sister's apartment after her first Monday in her new job with her head spinning—and a sinking feeling that two months, let alone two weeks, wouldn't be long enough for her to remember all that there was to absorb.

She was ready for bed and didn't think she had energy enough to eat a meal. Her sister had other plans. 'How was your first day?' she asked straight away.

'I'm on my knees!' Chesnie confessed.

'That good, huh? And how was the new boss?'

'I haven't seen him. He's in Scotland until Wednesday.'

'Right, now, don't take your jacket off. The flat Stephen told me about has come up. Come on, we'll go and take a look.'

Somewhere to live was a priority. From somewhere Chesnie conjured up some enthusiasm and, with her sister driving, went to view a small flat on the outskirts of the city.

The flat consisted of a sitting room, bathroom, a tiny kitchen and two bedrooms, though the second bedroom was no bigger than her parents' broom cupboard. 'If there's a chance, I'll take it,' Chesnie declared at once. The rent was astronomical—but so too was her salary.

'You're sure?' Nerissa questioned. 'You're welcome to stay with me for as long as you like—if you can put up with Tibbetts.' 'Tibbetts' being her husband, Stephen Tibbetts.

'This will do fine,' Chesnie assured her, and in no time Nerissa was speaking to her husband on the phone.

'You can move in any time,' she said the moment she had ended her call. 'Let's celebrate!'

Chesnie was grateful that the celebration was nothing more than a meal out with a glass of wine.

Tuesday proved every bit as busy as the previous day, with Barbara Platt trying to break her in gently but as aware as Chesnie that there was not too much time remaining before Barbara departed a week on Friday.

Joel Davenport had already been at his desk for over an hour when Chesnie arrived at her office on Wednesday. She was not late, was in fact fifteen minutes early. In the short time she'd been there she had heard that he simply ate up work—throughout that day he proved it.

Not that she had much to do with him. Though he did leave his office at one point to speak to Barbara and to pause in passing to ask, pleasantly enough, 'Settling in?'

She raised her head, maintaining her cool image to politely agree, 'Yes, thank you,' and he went on to Barbara's desk and Chesnie went back to what she had been doing.

By Friday, although she was starting to grow more confident that she was up to the job, she was nevertheless mentally exhausted by the time she arrived at her sister's home, to be greeted by Nerissa smilingly telling her, 'Philip Pomeroy rang. He wants to take you out.'

'You make me sound like a set of dentures! Who's Philip Pomeroy?'

'You're hopeless!' Nerissa complained. 'You met him at my party last Saturday. Tallish, wavy brownish hair, very slightly receding, pushing forty. Ring any bells?'

Chesnie did a mental flip back to the party, and placed Philip Pomeroy as a rather amiable man, interested in her, but inoffensive with it. 'Did you tell him I was busy?'

'I told him you'd ring him.'

'Nerissa!'

'Oh, go on, ring him. He's nice.'

Out of courtesy to her sister, who had promised a return phone call on her behalf, Chesnie reluctantly phoned Philip Pomeroy, who appeared pleased she had rung and straight away asked her to dine with him.

'I'm very busy at the moment,' she replied.

'You're too busy to eat?'

'I'm moving into a new flat tomorrow,' she explained. 'It will take me over a week to get everything unpacked.'

'I could bring champagne and caviar round, and we could snack while you unpack.'

She laughed and decided she liked him. 'Some other time,' she said, and rang off.

Chesnie had a change from mental exhaustion on Saturday, when she met the delivery van from Cambridge and set about placing her belongings and hanging up curtains.

On Monday Barbara Platt afforded her the most wonderful, if scary, compliment by telling her that Joel Davenport had a meeting at one of their other businesses and that Barbara was going with him. 'We won't be back again today, but I know you'll cope.'

Chesnie wished she had Barbara's confidence in that, but, to her delight—though bearing in mind it had gone seven in the evening before she finally switched off her computer—cope she did. She was not complaining—she was starting to really enjoy her job. She went home to her new flat feeling on top of the world.

Friday, Barbara's last day, arrived all too quickly. Chesnie spent the morning eagerly absorbing all and everything that Barbara was telling her of the more confidential details of their work. She supposed that with Barbara divulging such matters it must mean that she had satisfied herself that the new PA was worthy of such confidences.

Feeling enormously pleased with Barbara's trust, Chesnie was further delighted when at half past twelve the good-looking Joel Davenport came into their office and, instead of going over to Barbara's desk, came over to Chesnie.

'I'm taking my number one PA for an extended lunch. The office is all yours, Chesnie Cosgrove.'

Indeed, so delighted was she at this further show of trust in her abilities that her cool exterior slipped momentarily. She smiled, a natural smile. *'Bon appétit,'* she replied.

She became aware that Joel Davenport was staring at her as if seeing something new in her for the first time, but before she could change her smile back to her more usual guarded smile he muttered, 'Those incredibly long eye-lashes can't be real.'

'I'm afraid they are,' she replied.

'Amazing,' he commented—and took his 'number one' PA off for a parting lunch.

Feeling a mite disturbed by Joel Davenport's personal comment—even if it had sounded more matter-of-fact than personal—Chesnie was soon over any disquiet when she realised that if Barbara was his number one PA today, then on Monday yours truly, Chesnie Cosgrove, would be number one!

She had plenty to do, and was fully involved in her work when at five to three Barbara came back from what it tran-spired had been a champagne lunch.

'Joel has gone on to keep his three o'clock appointment,' Barbara explained. 'Now, what can I help you with?'

'I think you've filled in as many blanks as you can,' Chesnie replied.

And guessed she must have sounded a mite apprehensive when Barbara replied that she was confident she would cope admirably. 'A bit different from your predecessor.'

'My predecessor?' Chesnie was puzzled. Mustard had nothing on Joel Davenport's present PA.

'Didn't I mention it?' Barbara realised that she hadn't, and went on to correct that oversight.

Apparently Barbara's life had changed dramatically when she had met Derek Platt. In no time she had fallen in love and married him. Derek had been in the process of purchasing a small holding in the Welsh borders, and that had been fine by Barbara. A smart and mature woman, she'd looked forward to this change of lifestyle.

'I gave ample notice, and we thought we'd selected the right person. But she proved not up to the job, and Joel didn't think the other candidates were any better, so we advertised again. And—' she smiled '—here you are. And, I'm certain, more than up to the job.'

Chesnie fervently hoped she was right. 'That won't prevent you from leaving me your phone number, I hope?' It had been Barbara's suggestion that she would. But she laughed and, having more or less cleared her desk, began to expand on matters other than the work which Chesnie would be dealing with.

Barbara was full of praise for Joel. Yeatman Trading had been going through a very tough time when he had joined the firm. He had seen at once what needed to be done, and had done it—had transformed the company—and been rewarded with a seat on the board.

'And now,' Barbara continued, 'within the next year Winslow Yeatman is going to retire.'

'The chairman?' Chesnie had picked that up from somewhere during the past two weeks.

'None other,' Barbara agreed. 'And Joel wants that job—very badly. He has very progressive ideas, and believes that to be able to put those ideas into effect he needs to be chairman.'

'Will he get it?' Chesnie asked.

'If there's any justice he will,' Barbara answered. 'It's largely through his efforts that a firm that was heading for the rocks has gone from strength to strength this past ten years. He, more than anyone, is responsible for its growth and expansion. He's ambitious and hard-headed when it comes to business. But he's good. They certainly don't come any better.'

Chesnie had seen that much for herself in the short time she'd been there. 'You think he might not get it?' she asked.

'Nothing's certain. The problem here is that this started off as a family firm a hundred or so years ago, and, although new blood such as Joel has gradually infiltrated, over half the board are family members. Three of whom I know for a fact want a Yeatman to head the company. There are nine people on the board, excluding the chairman, and while I know there are three of the directors who are for Joel, he can't vote for himself, so that leaves two other votes as yet unaccounted for. Should the vote be split and Winslow Yeatman have to make the casting vote then it's more than likely he'll favour a family man.'

'One of his family?'

Barbara shook her head. 'A man with a family. He also wants what is best for the firm.'

'Doesn't J... Mr Davenport have a family?'

'He's not married.'

Chesnie felt a little surprised. 'Some woman named Felice phoned for him last week, and a woman named Gina phoned to speak to him on Monday. I put them in the wife and daughter slot.'

'Girlfriends.' Barbara corrected Chesnie's assumption. 'He's *more* than happy with his bachelor lifestyle.' She gave a wicked grin. 'Though his fellow director, Arlene Enderby, née Yeatman, recently divorced, non-working but taking her cut just the same—and who just happens to be the chairman's niece—has got her eye on Joel.'

'Does he know?'

Barbara gave a whoop of laughter. 'I've an idea that there's not much that goes on in the female mind that Joel doesn't know. He's taken her out a couple of times, so I'm positive she will have filled in any gaps.' At that point Barbara seemed to collect herself. 'And I'm talking too much—must be the champage—I'm not used to it. Either that or some instinctive feeling that you'll be better able to help him get what he deserves and has worked for if you know more of what's going on.'

At a quarter to five Joel Davenport, who must have entered his office by the outer door, rang for Barbara to go in to see him. She came out ten minutes later, emotional tears in her eyes, a cheque in one hand, a jeweller's box in the other, and a gorgeous bouquet of flowers in her arms.

'Oh, Chesnie,' she said, emotion still with her after the presentation she had just received, 'I do so hope you'll be as happy working here as I have been.'

'I'm sure I shall,' Chesnie answered with a smile, but more hoped that she could do the job. For, aside from the everyday difficulties and stress that were part and parcel of the job, from what Barbara had said earlier it seemed there was a lot of in-fighting going on too.

For a fact, there were three board members who were against Joel Davenport getting the chairman's job.

Chesnie suddenly felt swallowed up by an unexpected huge wave of loyalty, and she determined that if there was any small thing in her power she could do to help him get that chairman's job, she would do it. Then she laughed at herself. What on earth did she think she, a PA, could do that would help when it came to electing the new chairman?

CHAPTER TWO

IT WAS four weeks since Barbara had left, and Chesnie was thankful that in those four weeks she had not had to phone Barbara or needed to call on the services of Eileen Gray, a kind of floating PA who, while not wanting the pressure of being anyone's full-time PA, was so good at the job that the company did not want to let her go.

Chesnie drove to work that Monday four weeks after Barbara's departure and for the first time truly believed that she *could* do the job of Joel's number one PA.

It had not been an easy four weeks. Joel Davenport, for all he made his job seem effortless, had an appetite for work that at first had caused her to work in overdrive just to try and keep up with him.

She worked late; once, when he was out for the day, staying at the office until gone nine at night to catch up and so have her desk clear for the next morning.

Most evenings she staggered home to make a quick snack, get her smart business clothes ready for the morning, and fall into bed. Sometimes she dreamed of him, but that was hardly surprising; he had become a dominant force in her life.

On one weekend she had visited her grandfather in Herefordshire, and another weekend she'd gone to see her parents in Cambridge. Robina had been there, having left Ronnie for a 'final' time. She was divorcing him, she'd declared in floods of tears, she'd had enough. Ronnie had phoned, and there were more tears as Robina had screeched a list of his faults down the phone at him.

All that hate and recrimination had served only to freshly endorse for Chesnie that she'd got the better bargain when she'd decided never to marry. Though she had to smile—when would she get the chance? Working for and with such a high-powered, work-oriented man, she didn't have the time to date, much less to build any kind of relationship.

Which reminded her. Nerissa had telephoned last night to say Philip Pomeroy had rung again and could he have her sister's number?

'You didn't give it to him?' Chesnie had asked, guessing that Philip wanted to ask her out; she didn't have time to go out. By not letting him have her newly connected number, she was spared having to make excuses.

'I promised you I wouldn't,' Nerissa had confirmed.

With her new-found confidence in her ability to cope with her job, Chesnie parked her grandfather's car, swung into the building and took the lift to the top floor. It went without saying that Joel Davenport would already be hard at work. Unless he was out of town he was always in before her.

An involuntary smile lit her mouth as she recalled that first Monday after Barbara had gone. Hoping to look as cool and as poised as she was striving to look, Chesnie, feeling a bundle of nerves, had entered her office. No sooner had she sat down, though, and Joel Davenport had come to greet her as if it had been her first day.

'Good morning, Chesnie,' he'd said pleasantly. 'We haven't frightened you off, then?'

She had given him her guarded smile. 'Good morning, Mr Davenport,' she'd replied and, inwardly churning, 'I don't scare easily,' she had added.

He'd studied her, nodded, and then commented, 'That's what I like to hear. The name's Joel,' he indicated, and her first day as *numero uno* had begun.

The door between the two offices stood open today, as it sometimes did when she went in. 'Good morning,' Chesnie called to the dark-blond-haired man absorbed in the paperwork in front of him.

'Good morning,' he answered, but did not raise his head. Business as usual.

Chesnie had barely stowed her bag when Darren, the post boy, arrived. 'Good morning, Miss Cosgrove,' he said huskily, and as their hands touched as she relieved him of the bundles of post he blushed crimson.

Chesnie took her eyes from him, giving him time to compose himself. 'How's your mother?' she asked. 'I do hope she's on the mend.' She glanced at him, glad to see his blush had died down.

'She's going back to work today,' he answered on a gulp of breath. 'Thank you,' he added, and gave her a beautiful smile as his eyes glued to her face, he backed to the door.

Then he became aware that Joel Davenport had come from his office and was standing watching him—Darren bolted. 'That young man idolises you,' Joel said abruptly.

'It's only a crush,' Chesnie replied, and was ready to deal with any query her employer had when she discovered he wasn't ready to dismiss the subject yet.

'He'll never get over it while you treat him that way!'

What way was that? 'I'd rather be pleasant to him than not,' she answered, as calmly as she was able.

'Is that the way you treat all your admirers?'

What had this got to do with work? 'It depends how old they are,' she replied evenly. 'Young men like Darren, sensitive young men, deserve to have their blushes respected. Older, more cynical men,' she went on, looking one such straight in the eye, 'are too tough to need kid-glove treatment.'

A grunt was her answer. 'Bring the post through when you've sorted it!' he rapped.

Yes, sir, three bags full, sir. And, anyhow, he could talk! In the short time she'd been there she'd observed he had quite a fan club amongst the female staff.

The morning that had got off to a rancorous start did not improve much for Chesnie when, nearing one o'clock, Joel's office door opened. Observing he wasn't there, the most striking-looking blue-eyed brunette, sporting a sensational tan, fluttered through and into Chesnie's office.

'You must be Chesnie!' She smiled. 'Uncle Winslow told me all about you.'

'Uncle Winslow' must be Winslow Yeatman, the chairman. Chesnie had by then met him several times and found him a most charming gentleman. 'You must be Arlene Enderby,' Chesnie guessed—the non-working director of the company.

'You have it. I've come to take Joel to lunch, but he doesn't appear to be in.'

Chesnie, who managed Joel's diary with keen efficiency, knew for certain he did not have a lunch appointment with the chairman's niece. 'He's probably been held up somewhere,' she suggested tactfully. 'Perhaps...'

'Oh, we haven't arranged lunch. I've just got back from soaking up the sun on holiday.' She almost purred as she trotted out, 'We have such a lot to catch up on, I thought—' She broke off to exclaim, 'Ah!' as they heard a door open and saw Joel stride into his office. 'Joel! *Darling!*' Arlene Enderby cried, and was in the other office, flinging her arms around him as if he was some long-lost lover.

Chesnie met the eyes of her employer as Arlene Enderby snuggled into his arms. Chesnie did not smile; neither did he. She got up and deliberately closed the door—and discovered she was inwardly shaking, experiencing the strangest sensation of not caring to see him with his arms around some woman. How odd! Why should it bother her at all?

It wasn't in the least odd, she decided a moment later. This was a place of business and that was why she didn't care for it. Everything that happened in this office should be purely professional. Which wasn't what was happening next door. What *was* happening next door? It was very quiet in there. She half wished she had left the door open.

Chesnie was over the slight glitch in her equilibrium by the next day. She smiled and chatted lightly to Darren when he brought the post, and dealt pleasantly with the various heads of department—male ones—who seemed to find it necessary to stop by her desk for one reason or another. She had gradually got to know more and more of the people within the organisation, and it was good to be able to put a face to the various names that cropped up from time to time.

Though there was one new face she hadn't seen before. The tall white-haired man poked his head round her office door at a quarter to one and came in. 'Well, you're a decided improvement on Barbara Thingy,' he beamed, and, when Chesnie looked pleasantly enquiring, asked, 'Is my son around?'

'You're Joel's father?'

'I know, I know. I don't look old enough to have a son that age,' quipped the man Chesnie thought must be at least seventy. 'Magnus Davenport, at your service.' He extended his right hand, and Chesnie immediately decided she liked him.

'Chesnie Cosgrove,' she introduced herself, shaking his hand. 'I'm afraid your son is at a business lunch. Can I help you at all?'

'Oh, dear, that's a nuisance! I've driven all the way across the city hoping he'd take *me* to lunch,' Davenport Senior replied with a sigh.

Chesnie thought for a moment. The matter was settled when it came to her that Joel's father was only about ten years younger than Gramps. She wouldn't hesitate to take her grandfather to lunch. 'I'll take you if you like?' she offered.

'I thought you'd never ask!' he beamed.

Over lunch she discovered Magnus Davenport was a bit of a rascal. He insisted that she call him by his first name, but as he chatted away freely, about everything and everyone, she found that as well as being an outrageous gossip he was also a bit of a flirt—but quite harmless.

He openly told her that his wife, Joel's mother, had thrown him out and divorced him years ago. 'Said I was

shiftless. Can you believe that? And that she'd had enough.'
Chesnie was on the point of feeling sorry for him when all
of a sudden he laughed. 'D'you know, I can't really blame
her? I never did hold down a job for long. Come to think
of it, one of the happiest days I've had was when I retired.'

Chesnie had to laugh too; he had a sort of infectious
quality about him. 'I must think about getting back,' she
hinted, when he seemed inclined to linger over his coffee.

'I'm going to the races tomorrow. Fancy coming with
me?' he asked.

She smiled and declined, and knew she was going to be
late when Magnus Davenport drove her back to the
Yeatman Trading building. She was not unduly alarmed
that it was nearer half past two than two o'clock when
Magnus dropped her off. She had worked late many times,
and would cheerfully work late tonight if she hadn't finished her workload by five.

'I won't come in—give me a call if you change your
mind about the races,' he said, and handed her his card.

Chesnie was smiling as she bade him goodbye, but had
work on her mind as she opened the door to her office. She
noticed at once that the communicating door to her employer's office was open and that Joel was back from his
business lunch.

Courtesy demanded that she commented on her lateness.
She crossed that carpet and was aware that Joel knew she
had returned, even though she hadn't noticed him look up.

Nor did he glance up then, when she stood to the side
of his desk. For some reason it niggled her. She'd be
blessed if she'd say a word till he acknowledged her presence.

Just as she was about to turn around and go back to her
office, however, he carefully laid down his pen. Then his
head came up. He leaned back in his chair, silently ap-
praising her, from the top of her red-blonde hair, to her
slender but curvy figure in the royal blue suit, and all the
way down to her shoes. Then, while she was studying his

firm jaw, noticing that his mouth was pretty terrific even without the semblance of a smile, he moved his glance swiftly upwards and his blue eyes met her stubborn green ones head on.

Good, she'd got his attention. He waited—waited for her to speak first—and she felt quite irritated about that too. But she had been at pains to adopt a cool front; she wasn't about to let it slip now.

'Your father called,' she began evenly, pleasantly. 'He was disappointed not to see you,' she added. 'We went to lunch,' she informed him, when Davenport said nothing.

'No doubt you were able to help him over his disappointment,' he threw in sourly, and at that moment pugilistic tendencies awakened in Chesnie that she'd had no idea she possessed. To her amazement she felt a momentary desire to poke Davenport Junior in the eye with something sharp and painful. 'Who paid?' he asked abruptly, his tone toughening.

What was it with him? The nerve! 'Your father was my guest,' she answered primly.

'He conned you into taking him to lunch, didn't he?'

'Not at all. I liked him,' she began. 'He—'

'I'll reimburse you!' Joel Davenport cut in sharply—and her anger went soaring, and with it her cool image.

'No, you won't!' she flared hotly, and saw him smile—every bit as if he really enjoyed fracturing the cool front she'd displayed this past six weeks.

He shrugged. 'So I won't,' he agreed, his tone all at once silky, and picked up his pen.

Chesnie went swiftly back to her own office. She felt then that she hated him. He'd done that on purpose—made her forget her poise for a moment. She didn't want her front fractured; it made her feel vulnerable. She did not care for the feeling.

She slammed into her work and wanted nothing to do with him. This was what happened when you let personalities in on the scene. Meeting his father, liking him, laughing with him, had put a severe dent in the Chesnie Cosgrove she preferred to show the world. It seemed as if one Davenport had softened her up for another. Well, she wasn't having it.

By four that afternoon her cool exterior was firmly back in place. At four-fifteen Larry Jenkins from Accounts came into her office with a query that wasn't strictly in her domain, but she was pleased to be able to handle it. Though Larry didn't stay long when the door opened and Joel Davenport strode in.

Joel watched him hastily leave. 'I hear this corridor is alive with senior executives in need of guidance from you on some urgent matter or other,' he commented.

What was she supposed to answer to that? And how did he know? Though she supposed that not a lot got by him—even when he wasn't around! 'Is there something *you* need guidance with?' she enquired coolly of his visit—and didn't hate him any more when he actually laughed, as though the way she'd bounced that back at him had amused him.

'Are you still mad at me?' he asked, with such a wealth of natural charm there that she began to like him very much again.

'You deliberately provoked me!' she accused primly.

'Did I?' he asked innocently—and a moment later was all business and instruction.

Chesnie went home that night in a happy frame of mind. She liked her job, had never felt so stimulated by any work she had done before, and she liked her boss too. He was...Chesnie came to, to realise she had drifted off for quite some time to thinking of Joel Davenport, her good-looking boss. My, did he have it all. Gina had rung him this morning, but he hadn't stayed talking to her above a minute. Chesnie had an idea that Gina was on her way out.

Aware that her employer would be flying up to Scotland first thing on Thursday morning, Chesnie went into the office earlier than usual on Wednesday, so she could complete any information he needed to take with him before he left the office that night.

'Good morning,' she called as she went in, and hardly thought he would notice her early arrival.

'Couldn't sleep?'

She should have known better—there was no detail small enough that he'd miss. She grinned to herself and started her day.

She did not feel like grinning when, in Joel's office, taking notes later that morning, the phone on her desk rang. Saving time, Joel stretched out a hand and pressed a button to divert the call to his phone, and took the call himself.

Whoever it was had been put through to the right phone in the first place. 'Who wants her?' he demanded. And while Chesnie was thinking it must be some business call, because her family would only phone in the direst emergency, he was charmingly saying, 'I'm sorry, Pomeroy, my PA isn't available just now.' So saying, he put down the phone and terminated the call. Then, as cool as you like, he calmly carried on from where he had left off.

Feeling little short of amazed, Chesnie stared disbelievingly at her employer. Even while she was recognising that someone named Pomeroy had phoned to speak to her, and that the only Pomeroy she knew was Philip Pomeroy, Chesnie was astonished that Joel Davenport had not passed the call over to her.

She quickly found her voice. 'Anyone I should ring back?' she enquired politely, annoyance straining at the leash.

Joel looked across at her, his blue glance icy. 'How do you know Philip Pomeroy?' he demanded.

Ready to tell him it was none of his business, Chesnie decided that one of them should show some manners here. 'I met him at a party.' She forced the words out.

Joel grunted, didn't look impressed, and stated coldly, 'You *do* know he's with the opposition?'

'Opposition?'

'In case you didn't know he heads Symington Technology—our competitors in the technology field.'

'I didn't know,' Chesnie answered, and started to feel cross that Joel Davenport was as good as reminding her that the work she did for him was highly confidential. She resented that unsaid reminder, resented his icy manner, and tilted her chin a defiant fraction. 'You obviously know him better than I do,' she replied, her control back. And, knowing she was pushing it, 'Do you happen to have his number?'

Icy blue eyes bored into hers; she refused to back down. 'I shouldn't bother,' he replied shortly. 'He'll ring again.'

Chesnie was still silently mutinying against Joel Davenport when she went back to her desk. She didn't particularly wish to speak to Philip Pomeroy—and thank you, Nerissa, for telling him where I work—but that was for her to decide, not Davenport. He spoke to his girlfriends when they rang him at the office. Where did he get off not allowing her that same courtesy? Even if Philip Pomeroy *was* the opposition.

Chesnie was not feeling any more Davenport-friendly when, around midday, just as he had predicted, Philip Pomeroy rang again. Had the door between the two offices not been open, and Joel Davenport privy to everything she said, Chesnie might well have refused Philip's invitation to dinner. As it was, she knew full well he had heard her 'Hello, Philip' and would more than likely be tuned in. Stubbornly she determined that Davenport should know exactly what she thought of his offensive, if unspoken, reminder that her work was highly confidential.

'Say yes,' Philip was urging. 'You can't still be unpacking.'

She glanced through to the other office—Davenport appeared to be working, but she knew his capability to handle several things at once. 'I'd love to go out with you,' she heard herself reply—and loved it when Davenport turned his head to glance her way. He was unsmiling. She smiled—she couldn't help it—then dipped her head so he shouldn't see her smile, though she guessed he had.

'Tonight?' Philip was pressing. 'Give me your address and I'll pick you up at—'

'Er—I can't tonight,' she interrupted hurriedly. Heaven alone knew what time she would finish work tonight. Tomorrow, though, with Joel up in Scotland, should be much easier. 'I can make tomorrow if—'

Philip snapped up the alternative, asked again for her address, and when she had told him where she lived he, as busy as she, said he would look forward to tomorrow and rang off.

After that Chesnie was too busy to give thought to anything but the work she was involved with. She stayed late at her desk; so too did the man in the next room. At ten past seven she tidied her desk for the day, double-checked that Joel had all the information he would need for his trip, and went in to see him.

They spent another ten minutes finalising everything, then she said she was going home—and found she was looking into a pair of inscrutable sharp blue eyes.

He was unsmiling at first, but then relaxed to say quietly, 'You're turning out to be something of a treasure, Chesnie Cosgrove.'

Her heart gave the most peculiar bump, and she was so delighted by the compliment that she almost fell for his charm and smiled. But she wasn't forgetting his attitude earlier in the day, so she remained pleasant, but otherwise aloof, as—like any well-brought-up PA would—she wished him a pleasant trip and went home.

Strangely—or perhaps, she mused, it wasn't so strange— Joel Davenport was in her head very much that night. She could not remember ever being so annoyed with an employer before. Hector Browning didn't count; it was his father she had worked for.

Feeling unable to settle, Joel Davenport still in her head, she rang her sister at half past nine. 'I expected you to ring before this,' Nerissa said by way of apology. 'He rang, didn't he?'

'Did you have to tell him where I work?'

'What else could I do? You said not to give him your phone number. And anyway, I ran out of excuses. Where's he taking you?'

'I don't know. He's calling for me at—'

'Hah!' Nerissa cut in. 'You're going out with him!'

Chesnie had to laugh. 'Tomorrow,' she agreed, then chatted for another few minutes and rang off—to have Joel Davenport back in her head. He thought she was a treasure. She found she was smiling—and quickly cancelled that. Soft soap!

As anticipated, she was less busy on Thursday, and was extremely pleased that she seemed to coast through her work that day. True, there wasn't the same buzz about the office with Joel not there, but at least it looked as if she would be leaving on time that night. Which would suit her quite nicely. Time to go home, have a relaxing bath and get ready to go out with Philip Pomeroy.

At five past four she glanced at her watch, assessed the work she still had to do and knew for certain that she would be leaving at five. The best-laid plans...

At four-thirty her phone rang. 'Joel Davenport's office,' she answered pleasantly.

'Hello, Chesnie,' the man himself answered, and her insides went all kind of crumbly. Ridiculous, she told herself stoutly. 'I'm sorry to trouble you,' he began, not sounding sorry at all, 'but I've arranged an early meeting in London tomorrow. Do you think you can have some paperwork ready for me?'

'Of course,' she answered automatically, and had her notepad in hand. 'Fire away.'

She was getting writer's cramp before he was halfway finished. Was he joking? It would take her hours to complete this little lot! She almost stopped him then and there, to remind him that she had a date that night. But remembered in time how at her job interview he had asked her supposing she had a date but he needed her to accompany him at short notice. Without hesitation she'd indicated it would not be a problem—that she would change her plans for the evening. This wasn't accompanying him anywhere, but it amounted to the same thing.

'I haven't given you too much to do there, have I?' he asked, when he eventually came to an end.

'What are treasures for?' she found she had answered, before she could think about it.

'I knew I could rely on you,' he commented charmingly, and rang off.

Chesnie was busying herself making a start, collecting information together, before she realised that there was no way she could get everything sorted, no way she could type up reams and reams of confidential matter, *and* keep her date with Philip Pomeroy.

Her hand went to the phone, but before she could carry out her intention to put a call through to Symington Technology she had another thought. How about if she got all the paperwork already to hand checked over, then typed as much as she could of the new stuff before she went home? Then, with her computer installed at home in that apology for a second bedroom, she could work as late as she had to *after* her dinner with Philip. Brilliant, or what?

Having gone over the notion, Chesnie couldn't fault the idea. She'd have to get up early to have everything ready on Joel's desk for when he came in—she wished she knew what time that was—but couldn't see any problem. If this was what being a senior PA was all about, then she would prove she was very much up to the job.

She was glad to make herself comfortable in Philip Pomeroy's car on the way to the restaurant. It was the first chance she'd had to sit and relax since that half past four phone call. She had rushed from the office at five past six, laden with folders and stationery. She had taken the quickest of showers and had selected a short-sleeved, straight-skirted black dress. Although her wardrobe was not extensive it was of good quality. She had been ready and, anxious not to waste a minute, had been busy typing when the outer door buzzer had sounded, announcing the arrival of her escort.

The Linton, the restaurant Philip had chosen, was elegant, discreet, and, she didn't doubt, pricey. Chesnie found Philip Pomeroy a pleasant companion, too sophisticated to be obvious or pushy, and she began to relax more and more.

'I had no idea you worked for Joel Davenport,' Philip remarked as they began their meal. 'You can't have been at Yeatman Trading long or I'm sure I'd have heard.'

That surprised her. Then she wondered if it should have. Being a business rival, would Joel know the name of Philip's PA? Very probably he did, she mused.

'I've worked for Joel for almost two months now,' she saw no harm in admitting.

'You changed jobs around the same time you moved into your new flat,' Philip documented. 'How do you find working for Davenport? Is he—?'

'Hmm, I'm sorry, Philip, would you mind very much if neither of us talked about our work?'

He stared at her, plainly liked what he saw, and agreed. 'It's a pact. Business if off the agenda. But—' he smiled '—you can tell Davenport from me that he's a lucky devil, able to look at you every day. Now, tell me how you're settling in to your new flat?'

During their second course Chesnie learned that Philip had been married and divorced. That didn't worry her—who hadn't? She was growing to like him very much, even though she knew that it would never be more than that. He was amusing, and had just said something that made her laugh when, glancing from him, laughter still on her curving lips, she was startled to find she was looking into the steel-blue eyes of someone several tables away. The glint in those eyes warned her she was in trouble over something.

With a coolness she was suddenly far from feeling

Chesnie turned back to her dinner companion. She offered some light comment, she knew not what, her mind busy with the fact that Joel Davenport had flown back from Scotland and all too plainly, if her answers at the job interview meant anything, fully expected her to still be slaving away at the office.

It annoyed her that he should think she had fallen down on the job. And that annoyance caused her to smile more, perhaps laugh a little more, at Philip's amusingly light conversation than she would otherwise.

At any rate Philip seemed pleased, and she didn't give a button what Davenport thought. She knew what he didn't—that she was going home to do his work so he should have it on his desk for eight in the morning. So he could go and take a running jump.

'More coffee?' Philip asked.

'No, thank you,' she refused pleasantly. 'It's been a super evening, but…'

'But you're a working girl?'

'Something like that,' she answered with a smile, and smiled again when, having to pass Davenport's table—curse it—Philip civilly paused to say hello.

'Pomeroy,' Joel acknowledged, getting to his feet. 'Chesnie.' He included her, and introduced his sultry, if terrific-looking companion. 'Do you know Imogen?'

Brief introductions followed, where Joel did not mention that Chesnie was his PA and that he was saving a few short and sharp words for her. After the way she slaved for him! Let him try! Then she and Philip were moving on.

Philip came to the outer door of her apartment building with her. 'I hope you're going to allow me to see you again, Chesnie?' he asked.

She liked him, he was good company—and she had an idea it annoyed Joel Davenport that she went out with the opposition. 'I'd like that,' she answered. But, thinking he might have this coming Saturday in mind, added, 'I'll give you my phone number. Perhaps next week some time?'

'I'll look forward to it,' he said, and when he had her phone number he leaned forward. Though, perhaps sensing her instant withdrawal, he satisfied himself to kiss her cheek, and stood back to wait while she went indoors.

Despite the fact that her home had been cobbled together with pieces of furniture given to her by her parents, grand-parents and her sisters, and the few additions she had contributed herself, Chesnie had to admit everything blended in well to give her apartment a very homely feel.

But there was no time to make herself comfortable in it now. Time only to rinse her hands and head for that tiny second bedroom now laughingly called a study.

She had been at work for forty-five minutes when someone rang the outer buzzer. Philip? Why would he come back? She left her work and went into her small hall to take up the telephone that was connected to the outer front door.

'Who is it?' she enquired, and felt faintly staggered at the reply she received.

'Davenport,' he informed her crisply.

Davenport! Surely he hadn't left the lovely Imogen to have those few short and sharp words with his PA that had been brewing? At this hour? She didn't believe it—though he wasn't sounding too affable.

'You'd better come up!' she replied, equally crisply, while wondering—had she done anything that could be called grounds for dismissal? She didn't think so, and surely Joel Davenport wouldn't call at her home to sack her! Or would he?

She stayed in the hall to wait the minute or so it would take him to reach her door, and mentally braced herself for whatever he had called to see her about. At his first ring she had the door open. For several seconds, like warring adversaries, they stood coldly eyeing each other. He was the first to speak.

'You're still dressed!' he stated hostilely, his glance going over her black dress, drawn for a second to the delicate contours of her cleavage, which had never before been on view.

Feeling very much like holding her hands protectively in front of her bosom, Chesnie instead turned from him. 'Come in,' she invited, and led the way into her sitting room, realising that it would have been just the same to him if she had gone to bed—he would still have rung her apartment buzzer.

In her sitting room she turned to face him. But before she could ask him why he had called, *he* was telling *her*, 'You knew I needed that paperwork for the morning!' Clearly he had stopped by the office from the airport and discovered that the paperwork he'd ordered wasn't locked away in his drawer. 'Yet you deliberately—' He began to sort her out. But she'd had enough before he started.

'I'm glad you called,' she cut in calmly, inwardly boiling. 'There are one or two queries I need your help with. If you're not too tired after your busy day, I wonder if you'd help me?' He was looking at her with narrowed eyes, as if wondering what her game was. Oh, joy; oh, bliss. 'Have you a moment to come to my study?' Study? Pretentious or what? 'I'm working on your paperwork now.'

There was a definite glint in his eyes now, she saw. He had called looking for a fight. She had disarmed him—and he didn't like it. Tough.

Whether he was impressed or not that she'd had no intention of letting him down, she had no idea. But he followed her to her 'study', where she had already printed off some of the matter she had typed.

Swiftly he dealt with the queries which she had been going to make a note of, but from the unsmiling look of him she suspected he didn't care at all to have his cause for righteous anger taken away from him, and was still looking for a fight.

'Naturally, I intend to have everything completed and on

your desk by eight in the morning.' She nicely rubbed it in.

A hostile look was the thanks she received for her trouble. She was almost purring as they left her workroom and she accompanied him out to the hall. He soon put an end to any lofty feelings, however.

Joel Davenport had his hand on the door latch when he looked down on her from his superior height, paused, and then commented shortly, 'After our discussion yesterday, I hardly expected you to be out with Pomeroy tonight!'

What discussion was that? Her memory of it was that Joel had enlightened her to the fact that Philip Pomeroy was head of the opposition. And she felt incensed again that Davenport, for a second time, felt he had to remind her of the confidentiality of her position!

'Do you honestly believe that Philip would have telephoned me at the office and told you who he was if he was after sensitive information from me?' she flared. And, her cool image suddenly in tatters around her, 'Do you honestly think, when I've worked for you for almost two months now, that I would part with any information, confidential or otherwise?' she erupted—and came the closest yet to setting about him when, infuriatingly, he stared at her, seemed again to enjoy seeing her lose her cool front, and then had the sheer audacity—to smile!

'It seems a shame that, because of pressure of work, you sent him from your first date without even a goodnight kiss,' he commented charmingly.

Oh, to kick his shin! Chesnie strove hard for control. 'It rather looks as if you're going to bed kissless too,' she answered sweetly—and was on the receiving end of a look that very clearly stated *'Fat chance'*. Though he made no comment with regard to whether the delectable Imogen was waiting for him somewhere.

Instead, he opened the door, and was on his way out when he bade her silkily, 'Don't work too late.'

Chesnie glared at his departing back. Pig!

CHAPTER THREE

OVER the month that followed Chesnie grew more and more comfortable with her job, and now found the work well within her capabilities. It was hard work, many late evenings, and once, when there had been a big boardroom pow-wow, she had worked a whole weekend. But she loved it, thrived on it, and couldn't think of ever doing anything else. It was as though she had found her niche in life, as though working for Joel was what she was meant to be doing.

Ever since that night when he had called at her flat and found, contrary to his expectations, that she had not fallen down on the job and that his paperwork would be ready for him for the next day, as required, they had settled down to a good, mutually respectful, harmonious working relationship.

Since that night too, the night she had given Philip Pomeroy her home number, Philip had made frequent use of it—but had not again telephoned her at her office. She sometimes went out with him, but he knew by then—or she hoped he did—that she was only interested in being friends. True, he always kissed her cheek on parting—but friends did that sort of thing. She was seeing Philip again tomorrow evening.

But Philip Pomeroy was far from her thoughts that Friday morning when the phone on her desk suddenly called for attention. 'Joel Davenport's office,' she answered automatically.

'That has to be the delightful Chesnie,' said a mature voice she took a moment or two to place.

'Magnus!' she exclaimed, a smile in her voice. 'I'm

afraid Joel's out for the rest of the morning, and part of this afternoon. Did you want him for anything in particular? Or is there something I can help you with?'

'I haven't had a chat to you in a long while,' he replied.

That was true. It must be all of five, maybe six weeks since she'd taken Joel's father to lunch. 'How are you?' she asked, sensing he wanted to chat a little.

Several seconds of silence met her enquiry, then, his voice sounding frail and elderly all of a sudden, he answered at last. 'To tell you the truth, Chesnie, there have been days when I've felt better.'

'You're unwell?' she questioned, starting to feel worried. From his earlier bright tone—clearly a front—he had gone to sound alarmingly shaky.

'I'll—be all right,' he replied bravely.

That wasn't good enough. 'Have you seen a doctor?' she asked, not feeling at all as calm as she was pretending to be.

'I'll be all right,' he repeated, which she took to mean that he hadn't.

'Do you think you should?'

'I'll think about it,' he said, which she just knew meant he had no intention of seeing a doctor.

'Do you have anybody with you?' she asked.

'Who wants to keep company with an old codger like me?' he answered, plainly not feeling his best.

Chesnie chatted to him for about another five minutes, trying to find out what the exact trouble was. He wasn't saying. She gave up when she realised it might be something he was a little embarrassed about.

She was still feeling worried when Magnus rang off. It could be something; it could be nothing. She knew where she could contact Joel—but what if it was nothing? What would Joel do, anyway? Leave his meeting to go and check on his father? From what she'd gleaned, Joel wasn't over-struck on his father anyhow.

For the next half-hour thoughts of Magnus Davenport

being unwell and on his own chewed at her. It was a quarter to one when she couldn't stand it any longer. She liked him. She decided to contact the switchboard, ask them to take messages for her and go for an early lunch. She had his card somewhere—she'd drive over to see him.

It took her three quarters of an hour to get to Magnus Davenport's address, and, having pulled up at the very nice-looking house, Chesnie hoped he would be fit enough to come to the door. It might be that he hadn't moved from where he'd been sitting when he had telephoned her.

She was, she discovered, wrong in a lot of her assumptions. Her ring at the doorbell was answered immediately, and, standing there smiling, Magnus Davenport looked as sprightly as ever.

She opened her mouth—he spoke first. 'I thought you'd never get here!' he exclaimed cheerfully.

He had been expecting her? 'You're—not ill?' she questioned. He looked and sounded in the best of health!

'I'm lonely,' he answered.

And Chesnie just stared at him. There was *nothing* wrong with him, and she was going to have to work late tonight to make up for her earlier lack of concentration and the time she'd taken out when she should have been working. 'You want me to take you to lunch?' she guessed—he was dressed as smart as new paint.

'I've had a few winners lately.' He grinned. 'I'll pay.'

She wanted to be cross with him—he had conned her into driving to see him. But how could she be cross? He was grinning like a mischievous schoolboy, and had admitted to being lonely.

He was his usual indiscreet chatty self over lunch, with tales that most often began with, 'When Dorothea threw me out…' This way Chesnie learned he had been on his uppers with nowhere to go when Joel had come to the rescue and had bought him his house. Joel, it seemed, also gave him a monthly allowance.

'I'd rather have had a lump sum, but Joel said I'd be

bound to spend it all in one go on the gee-gees. He knows me too well,' Magnus complained wryly. 'Arlene Yeatman's still after him, I suppose?'

Arlene Enderby, née Yeatman. 'I've no idea.'

'She was after him even before she ditched her husband and got her divorce. She—'

'I don't think you should tell me...'

'Not you as well!' He laughed. 'Dorothea always used to accuse me of being worse than some gossipy old washerwoman.'

Chesnie smiled a gentle smile. 'You still care for her, don't you?'

'Dorothea? Adore the old battleaxe,' he admitted, and Chesnie's smile turned into a laugh. He really was incorrigible.

She was very late getting back to her office. It had gone three when she hurried in— Lord knew what time she'd be working until that night. And Joel was back, the door between the two offices open.

First dropping her bag down on her desk, she went in to see him. 'Sorry I'm late,' she apologised, out of courtesy. 'I hope you didn't need me for anything?'

'Been shopping?' he enquired mildly, his glance going over her sage-green short-jacketed suit, its just-above-the-knee skirt showing the long, slender length of her legs and trim ankles.

'I've been out to lunch,' she answered.

'The time you put in you're entitled to more than an extended lunch,' he replied, and she knew she was right; their working relationship really was harmonious. Or she'd thought she was right, until all at once his relaxed manner vanished and, 'Who with?' he demanded.

Slightly shaken by his change in attitude, it took all her will-power to stay looking calm. 'As it happens, I had lunch with your father,' she replied coolly—she had intended to tell him anyway, and to mention his father's loneliness at the same time.

'The devil you did! He came here, conning you—'

'He rang,' she cut in, starting to get cross and having great difficulty in hiding it. 'I got the impression that Magnus wasn't feeling well. You weren't here, and I didn't want to disturb your meeting if—'

'You would have interrupted my meeting on account of that cunning old fox spinning you some yarn?' he queried, looking astounded.

Chesnie, realising from that comment that Joel knew his father only too well, ignored Joel's look of astonishment, though didn't feel too clever at how easily she had been taken in.

'He didn't actually say he was ill,' she confessed, recalling that Magnus had merely said that there were days when he had felt better.

'But he alarmed you sufficiently for you to decide that rather than contact me—for which I thank you,' he inserted sarcastically, not looking in the least grateful, 'you'd meet him for lunch.'

'I didn't plan it at all. I just—got worried. So in the end I drove over to see him.'

'You went to his house?' Hostility was rife. 'How did you know where he lived?'

What *was* this? 'He gave me his card so I could ring him—the last time I had lunch with him.'

'He wanted you to call him?'

If Joel was getting angry, Chesnie was getting furious. 'Only if I wanted to go to the races with him, which I didn't. Anyway—'

'Anyway, you went over to his home and found he wasn't at all unwell, but merely wanted to dupe you out of another lunch.'

'He paid!' she erupted, no longer able to hold it in. 'And don't talk about him like that!' she snapped, her control flying. She was too furious to care that his eyebrows shot up in amazement. 'He's your father,' she stormed on. 'And he's lonely, and—'

'And no doubt you cheered him up!' Joel snarled, getting angrily to his feet, not at all enamoured of her telling him what not to do, nor her nerve in taking it upon herself to defend *his* father.

'What are you implying?' she flew, angry sparks flashing in her furious green eyes.

'You tell me! What's going on?' he demanded, coming round to where she stood.

'Don't *you* start!' she exploded, hurling the words at him, feeling within an ace of hitting him. She strove desperately for control. No man had ever riled her so! Somehow, though, she managed to harness her fury, sufficient anyway to inform Joel Davenport crisply, 'Just as I had no intention of becoming Hector Browning's stepmother, I've no intention of becoming your stepmother either!'

She saw his jaw clench, but recognised that he seemed to have got to grips with his anger too. Though she wasn't feeling in any way friendly to him when, 'Close the door on your way out,' he instructed her coldly.

Chesnie marched back to her own office, her control hanging on sufficiently that she didn't give in to her urge to slam the door hard enough behind her to make the fixtures and fittings rattle. It would not have taken much for her to pick up her bag and to keep on walking. She had to admit she felt very much like doing just that.

But her control held. Swine of a man—what had happened to 'harmonious'? She slaved for him! He didn't deserve her! How on earth had Barbara Platt put up with him? In the absence of slamming the door, Chesnie slammed into her work, mutinying angrily against the man she had the misfortune to work for.

She was still inwardly raging against him when she had work ready that required his signature. He could jolly well come and get it! But her professionalism chose that moment to trip her up.

She got to her feet, collected everything together in a folder and, opening the connecting door, went smartly into the other office. He was seated behind his desk. If he looked up from what he was absorbed with she didn't notice—she wasn't looking at him. She spotted a clear space on his desk, placed the folder down and, without comment, went smartly out again, closing the door behind her.

Quite when during the next sixty minutes Chesnie began to see things from Joel's angle, she didn't know. She didn't want to see things from his point of view, she knew that; she wanted to stay furious with him. How dared he ask 'What's going on?' just as though she was some harpy with designs on his father?

Against that, though, who did she think she was, defending his father to him? Joel had known his father for longer, and knew him far better than she. He probably loved him, though he'd probably never admit to it. Knowing his father for the con-merchant he undoubtedly was hadn't stopped Joel from seeing to it that his father had a roof over his head and money in his pocket.

That was no reason for him to speak to her the way he had, though, she fumed in another moment of rebellion. But she knew that her rebellion was not as strong as it had been.

It was a little after six when Joel came through to her office with the folder she had placed on his desk. She thought he would just put it down and leave. But he didn't, and the mere fact of him holding on to it made her look up.

He was unsmiling, but he was no longer angry, she saw. And as he held out his right hand to shake hands she realised he had cooled down and was making a gesture of truce.

'I can't go home wondering if I'm still going to have a PA come Monday,' he said quietly, every bit as if he was aware she had come close to walking out earlier.

Selfish devil! All he cared about was his work! 'We were both in the wrong,' she felt fair-minded enough to reply, while at the same time wondering what *else* should he care about, for goodness' sake? Her? Don't be ridiculous. 'But since you apologise so nicely...' She extended her right hand—and felt an undeniable thrill when Joel took it in his firm grip. Grief! Their furious spat must have unhinged her!

'Have you much more to do?' Joel asked, letting go her hand.

She did a rough calculation. 'I should be through about seven,' she calculated.

'Same here. I'll take you for a spot of dinner, if you like.'

She'd had better-phrased offers. 'I had a big lunch,' she refused. 'Thank you all the same.'

Chesnie had known many emotions that day, but as she later drove home she realised she was feeling almost tearful—and could only put that down to the fact that, having felt more furious that day than at any time in her life, she was so very glad that Joel had been big enough to put an end to hostilities. She must be feeling tearful out of relief that they had made it up.

Philip took her to a symphony concert on Saturday. It was enjoyable, but the evening took a quite alarming turn when, after pulling up outside her apartment building, Philip said that he wanted to have a talk with her about something.

He sounded serious and, while she hadn't a clue what he wanted to talk to her about, she liked him too well to suggest he tell her in the car what he obviously thought was important.

'Would you like to chat over coffee?' she offered.

She was in her small kitchen making coffee, and wondered, for all they had agreed on their first date not to talk business, if he was perhaps bursting with news of some coup or other that Symington Technology had just pulled off.

Hearing a sound behind her, she turned and saw that Philip had just come into the kitchen. She was just about to make some laughing comment to the effect that the kitchen wasn't big enough for two when, to her utter consternation, Philip exclaimed, 'You're driving me mad, Chesnie!' She stared at him in astonishment. 'I'm in love with you, yet I'm not allowed to touch you, to come near you. I want to marry you, but...'

'Philip—don't!' she cried in total dismay.

'You're shutting me out again!' he protested.

'Philip, I...' she said helplessly, all thought of coffee forgotten.

'I'm sorry. I'm not doing this very well. I hadn't meant to blurt it out like that. At my age you'd think I'd have more control.'

She was starting to feel claustrophobic. The kitchen was small, and Philip was blocking the doorway. 'Let's go and sit down,' she suggested, and was relieved when, like a lamb, he moved to let her out. But in the sitting room Chesnie was stumped to know what to say. 'I'm sorry,' she in turn apologised, 'I had no idea I'd encouraged you to think...'

'That's just it. You haven't given me any encouragement at all. I would dearly love to hold you close, but I know you'd never consent to go out with me again if I attempted it.'

She was starting to think it would perhaps be better if she didn't go out with him again anyway. But he seemed to read her mind and, over the next ten minutes, implored her not to break with him and to let him see her again. He looked so strained, so anguished suddenly, that she found she could not do what her every instinct told her to do.

'I want to marry you, that's irrefutable, but promise to see me again and I'll promise not to mention it again until I see some sign that you want me to,' he urged. 'It wouldn't hurt you. *I'd* never hurt you, Chesnie—and it's not as if you're in love with anybody else.'

Why in creation a picture of Joel Davenport giving her one of his rare smiles should come into her mind's eye, she had no idea. 'No,' she agreed, 'I'm not in love with anybody else.'

'There you are, then.' He smiled winningly. 'Say you'll have dinner with me next Saturday, no hard feelings. Then I can ask you what I meant to ask you before the sight of you looking so beautiful in the kitchen turned my insides to jelly and my brain to mush.'

Good heavens! She made a mental note to stay out of the kitchen whenever Philip was near. 'That wasn't it?' she questioned. 'Er—that—your…'

'My proposal? No. I knew the time wasn't right. It doesn't alter what I feel, what I want—I just got my timing all wrong.' He looked at her for long moments, then collected himself to state, 'My long-suffering PA has today told me she's had enough. I wanted to ask you if you fancied coming to work for me?'

She hadn't got over her first surprise yet, and here he was issuing another one. 'I don't think…' she began.

'You can name your own salary,' he jumped in quickly. 'Any package you want is yours. You—'

'You're chancing it!' She had to smile. 'You don't know if I'm any good at my job or not.'

'Davenport wouldn't keep you on for a minute if you weren't. Besides, I've heard that you're close to being brilliant at the work you do.'

Chesnie wasn't so sure she liked the sound of that. When all was said and done the firm Philip was head of was still the opposition. Did Symington Technology have a spy in the camp of Yeatman Trading? She realised that it was a fact of life that staff were invariably constantly on the move. It wouldn't be a highly confidential matter for some one-time Yeatman employee on transfer to a similar company to comment that Joel Davenport's new PA was proving up to the job.

Having declined Philip's job offer, Chesnie was still feeling a little shaken by his surprising marriage proposal the next morning when her mother telephoned—mainly, it seemed, to give her a catalogue of her father's wrongdoings. Chesnie knew that her mother would not be entirely blameless—the plain fact was that her parents didn't see eye-to-eye on *anything*. Long experience had taught Chesnie not to take sides, but at the end of that phone call she felt emotionally drained.

Marriage! Who wanted it? Marriage—you could keep it as far as she was concerned. One way and another she was having quite an emotional time of it. It had started with her argument with Joel on Friday and gone on to Philip last night, her mother just now—if any of her sisters phoned to complain about their lot, she'd tell them to ring some other time.

Monday started the busiest week she had ever known. Joel spared neither himself nor her. The morning flew by. She had a sandwich at her desk at lunchtime.

Knowing that there was a full board meeting at two, Chesnie went into Joel's office at a quarter to the hour and was taken aback to see Arlene Enderby, sitting cosily with Joel at his desk, her tinkly laugh trilling out at something he had just said.

For no reason it irked Chesnie that Arlene Enderby had come in through the other door to see Joel. But, masking her feelings, Chesnie handed Joel the figures he required and went back to her desk, wondering what on earth was the matter with her? If any of the other directors wished to see Joel they often used that self-same door.

Joel was back from his meeting at four. He called her in to his office. 'A few notes,' he said, and proceeded with a list so long she felt like checking the dictionary meaning of the word 'few'. Nor had he finished when, notes taken, he informed her, 'We're in Glasgow tomorrow.' We? Him and Arlene? Chesnie felt her stomach muscles cramp up. 'Book accommodation for one night,' he went on, 'and an early flight.' And while Chesnie, to her own amazement, was fiercely determined he and laughing-girl would be having separate rooms, he looked up to enquire, 'You do know the way to the airport?'

She almost exclaimed *Me?* but in time remembered her

cool image. 'Of course,' she lied. *She* was going to Scotland with him! She was going on her first trip with him!

Joel relaxed for a moment to comment dryly, 'I trust you won't have to break a theatre date.'

Her lips twitched. She controlled herself, but, looking at him, saw that his gaze was on her mouth, and knew that he had noticed she had almost lost her cool front for a moment then.

When Chesnie fell into bed that night she knew she was going to sleep soundly. She was exhausted. Work had been non-stop that day, and she only hoped she had got everything right. She had contacted the hotel Joel usually used and, bearing in mind Barbara Platt had told her that he did not hold with the antiquated nonsense of his PA being on a separate floor— 'In other words if he wants to contact you around midnight with some query or work to be done you'll be near at hand.' —Chesnie had booked their accommodation on the same floor. Because she couldn't see the point of her going if she was not intending to work, she booked a suite of rooms with a computer facility for him, and a room for herself.

The only respite the next day was during the seventy-five-minute flight. But even then Joel spent time instructing her and filling her in on the meeting she was attending with him.

A car was there waiting for them at Glasgow airport, and whisked them off to their hotel. Since she had thought to freshen up at the airport, while waiting the short while for their overnight bags to arrive, it was just a matter of taking their luggage and the laptop Chesnie had decided to bring at the last moment up to their hotel rooms, and going straight out again to their first meeting.

Joel was indefatigable; she'd give him that. Even in the late afternoon he was assimilating in moments complicated matter that had her struggling. By the skin of her teeth she managed to keep up, but she wasn't sorry when at six-

fifteen the last of their meetings that day wound down and
Joel said they'd go back to their hotel.

Chesnie had no doubt that she had not finished for the
day, but was pleasantly surprised when, having collected
their keys, ridden up in the lift and stepped out at their
floor, Joel suggested, 'See you in the bar for a drink before
dinner? Around seven?'

'Good idea,' she agreed, and left him, no longer wondering why businessmen—or any true worker, for that matter—liked a pick-me-up at the end of a hard and strenuous
day. She knew just how they felt.

She had packed a crease-resistant casual trouser suit and
was pleased she had. She was glad to get out of her 'office'
clothes, take a shower and get dressed again in something
casual.

Chesnie applied the small amount of make-up she normally wore, brushed her shoulder-length red-blonde hair,
and at a few minutes after seven left her room and went
down to the hotel's bar. She admitted to herself that, for
someone who had earlier been very much feeling the effects
of a non-stop working day, she was now feeling a little
excited. How strange!

Joel was already in the bar. He was nursing a Scotch,
but was on his feet when he saw her, and she saw his glance
flick over her long-legged trouser-clad form. 'What are you
having?' he enquired pleasantly.

She asked for a gin and tonic but, mindful that he would
probably want to put in a few hours of work after dinner,
decided one gin and tonic would be sufficient alcohol to
'pick-her-up'.

Joel was good company away from the office, she discovered, chatting lightly and easily away, his manner remaining pleasant and just as easy when they went into dinner.

They were into the main course of their meal when, having briefly discussed a play they had both seen, Joel paused,

studied her, and then enquired casually, 'Still seeing Pomeroy?'

Chesnie studied Joel in return, trying to gauge from his equally casual expression what, if anything, lay behind his question. 'Occasionally,' she replied steadily, her insides starting to knot up, hoping they weren't going to have a fight in a public dining room.

Blue eyes fixed on her green eyes. 'How is he?' he asked civilly.

As if he cared! 'We have a pact never to discuss business,' she replied to the question she was certain he was asking.

'A pact!' His look was sardonic. '*That* occasionally?'

Oh, stuff it! Somehow Chesnie managed to stay looking outwardly calm, admitting that to have such a pact with a man she saw only 'occasionally' did sound a bit odd. 'That confidential,' she replied, her hackles starting to rise as she recalled Joel's icy manner that day Philip had phoned her at the office.

'I don't doubt it,' Joel replied pleasantly, and at that vote of faith Chesnie's raised hackles disappeared. She even smiled, a natural and—for the moment—unguarded smile. It was a mistake. She saw his glance go to her mouth. Indeed, he was still surveying its pleasing curve when, clearly not done with the subject of Philip Pomeroy yet, Joel abruptly left his contemplation of her mouth and, looking straight into her eyes, bluntly asked, 'So what package did he try to tempt you with?'

'Package?' she questioned, for the moment not with him.

'Don't tell me he didn't come head-hunting!'

'Head-hunting!' she exclaimed, catching up fast. 'I'm that good?'

'You're prevaricating!' he accused toughly.

'Why on earth would I want to leave you?' she retaliated, and could have sworn she saw a hint of a twitch on his superb bottom lip. Superb! Yoiks!

Any notion she might have nursed that he had found her

answer a touch humorous was proved erroneous, however, when, as bluntly as before, he stated, 'So you turned him down.' But, his eyes suddenly alert, he leaned back in his chair and questioned tautly, 'A job wasn't all this man you see only "occasionally" offered, was it?'

Honestly! She worked for this man; he didn't own her! Stubbornly Chesnie looked back at him—as if she'd say! She put down her knife and fork and smiled her guarded smile. 'That pie was delicious.'

'So you turned down that proposal too?'

She stared at him, wondering how she could like this tenacious man and yet, at the same time, would be quite happy to punch him on the nose. 'Look,' she said on a hiss of sound, 'I don't know how we got onto the subject of Philip Pomeroy—' they had been enjoying a perfectly pleasant evening up until then—well, at least she had '—but if your questioning is on account of some notion you have that I may give up my job at a moment's notice— and I'm sure Eileen Gray or any one of the other PAs would fill in quite adequately until you could get someone else—then I'll tell you what I told Philip. I have no intention of leaving Yeatman Trading.' She stared forthrightly into a pair of unflinching sharp blue eyes. 'Unless I'm pushed,' she added. 'And I'd remind you of what I said at interview—that I am not, repeat not, remotely interested in marriage!' There! It had been quite a speech, and had been spurred on by a growing niggle of annoyance, but she didn't regret a word of it.

That was, she hadn't thought she did until Joel Davenport's brow went up and, 'Marriage!' he exclaimed. 'Pomeroy offered you marriage?'

'What the Dickens did you think he'd proposed?' She was starting to get really angry, and was glad the dining room was spacious and that their table seemed to be a cosy one, not too close to other diners.

Joel looked at her—looked at her as if really seeing her. 'Oh, Chesnie Cosgrove,' he answered, a smile coming to his wonderful mouth. 'Looking at you, half a dozen offers spring to mind.' She blinked. Surely he wasn't being personal? 'Not for myself, of course,' he hastened to assure her. 'I'm more than happy with the relationship we have—our working relationship.'

At that point the waiter came to clear the used dishes away and returned with the pudding menu. And Joel Davenport went back to being a pleasant host and boss, and spoke of anything that came to mind other than business.

But it ferreted away at Chesnie that she had revealed what she considered to be personal to Philip. She hadn't meant to, she had just let her guard slip for once, and Joel now knew that the proposal Philip had made was one of marriage.

She and Joel were standing waiting for the lift when Chesnie knew that she wouldn't be able to go to bed until she had said something. She turned to the tall man by her side, saw that he was looking down at her, that she had his attention, and the words just came bursting from her. 'I didn't mean to say—about Philip.' Joel looked as though he might laugh. 'I wish I hadn't,' she went on. He had to know she was serious. 'It was unfair to him. It's—'

'What a truly nice person you are,' Joel cut in. She stared at him—he was good at soft soap. Was this some more of it? 'Nice, sensitive—and I promise I'll respect your confidences.'

Whether it was flattery or not, she knew she could believe him. 'Thank you, Joel,' she said quietly, and went into the lift with him.

They had the lift to themselves, and he had pressed the button to their floor when he turned to her to ask, 'What is it exactly you have against marriage?'

'Apart from the divorce statistics, you mean? Where would you like me to start?'

'You've never been married?' he asked abruptly.

'No!' she replied, more sharply than she'd meant to.

'I've seen enough of other people's marriages to know I don't need it.'

'In your own family?' he guessed.

She knew his parents were divorced, so deemed it a fair question. 'I have three sisters—their marriages range from rocky, shattered to divorced. Though the divorced one did try again.' She broke off jerkily. 'I shouldn't be telling you this.'

'Yes, you should,' he contradicted. 'Besides, I asked you. How's the remarriage going?' Chesnie decided she didn't want to tell him anything more. What went on between Nerissa and Stephen was private. To his credit, Joel didn't press her for a reply to that question, but as the lift doors opened he had not yet done with his questions. 'How about your parents' marriage?' he enquired. 'Still surviving?'

'It's been hanging by a thread for years,' she found she had replied, before she knew it. And, in a bid to get the conversation on a work-oriented course, quite off the top of her head invited, 'You have my room number if you need me during the night.' She would have thought no more about it had not Joel stopped dead and stared at her. She stopped too, and looked at him. Then suddenly she went scarlet. 'Work!' she said hurriedly. 'If—if you want me to work...' She felt hot all over.

'You're blushing,' Joel remarked. 'Well, well, my cool Miss Cosgrove.'

'Goodnight!' she said abruptly, and marched off to her room. Pig! she fumed. Pig!

Inside her room, she strove to get herself together. It wasn't her fault; she'd thought he might want her to work late into the night. As he hadn't mentioned anything about work, it was only natural that she should have offered, made herself available...

Oh, hang it. What was it about the man? She couldn't understand it, him either, or even her own self. Some things—family things, Philip things, confidences such as those—were sacrosanct. Wild horses, she would have said, prior to this evening, would not have dragged from her what she had just told Joel Davenport about her personal life.

So what was it about him that had seen her opening up the way she had? She had never opened up to anyone else that way before. True, she had every faith that what she'd said would go no further. But if Joel could keep such matters to himself, why in the world hadn't she been able to do the same?

She was forced to admit that the answer to that was simply that she didn't know why. But what she *did* know, as she considered how easily Joel was able to get under her carefully built up guard—be it by annoying her, making her angry, making her furious, and now even making her blush—was that no man she had ever met had his power to so effortlessly shatter her equilibrium.

CHAPTER FOUR

THEY arrived back in London early the next afternoon. While Joel had gone to another meeting Chesnie had spent the morning beavering away on the previous day's notes. She still hadn't finished when Joel had returned to the hotel, but after a snatched meal they'd gone straight to the airport and on to the office.

The London office was buzzing, as usual, and there didn't seem a minute to spare. Chesnie at last caught up with her work, and the previous day's messages—though if she worked hard, she just had to admire the amount of work Joel got through. No sooner had he caught up on his backlog than he was off to an 'in-house' meeting. He returned to instruct her to set up another meeting, for nine the following morning, and stayed at his desk to make some phone calls.

At half past six Vernon Gillespie and Russell Yeatman, two of the directors whom Chesnie knew were in favour of Joel taking over the chairmanship, stopped by Joel's office briefly before the three of them went off to a conference.

Chesnie, knowing that the conference Joel was attending would go on for hours, worked until seven. She hoped they would have some kind of refreshment at the conference. Joel had barely eaten... Abruptly she brought herself up short. He was a grown man, for goodness' sake! Well able to look after himself and find himself something to eat.

Chesnie went home certain that her concern for Joel was nothing more than a natural interest anyone would have when they witnessed at first hand the sort of day Joel put in.

That feeling of concern was still with her, however, when she changed from her smart business suit. She usually showered last thing at night, but, feeling in need of revitalising, she took a shower, donned jeans and a tee shirt—and her concern over Joel was still there. It remained with her when, feeling too tired to want to cook properly, she made herself some cheese on toast. Somehow she couldn't stop thinking about Joel.

By ten she was half decided to go to bed. She admitted she felt tired enough to sleep the clock round—yet at the same time she felt restless, unable to settle. She decided instead to have a tidy round.

Her flat was usually fairly neat and tidy, and was soon dealt with. She was again considering going to bed when, to her surprise, her telephone rang. She answered on the second ring.

'Good, you're still up!' Joel said. Her heart gave a most unexpected flutter, and even as she wondered why Joel would phone at this hour she found she was smiling. Though not for long when, abruptly, and not very pleasantly, 'Are you alone?' he fired.

Chesnie took a steadying breath. 'Good evening, Joel,' she replied sweetly, her ultra-pleasantness making up for his lack of it. 'How did your conference go?'

'Funny you should ask,' he answered, sudden good humour pushing away any sign of aggressiveness. 'I've just come away now. Um—I could really do with some paperwork for that meeting tomorrow.'

'Your nine o'clock meeting?' she enquired carefully, not thrilled at the idea of getting dressed in her business suit at this time of night and driving to the offices of Yeatman Trading. For preference she'd rather get up before dawn cracked and get to the office around five.

'You've remembered,' he flattered.

'Cut the flannel!' she retorted, quite without thinking, and added, 'Sir,' for the hell of it. 'It would take me half an hour to three-quarters to get to the office tonight. But I could—'

'I wouldn't dream of asking you to turn out of your cosy apartment at this time of night,' Joel cut her off.

'You—wouldn't?' she questioned slowly, not believing it for a second—and was staggered by his answer.

'I'm outside your place now,' he said matter-of-factly. He was outside now! On his mobile phone! But there was no time for her to think further because he was going on succinctly, 'And you've got a computer...'

She hadn't a scrap of make-up on, and looked down at her jeans—clean, neat—but she didn't want to be seen by him looking anything but her best. Ridiculous! she scoffed the moment the thought was born. 'Ring the buzzer; I'll let you up,' she said in her best PA voice.

Joel rang off and she had time just to run a comb through her hair, check her appearance—then the buzzer sounded. She pressed the button to unlock the front door and in no time was opening her door to the man she worked for.

'Come in,' she invited, and he stepped into her hall.

She closed the door, but before she could follow through her intention to lead him straight to her 'study' she was arrested by the way he was looking at her. 'Lovely.' The word seemed to escape him. 'You know you're lovely.'

Her throat went suddenly dry. He thought her lovely— without a scrap of make-up, he thought her lovely! 'If you say so,' she somehow managed lightly. 'I wouldn't dream of arguing.' His glance went from her face to flick over her shapely figure and she was very much aware that this was the first time he had seen her in casual attire. 'Have you eaten?' she asked in a rush, having not meant to ask anything of the sort.

'Of course,' he answered, 'at lunchtime.'

He hadn't eaten since lunch! 'How does cheese on toast sound?' she offered, reflecting that fifteen minutes either way would make no difference to the time they finished work.

'A feast,' he accepted, and she led the way to the sitting room.

He had been up early that morning, as had she, but she'd had time to rest between now and then—and his day wasn't over yet. She left him seated on her sofa, hoping that perhaps he might relax for five minutes while she was in the kitchen, but he was already delving into his briefcase.

While he demolished cheese on toast and drank a couple of cups of coffee Joel talked her through the business of the next few hours. It was eleven o'clock by the time Chesnie had her computer turned on. While she worked Joel was busy with more work of his own, but was on hand for queries—the hours just flew.

At three minutes past two Chesnie switched off her computer. 'That's the lot,' she said, getting up and putting all the paperwork together. Only then did she allow herself to acknowledge how tired she felt. But, aside from the fact she was paid a whale of a salary, Joel was good to work for, stimulating to work for—but now he must be feeling as drained as she.

He admitted as much when, all the documents safely in his briefcase, he strolled with her back to her sitting room. She thought he might wait for a short moment before saying goodnight. And, though he did pause, it was not as a prelude to saying goodnight, but to all at once ask, 'How does your landlord feel about gentlemen callers staying the night?'

Her heart suddenly began to hammer. It was late, and she was tired, and it took every scrap of her remaining energy for her to keep her expression bland. Her pulse was leaping all over the place as she pondered—surely to heaven Joel wasn't thinking of sharing her bed!

'I haven't lived here long enough to find out. But—' She broke off to look pointedly at her sofa. 'If you think you'll be comfortable there, you're quite welcome.'

His lips twitched. As tired as he was, and she calculated he must have been on the go for close on twenty hours, his lips definitely twitched. But he took her up on her offer. 'I'd much prefer to rest my eyes here for an hour before I tackle the hours drive back to my place, if you wouldn't mind.'

Chesnie found him a blanket and a couple of pillows and, more than ready for bed herself, said 'Goodnight,' and, unused to having any male 'staying over', went hurriedly to her bedroom.

As exhausted as she was, though, sleep was elusive. She still felt restless, fidgety, and, she had to admit, emotional. Emotional without knowing why she should feel so. She couldn't hear one single, solitary sound coming from the sitting room, so presumed that Joel had gone 'spark out'.

Proof, however, that she too had gone 'spark out' at some time, came when she opened her eyes to find that it was six o'clock—and that Joel was in her room.

Joel was *in her room*! 'What…?' was as far as she could manage as, pushing a cloud of hair away from her face, she struggled to sit up.

'I did knock,' Joel informed her. 'You were sound asleep.'

'Er—yes. Well…' Her brain was still asleep—and he could hardly have had much more than three hours' sleep. That thought abruptly vanished when, startlingly, she suddenly became aware of her bare arms—the narrow straps of her nightdress no covering at all—and the front of her nightdress, more *décolleté* than *décolleté*—none of which was lost on Joel.

'I thought I'd mention I may be out of the office for most of today,' he stated, his glance flicking to where the tips of her breasts were showing dark through the fine white lace material. Hastily she pulled the covers up to her chin. He looked amused—she wanted to hit him! 'You'll have to rearrange my diary accordingly,' he instructed.

She'd had enough of him. 'Naturally I'll rearrange your diary!' she answered tartly, and, for good measure, 'Goodbye!'

He looked at her for perhaps one second longer, then commented nicely, 'If you're like this with all your gentlemen callers, it's no wonder none of them stay the night.'

With that he went, and she would dearly have loved to throw something after him. Good grief—what was wrong with her? She was feeling emotional again.

It was business as usual the next time she saw Joel. He made no mention of the comfort or otherwise of her sofa, for which she was very glad.

By Saturday her emotions were on a much more even keel, and she enjoyed dining with Philip. He did not refer again to his feelings for her and, given that he kissed her cheek on parting, his behaviour was impeccable.

On Sunday she drove to Cambridge to see her parents. She loved them both dearly, but had soon had too much of their bickering and was much relieved when the time came that she could say she had to get back.

That night she rang her grandfather. 'Dad tells me you've found the house you're looking for,' she said brightly, loving him to bits.

'It's only a two-up, with bathroom, and two-down, but it's sufficient for my needs.'

'You'll be wanting your car back?' she suggested.

'No hurry,' he replied. 'It'll be some time before the purchase is completed and I have the rest of my furniture out of storage. Now, how are you?'

Chesnie came away from the phone, her good spirits restored. She was earning better money now. She would start looking for a car at the first opportunity. Something small, and not too expensive.

Though when, she wondered, when the two weeks that followed saw her working late each night, would she ever find the time to go looking for a car? Although there were quite some months to go yet, things were already starting to warm up in the battle for who would win the chairmanship when Winslow Yeatman retired.

She had met all the other directors—Arlene Enderby was

a most frequent visitor to the office next door. Some were directors by virtue of either being a Yeatman, marrying a Yeatman, or, like Joel, working their way up by their own merit.

Fergus Ingles was one such. He was not putting up for chairman, and had not as yet declared which candidate he was likely to support. Of late, Fergus had taken a leaf out of Arlene Enderby's 'just popping in while passing' book. But where Arlene popped in to see Joel, Fergus always made a bee-line for Chesnie's desk.

On Friday he 'popped in' to see if she fancied going to the theatre with him the next evening, and, having been turned down, was just leaving when Joel came from his office to discuss some matter with her.

The two men acknowledged each other, but Fergus had barely closed the door after him when Joel was asking, 'What did Ingles want?' He didn't sound thrilled.

Chesnie stayed calm to reply, 'Someone to go to the theatre with tomorrow.'

'Someone? Anyone?'

As ever, Joel wanted all the 'i's dotted and all the 't's crossed, though Chesnie knew that he was quite well aware that the invitation had been to her personally. 'Me,' she admitted.

'You haven't time for a social life!' Joel told her sharply, and just the preposterousness of that remark caused her to break free of her cool image for once. She laughed out loud. But clearly Joel didn't see anything to laugh at, and his tone was sharp still when he barked, 'You're not going?'

Honestly! She slaved for this man—her free time was her own. 'I might,' she replied. 'And then again, I might not.' For her sins she was on the receiving end of a murderous look, and Joel kept her working late that night.

In actual fact she loved her work, and didn't mind a bit working overtime. 'Goodnight,' she said pleasantly, when at last everything had been completed. He looked up and seemed to study her intently, as if she was a new species to him. She smiled. 'Have a good weekend.'

But as she drove home she started to feel a little annoyed over the way Joel had seemed to take exception to the idea of her seeing one of the directors outside of work. Surely Joel didn't think Fergus would try and find out from her anything highly confidential Joel had told her with regard to his bid to be chairman? Surely Joel didn't think that she would be so indiscreet as to let anything slip? She began to feel exceedingly irritated—didn't Joel trust her?

Chesnie had dinner again with Philip Pomeroy the next night. But it was over that meal that she began to see that maybe Joel had some excuse to be a shade wary where PAs were concerned. She and Philip had been congenially chatting on and off through their meal when Philip suddenly looked at her, sighed very softly, and said, 'I know we have a pact not to talk business, Chesnie, but I've recently come across an item of news that just has to earn me a few stars if I share it with you.'

She looked back at him. 'Oh?' she queried warily.

'I'm not asking you to tell me anything,' he quickly assured her, 'but you might be interested to know I yesterday interviewed a woman named Deborah Sykes for the job as my PA.'

Deborah Sykes! Chesnie knew her. Until only a couple of weeks ago, when the company had found serious reasons to dispense with Deborah's services, she had been one of the senior PAs at Yeatman Trading.

'Oh, yes?' Chesnie answered non-committally, not certain she should be having this conversation with Philip. But since he had stated that he wasn't asking her to tell him anything she decided to stay with it—for the moment, anyhow. She felt she could trust Philip, but the minute this called for her to contribute something she would close the conversation down.

'As you're no doubt fully aware, Deborah Sykes was PA to Russell Yeatman until, by mutual agreement, they parted company.' From what Chesnie had heard there had been nothing mutual about it. 'What you are probably not aware of,' Philip went on when Chesnie made no reply, 'is that her boss—or should I say her ex-boss—while pretending to support your boss, Joel Davenport, is planning, when he feels the time is right, to put in his own bid to be chairman of Yeatman Trading.'

How Chesnie managed to keep her jaw from hitting the table in shock, she had no idea. She wanted to argue, wanted to tell Philip that he was mistaken, that Russell Yeatman was most definitely intending to support Joel when the time came to vote. But Philip wouldn't lie, and who had been closer to Russell Yeatman and in a position to see what went on other than Deborah Sykes—who'd been his PA?

'It was kind of Deborah to share that snippet with you,' Chesnie commented lightly.

'I rather gathered she thought it might help Symington Technology to know who was likely to be the next chairman of Yeatman Trading, and that I would be suitably grateful.'

'And offer her the job?' Chesnie suggested, her mind reeling at the implication that Russell Yeatman, because he was a Yeatman, might get the chairmanship. How dared he pretend to support Joel!

'A waste of time.'

'You didn't offer her the job?' Chesnie asked.

'Why would I want a PA who can't keep her mouth shut?'

Chesnie parted from Philip in her usual friendly manner that night, but she was glad to be alone—her head was still spinning with the implications of what Philip had told her. If he was right, and she was sure he was, then the most votes Joel was certain of were two. That meant there were six votes, including Russell Yeatman's vote, that could go against him. The present chairman's vote wouldn't need to be involved. If the Yeatmans wanted a Yeatman, it was a foregone conclusion that Russell Yeatman would win.

Chesnie spent Sunday with her mind in a turmoil. Should she phone Joel and tell him what she had learned? But he'd worked so hard that week. Surely he was entitled to one day of rest. Would he want to know anyway? Well, of course he would want to know. But perhaps he knew already. And what could he do about it anyhow?

In the end Chesnie decided against contacting Joel, but she went into the office early on Monday morning. As ever, Joel was in first. She went straight in to see him.

'Uh-oh, this looks ominous!' Joel said, looking up to observe her serious expression. 'If you've come in early to give me your resignation, I'm afraid I have to tell you I don't take resignations on Mondays.'

He smiled; she didn't. Something—or someone—had obviously put him in a good mood. She didn't want to consider what he might have been doing over the weekend.

There was only one way to say this. 'I've heard a whisper that you have serious competition for the chairmanship,' she stated flatly—and that took the good humour out of his face. She'd almost forgotten how very, very determined he was to have that chairmanship.

'The devil you have!' he retorted bluntly. 'Where did this whisper come from?' he demanded.

'Is it important where it came from?'

'Of course it's important!' he barked. And, apparently having not forgotten her visitor of Friday afternoon, 'Fergus Ingles!' he guessed. 'He told you? You went to the theatre with him on Saturday and he told you he intended to oppose me!'

'No, I didn't!' she denied crossly. 'And it isn't him. He isn't the one who's going against you—it's—Russell Yeatman.'

'Russell Y...' Joel stared at her in disbelief. 'You're seriously suggesting that Russell Yeatman has defected from my corner and intends to go for the chairmanship himself?'

'That's the way I heard it,' she confirmed.

'Where?' he demanded toughly. 'If you didn't hear it from Fergus Ingles, where did you hear it?'

Chesnie knew she was going to have to tell him. In order to gauge the strength of her source, Joel was going to have to know. 'I had dinner with Philip Pomeroy on Saturday—'

'Pomeroy! You're still consorting *occasionally* with the enemy?' Chesnie knew this Monday morning had started off badly, but was determined not to let Joel Davenport's sarcastic jibes get to her. That was until he went on, 'So what happened to the pact you had with him not to discuss my office business?'

'I did *not* discuss your business!' she flared.

'You had to tell him something to gain that little nugget!' he accused harshly—and Chesnie's usual grip on her temper went flying.

She had once before felt like walking out—she came close a second time. But, instead of walking, this time she stayed rooted. 'You don't fully trust me, do you?' she blazed. And, not giving him a chance to say yea or nay, she stormed angrily on. 'That much became clear last Friday, when you objected to the notion I might consider dating one of your fellow directors! Well, let me—' She broke off when she saw that Joel was looking at her with something that looked, if she wasn't mistaken, very much like admiration in his eyes. 'What...?' she challenged belligerently.

He rose to the challenge. 'Did you know that when you forget to look out at the world through your permafrost, your eyes sparkle like emeralds?'

She wanted to stay mad at him—but couldn't. 'Soft soap,' she muttered, supposing this was the reason he left a trail of PAs, and women in general, swooning in his wake. Though not her. Assuredly not her.

'I do trust you, Chesnie. If I didn't you wouldn't be working for me.' His expression was unsmiling. 'I apologise if anything I said on Friday upset you, and that goes double for this morning. I confess that what you've just told me has come as a bit of a bombshell.' He was still looking serious as he continued, 'If your news checks out I shall need to take some kind of drastic action. You'd better take a chair and tell me all you know.'

Chesnie became aware as that week progressed that Joel was keeping as much home-based as possible. She rather liked having him working in the next-door office, and had to admire the way in which he acted in the same outwardly affable way he'd always acted when Russell Yeatman, the man who was preparing to stab him in the back when his chance came, dropped by to see him.

What Chesnie did not enjoy was the way Arlene Enderby, who didn't even work there, director though she might be, seemed to appear in Joel's office on a daily basis. Arlene, without a doubt, as Joel's father had suggested, was still after him.

The fact, however, that Joel was not so keen on the idea of being chased became apparent to Chesnie on Friday, when Arlene rang to speak with him as he was about to leave the office for a meeting. Chesnie knew for a fact he had two minutes available in which to take the call. But, 'I'm not available,' he told Chesnie, and went.

'I'm afraid Joel's at a meeting. May I take a message?' Chesnie suggested tactfully, aware, as she was sure Joel must be, that if he wanted to court Arlene's chairmanship vote it wouldn't do to upset her.

'What time is he due back?' Arlene asked, a touch put out.

'He may go straight home from his meeting, but I can leave a message on his desk in case he comes back when I've gone,' Chesnie offered.

'Damn!' Arlene muttered. 'I wanted him to come to a party with me tomorrow. I suppose if I ring his home I shall only find myself talking to his answering machine.'

Arlene rang off, and Chesnie had several messages from other sources for Joel when he returned an hour later. She left telling him about Arlene Enderby's call till the end. '...and Arlene Enderby would like you to go to a party with her tomorrow,' Chesnie relayed nicely.

He took the message without so much as a blink, and asked, 'And what are your plans for tomorrow?'

'You want me to work?'

Joel looked at her with humour in his eyes. 'I don't deserve you,' he told her.

'True,' she answered—and loved it when they shared a small laugh together.

'I think you can have tomorrow off,' he said, after a moment, but hadn't lost sight of his original question, it seemed, when he rephrased it. 'Are you off partying tomorrow?'

'Tomorrow I'm off to visit my grandfather,' she stated.

'He lives where?'

'Herefordshire. He's in the process of buying a cottage,' she volunteered, then suddenly realised how well and truly she had departed from the cool image she was at pains to show the world. 'If you would just sign these letters, I'll get them in the post.' With that she turned and went back to her desk.

She knew she enjoyed seeing Joel laugh, enjoyed seeing him relax every now and then from his busy day. She by far preferred to see him that way than as the short, sharp, snarling brute he could be sometimes. And she knew she wanted to be on friendly terms with him—yet at the same time being on those amicable terms with him seemed somehow to make her feel strangely vulnerable—and she didn't want that.

Chesnie stayed overnight with her grandfather on Saturday, and together they inspected his new purchase. 'It's a delightful cottage, in a beautiful spot,' she replied when he asked her opinion.

'I think it's plenty big enough for me,' he said, and smiled as he added, 'I don't hold with too much housework. Although Mrs Weaver, a few doors down, has said she'll come in and give the place a "going over" whenever I give her a call.'

It was good to know that her grandfather would soon be settled in his own place. Chesnie drove back to London on Sunday, having assured herself that he was managing, and would be able to manage very well on his own. It was what he wanted. Since her grandmother's death he had become something of an insomniac. When he'd lived with her parents her mother had carped on about him getting up in the middle of the night to make himself a warm drink—he wasn't going to give up his independence again in a hurry.

Her visit to Herefordshire at the weekend was far from her mind on Tuesday. Arlene Enderby had outstayed her welcome in Joel's office yesterday, and Chesnie had picked up very clear vibes when she had gone in that Joel, wanting to get on with work which he considered of far greater importance, had been doing his best to shake her off. Arlene, clearly, was having none of it.

Arlene made a visit to his office again on Tuesday. A visit of which Chesnie was entirely unaware until, pausing only to stow her bag on her return from lunch, she walked over to the communicating door and went in. Arlene was there, and so too was Joel, but there was an odd sort of tension in the air. They were not looking at each other, but had turned and were looking at her.

All Chesnie's instincts were suddenly alert. Something was telling her to retreat. To leave the room, and to come back later. But, 'It's you!' Arlene suddenly exclaimed. 'It's you, isn't it?'

Chesnie hadn't a clue what she was talking about, and glanced swiftly to Joel—he glanced blandly back. But, like the professional she was, Chesnie thought she'd better show a cool front until she knew more of what Arlene Enderby was referring to. 'I—er...' What in creation was going on?

'Joel's just told me he's getting engaged, but won't say to who,' Arlene informed her, and while Chesnie felt distinctly shattered to know that Joel was to be engaged,

Arlene, plainly striving hard to hide how she felt at this news, had recovered sufficiently to state, 'He's said no to all the names I could think of—and then you came in.' Arlene turned back to him. 'It is Chesnie, isn't it?' she asked.

Chesnie's momentarily stunned brain at that point came out of its shock, and she was suddenly working at full brain power. Of course Joel wasn't getting engaged! He'd run like fury at the thought of getting that close to marriage. All too obviously Arlene had backed him into a corner, perhaps with yet another party invitation, and in order to kill any future invitations—or maybe to head off her chase, perhaps to let her down gently—he had fed her the line that he was going to get married. Arlene, not one to duck from asking questions, wanted to know who.

Chesnie allowed herself a small smile. She had seen Joel diplomatically handle quite a few difficult situations. She knew he was going to deny it, but she also knew it was going to take all his diplomacy skills to deny any attachment to her while at the same time keeping Arlene out of his hair.

Chesnie raised her eyes to look at him. She saw that his glance was on her mouth, but as she watched she saw that glance flick upwards, and suddenly he was looking straight into her green eyes. After a momentary pause, all at once he, too, was smiling. He'd thought up something good, Chesnie knew he had.

But she just could not believe her ears when, his glance moving to Arlene, he replied, 'We weren't going to say anything just yet...' He turned back to Chesnie and, still smiling, added, 'Were we, darling?'

That took the smile off her face. He surely hadn't said what she thought he had just said? She knew he hadn't. Chesnie didn't believe it! Couldn't believe it. But all at once Arlene Enderby was brilliantly hiding whatever her inner feelings were and had gone over to Joel to give him a kiss of congratulation.

'You'll have all the other PAs after your blood,' she turned to Chesnie to say lightly, and while Chesnie was having a hard time hiding her own feelings—only her years of practice aiding her to keep a calm front until she got to have a private word with her 'fiancé'—the door to her office opened. Unannounced, unexpected, Joel's father came in. It was all she needed.

'Magnus!' Arlene exclaimed, greeting him like some long-lost friend. Magnus started to walk through into his son's office. 'I suppose you knew all about Joel and Chesnie?' she trilled, going over and giving him a hug.

'What's this, then?' he asked when she let him go.

'Don't tell me you didn't know that Joel and Chesnie are engaged?'

Magnus's face lit up. 'I couldn't be more pleased!' he beamed, and came over to where Chesnie, wondering if the world had gone mad, was standing. For the moment she was somehow still managing to conceal her feelings, and stood rooted while Magnus gave her a kiss and exclaimed, 'I couldn't ask for a more terrific daughter-in-law!' And, while Chesnie was only just managing to mask her horror that she should be anybody's daughter-in-law, he went over and shook his son warmly by the hand.

'This calls for champagne!' Arlene declared.

Ye gods! Chesnie looked directly at Joel and guessed he must have read in her expression that she was about to burst a few blood vessels. 'This calls for Chesnie and me to get on with some work,' he stated unequivocally, but he still was smiling.

'Which means you and I will have to go off and drink champagne on our own, Arlene,' Magnus said, taking his son's hint wonderfully.

Chesnie thought they would never go. But eventually, after Joel's father gave her another kiss, they both departed. And with their departure so too did Chesnie's composure leave her.

'What on earth do you think you're playing at?' she

turned to Joel to demand the moment she heard the outer door close.

'It was your fault!' he tossed back at her, equally un-smiling.

The cheek! His sauce took her breath away. 'How?' she challenged. 'I've just come back from lunch! I didn't say a—'

'It was the way you *looked*!' Joel interrupted her. 'The smug way you smiled!' he told her bluntly. 'I'm just about up to here with one woman trying to manipulate me—then there are you too, believing you know exactly how I'll re-act.'

Chesnie had to admit that perhaps she had been a bit smug as she'd waited for him to 'diplomatically' own up to the truth of the matter. But she was still furious. 'I know you want Arlene's vote, but you—'

'For your information,' he chopped her off curtly, 'Arlene Enderby's a realist, and, regardless of whether it's a family member or not, she'll vote for whoever she believes will ultimately bring her the best rewards!'

'Whatever,' Chesnie snapped. 'That still doesn't give you the right, whether or not you're fed up with manipulative women and smug women, to say what you did.' And, unsure of Arlene's gossip level, but knowing his father's penchant for chatting freely on everything and everyone, 'It will be all over the building in two minutes!'

He shrugged. 'So, we'll deny it.'

'A fat lot of good that will do!' Chesnie erupted, outraged that he thought he could shrug it off and it would all blow over. 'We've been away together,' she charged on, digging her heels in when she could see she just wasn't getting through to him. And, while he did look a shade startled at what she had just said, she sought for something else to really make him sit up and take notice. 'You've stayed overnight in my flat!' she reminded him, when nothing else very clever presented itself.

That was sufficient, anyhow; she could tell that from the

astounded expression that came to his face. 'Hell's teeth!' he exclaimed, appalled, looking absolutely aghast. 'Surely you're not suggesting I should actually *marry* you!'

That hurt! The pain of it was stupefying. And the pain of what she had just realised rocked her. 'You should be so lucky!' she managed to slam back—before deciding she needed to hide. She turned from him and marched quickly out from his office, straight to the bottom drawer of her desk.

She didn't know Joel had come to the door and was watching her until, as she collected her bag and closed the drawer, he demanded 'Where are you going with that?'

Chesnie had a feeling she was going to break down any minute—and no man was going to do that to her. 'Home!' she retorted, afraid to say more lest her voice gave her away.

She had twice before come close to walking out. This time she went at speed—straight out from her office. She had resigned, and knew that she was never going back. How could she go back? She had only a few moments ago realised that she had fallen in love with Joel. In his book that was probably a sackable offence anyway!

CHAPTER FIVE

CHESNIE was in shock for the rest of the day. She went to bed that night still reeling. How had it happened—this love she had for Joel? This feeling that had exploded in on her so unannounced. Why hadn't she seen it coming? Had she done so, then surely she could have taken some evasive action.

Oh, she liked him. Most of the time she liked him quite a lot. She admired him tremendously too; the man positively ate work. But—love him? She shook her head—oh, that it would so easily go away. But it wouldn't, and she knew that it wouldn't. It was there, this love she had for Joel and she could do absolutely nothing about it.

Over and over that night, as she lay in her bed, Chesnie relived that scene that had led up to her walking out of her job. That job she loved so much. She tried to get angry with Joel. How dared he, with that, 'We weren't going to say anything just yet. Were we, darling?' confirm for Arlene Enderby that he and his PA were *engaged*.

And what about Arlene Enderby? Joel plainly knew her to be hard-headed enough to vote where it might affect her bank balance. Equally plain was that for him to have used the desperate excuse he had to shake her off must mean he had used up all other reasons to stop her from chasing him. Chesnie supposed that she had appeared at just the wrong moment, and her smug look must have been the last straw as far as Joel was concerned.

But—engaged! No, it was too much. Even though Chesnie was sure that by now Joel would have put the word out that there was absolutely not the slightest truth in any despicable rumour that he and his PA were engaged,

77

Chesnie thought it too much. Once that rumour had got round it was not going to be so easy to scotch. And 'engaged' spelled commitment. And commitment in that area spelled disaster. Love him she might, but Chesnie wanted no part of it.

She got up the next morning at her usual time, but with her anger spent. It was negated by the fact that she would never work with Joel again. Negated by the fact that he would not want her to work in his office. By walking out she had walked out on all chance of ever seeing him. And that hurt.

That Wednesday was a most unhappy day for Chesnie. It seemed to drag by endlessly slowly. The logic of her head told her that what she should be doing was getting out there and finding herself another job. So far as she knew that job in Philip's office was still open. But she didn't want to work for Philip, and nor did she wish to listen to logic. She could easily have telephoned one of her sisters and arranged lunch somewhere, or have spent the day searching for a car, but she didn't have the heart to do any of those things. What she wanted to do was what she did—stay home to lick her wounds in private.

She did see someone before that day was out, though. It was just after eight that evening when the outer buzzer sounded. She ignored it; she didn't want to see anyone.

The buzzer sounded a second time. Surely if it was Nerissa she would have telephoned first? Though perhaps not if she was in something of a 'fume' over her husband's latest misdemeanour. Not wanting her sister to have had a wasted journey, Chesnie went out into the hall. 'Hello?' she said into the intercom.

'Are you still sulking?' questioned an all-male voice.

Joel! Wonderful Joel! Before she had thought about it, joy in her heart after such a miserable day, Chesnie had pressed the button to let him into the building. Then, when she did get round to thinking about it, a dozen other thoughts flashed through her mind. Joel—here! Her hair!

She who had previously had little to do with vanity, raced to her bedroom. Did she look all right? She ran a comb through her lovely red-blonde hair and tucked her silk shirt more neatly into the waistband of her tailored trousers. Her doorbell sounded before she could do any more. Joel was here! Why had he come? She wasn't ready to see him again. Yes, she was. A day without seeing him had been unbearable.

She hurried to the door. Calm, she instructed before she opened it. Be calm, be cool, be composed. Those were the instructions she gave herself. Then she opened the door, and there he was, the man she loved, tall, straight, good-looking, and her insides went like jelly.

She couldn't speak, she turned away, and Joel followed her into her sitting room. When she felt she had a tighter grip on her emotions she turned, but, still not trusting herself to speak, she instead gave him what she hoped was a cool, questioning look.

He looked back equally unspeaking, his glance going over her trim but curvy shape, taking in her shining hair and coming to rest on the face he had called lovely.

Seconds passed. She saw his glance flick to her mouth, and she wanted to swallow—but that would be letting the side down. 'To what do I owe this unexpected pleasure?' she asked, when she could bear his inspection, the silence, no longer.

He smiled, and she found a little bit of hate for him. He, by his very silence, had made her speak. 'I thought I'd better call in person,' he said pleasantly. 'We've had an invitation to dine with Winslow and Flora Yeatman.'

The chairman and his wife! *We!* 'Didn't you tell them I no longer work for you?' she responded.

He smiled again, a charming smile. It was a smile she did not trust. And was right not to trust, she discovered, when, coolly, he replied, 'We weren't invited in that capacity.'

What other capacity was th—? Her eyes widened in

shock, that *we* starting to make sense. 'You…' she said on a gasp of sound. She couldn't believe it. But, it had to be, didn't it? She did swallow then—there was only one way to find out. 'Are you saying,' she began slowly, 'that you have not yet corrected the impression that you and I—are engaged?'

'What sort of a cad do you take me for?' he enquired silkily, and at that hint of devilment in his eyes she knew that he was playing with her. Why, she couldn't fathom— unless, of course, he hadn't taken too kindly to her walking out on him and leaving him without the assistant he needed.

'What do you mean?' she flared.

'What would I mean?' he answered smoothly, his blue gaze taking in the angry sparks in her wide green eyes. 'Surely it's the woman's place to announce to everybody that she's ditched her man.'

'D-ditched…'

'It would be the height of caddishness, surely, should I be the one to tell everyone that I was the one who did the ditching.'

Chesnie, recovering slightly, did not thank him for his consideration, and rounded on him angrily. 'In the first place, you are not "my man". In the second place, but for me covering for you when your love-life blew up in your face—'

'Hardly my love-life,' he butted in. 'Nor did you cover for me—you just stayed smugly and silently watching, while you waited to see how I was going to handle a tricky situation.' He shrugged nicely. 'So I handled it—we got engaged.'

'We were never engaged!' she erupted. 'Nor are we engaged.'

'That's not the talk at the forum,' he replied charmingly.

'You're saying…?' She couldn't finish it.

Joel had no such problem. 'As you rightly suggested, word about "us" spread like wildfire.' Oh, no! His words winded her, and she had to struggle to find a modicum of her former outward composure. But then, having all but floored her, 'Well?' he enquired evenly. 'Will you come with me?'

'Where to?' she asked, still feeling stunned.

'Dinner with Winslow and Flora,' he reminded her—and at his so easily asked enquiry some of her former spirit returned.

'No, I won't!' she erupted.

'Why not?' he asked, sounding so reasonable—making it seem as though she was the unreasonable one—that she wanted to hit him.

'What—and further perpetuate this myth that you and I are engaged? Why would you want to anyway?'

'I don't want to,' Joel answered, confirming what she already knew. 'It's just that the Yeatmans have such a happy marriage. Flora has kind of picked up the ball and run with it—she's in raptures that I appear to have at last been snared.'

'Snared!' Chesnie exclaimed, affronted. There was more here than he was saying. It was probably all to do with business, but she was too churned up just then to be able to work it out. That word 'snared', however, just as if she'd trapped him, caused her pride to furiously rear up. Who did he think he was? What about *her* being snared? She set about showing him that she had offers of her own and didn't need to 'snare' any man. 'Apart from the fact that you and I are not engaged—or ever likely to be—what about my present relationship?'

'You mean—there's some other man?' Joel questioned, and Chesnie knew that if he carried on like this for very much longer she was definitely going to have to hit him! She saw his glance go round her sitting room, as if searching for some evidence that she had a man about the place. Of course there wasn't so much as the merest sign. His glance came back to her. 'Trust me, you won't have time to conduct a relationship.'

'I—won't?' she questioned, not with him at all.

Joel shook his head. 'Not while you're working for me. Things are hotting up.'

Things were hotting up? He had to be meaning the fight for the chairmanship. Chesnie suddenly glared at him—she had actually been thinking in terms of helping all she could! 'I'm not working for you!' she exploded.

'Ah, Chesnie,' he murmured softly, 'don't say that. You know you've been bored out of your skull staying home all day today.'

That was true—the day had stretched interminably. It occurred to her to wonder, *if* she went back to work for him, if she would be so busy she wouldn't have time to think about her feelings for him. 'So I'll stay bored!' She refused to give in to the weakness of love that, foolish though it was, still made her want to see him every day.

Joel heaved a dramatic sigh, and came a couple of paces closer. 'You want me to tell you that I can't cope without you?' he asked, close enough to look steadily into her eyes. 'You want me to tell you that already the office is falling apart? Without you there at—'

Oh, she did love him so. 'I'd love it,' she butted in, and—against all inclination—she just had to laugh.

Joel's eyes went to her mouth and, as if he enjoyed seeing her laugh, his own mouth started to curve upwards. 'Come back, Chezz,' he urged softly, and, unhurriedly coming those few steps closer, took a light hold of her upper arms. As if to add weight to his request, he placed a light kiss on her cheek.

Her control was instantly shot. Just the feel of his wonderful mouth against her cheek and, shaken rigid by his spontaneous kiss, his unexpected hold, Chesnie was desperately fighting to regain her shattered control.

Swiftly she pushed him away, and more than ever needed the cool front which over the years had become second nature to her. She found help in her struggle that, when she pushed him away, Joel immediately let go his hold on her arms.

She was still recovering her composure when, 'What do you say?' Joel pressed. 'A life at some boring other job, or a return to the demanding job you love? Say yes,' he urged.

'I...' she faltered. Yes, the work was demanding, and did sometimes stretch her, but... Chesnie made the mistake of looking at him—and was weakened. Oh, how could she deny herself the chance of seeing him every day? 'I'll—er—I'll come back, on one condition,' she agreed, her nerve-ends still all of a jangle.

'Name it,' he replied promptly.

'You ever kiss me again, Joel Davenport, and I'll walk out on you permanently.'

Solemnly he studied her. Then silently his hand came out to shake on it. 'I'll see you in the morning,' he agreed, shook hands with her—and went striding from her apartment.

Chesnie collapsed into a chair the moment he had gone, a hand going up to touch the side of her face that he had kissed. She loved him, and had given in to the weakness of love, and—she couldn't regret it. She loved him, and would see him again tomorrow.

The next day dawned bright and beautiful and Chesnie drove to Yeatman Trading full of enthusiasm for her work. The day did not go well. For one thing Joel had left her apartment the previous evening with the only issue resolved being that she was going to continue working for him.

The issue of their 'engagement', however, had not been resolved. What Joel told Winslow Yeatman when he said they would not be accepting his invitation to dinner was, she had decided, entirely up to Joel. For her part, and at the very first opportunity, she intended to stop any rumours that she and Joel were engaged.

Unfortunately, her first chance came when, Joel out of the office and not expected back for a couple of hours, one of the directors came in. Muriel Yeatman, a square-set, mid-fifties woman whom Chesnie had met before, had come purposely, it seemed, to wish her well on her engagement. The unfortunate part was that Arlene Enderby came in with her aunt, thereby putting Chesnie in a dilemma about what she wanted to do, and what, for Joel, she had to do.

'Isn't it wonderful, Aunty?' Arlene gushed when Muriel had said how delighted they all were by the news. And while Chesnie had to give Arlene top marks for covering whatever she was feeling about Joel now being out of her orbit, Chesnie was left with little choice but to go along with it—if she didn't want to let Joel down.

For a short while after they had gone Chesnie mutinied against Joel. Why in thunder couldn't he have told the predatory Arlene straight out that he wasn't interested in her and would she please stop coming to his office, wasting his time?

Very probably, in the politest way he knew, he already had, came back the answer. But precisely because Arlene *was* predatory, and once she had set her sights on him wouldn't so easily give up, it hadn't worked. So he'd invented a steady girlfriend—and don't forget *smug*.

Vowing never to be 'smug' ever again, Chesnie got on with her work—whenever she could. She was interrupted many times that day, Muriel Yeatman being not the only director of Yeatman Trading to call by and offer their good wishes on her engagement.

Heartily wishing that she had sorted out something, *anything*, with Joel before this—simply because half of the directors happened to be Yeatmans, and thereby related to Arlene Enderby—Chesnie saw that there was nothing for it but to go along with it until she had chance to talk to Joel.

He was back in the office just after two, but with little time to spare before he went off to his next appointment. Chesnie did not care—this matter had to be settled—*now*.

She went into his office with some data he would need to take with him, and after a few minutes of business discussion she informed him bluntly, 'Muriel Yeatman came in to wish me well on our engagement.'

Joel paused in placing the papers in his briefcase, and turned to study her stubborn expression. 'And you said?'

'What could I say? Arlene Enderby came in with her!'

'Ah!' He smiled then. 'I know I don't deserve such loyalty, but thank you, Chesnie.'

'That's not good enough!' she erupted, refusing to be charmed. 'They weren't the only directors to call in with their good wishes. What in creation am I supposed to say?'

'Why say anything?' he replied, his expression as serious as hers. 'By the sound of it, very few people haven't heard about "us".' He thought for a moment and then, clearly having no time to set about denying it, 'It will only be a nine-day wonder,' he decided, 'then something else will happen to take precedence.'

'You think our "engagement" will so easily be forgotten?' she asked, incredulous at his attitude.

'Of course,' he stated confidently, and, his mind plainly more on the importance of his work than on the unimportance of a mere matter of an engagement, 'Take my word for it, the whole business will die a natural death—especially when you and I show no sign of taking that diabolical trot up the aisle.' He paused to take a quick glance to his watch. 'Back around four,' he said, and was gone.

Chesnie was still staring after him, dumbstruck that he could be so unconcerned, when business called for her attention in the shape of a ringing telephone.

She had little time herself during that afternoon in which to give the matter much thought. As Joel had said, things were hotting up, and she was working flat out to cope. She had a brief moment to suppose that, as Joel had so quaintly put it, when they didn't show any signs of trotting up the aisle all talk of them being engaged would probably fizzle out—she only hoped it would 'fizzle' this week rather than next. Then it was all work.

As well as dealing with the general day-to-day business

of seeing to it that Joel's office ran on supremely smooth-oiled wheels, Chesnie had the previous day and half's work to catch up on. The interruptions she'd had that morning did not help.

She was still catching up on Friday afternoon, and it was a matter of pride to her that she had all her work completed so she should start with a clear desk come Monday.

At four-thirty she knew she was just not going to be able to make her date with Philip that night. That did not particularly bother her, other than she did not like to let people down. They had been going to a party some friends of Philip were giving, but she had been wondering more and more of late if it wouldn't be kinder to him in the long run if she told him it would be better if she didn't see him again.

She looked through to the other office. The door had been open for the last hour, while Joel needed to frequently check over some details. With that job out of the way she would have liked to get up and close the door, knowing that because of Philip being a competitor Joel didn't care for her going out with him. But she suddenly found she was feeling a touch rebellious. Tough! A slave for Davenport she might be, but he didn't own her. She picked up the phone, asked for an outside line, and dialled.

'Mr Pomeroy, please—Chesnie Cosgrove,' she informed the telephonist and, her eyes on the man making notes in the other room, she saw his pen momentarily pause before moving on. Then Philip was on the line and she tried to forget that Joel was very likely tuned in. 'I'm sorry to call this late,' she apologised to Philip, 'but I'm afraid I'm just not going to be able to make the party with you tonight. I had a day off on Wednesday,' she excused, 'and I'm still catching up.'

'You weren't ill?' Philip questioned in concern.

'No, no. I've been fine.' She smiled.

'Good. We can go to the party late,' he suggested. 'They won't mind.'

'I'd rather not.'

'How about tomorrow?'

'I'm sorry. I'm going to my parents for the weekend,' she explained, and for no reason glanced at the man in the other office. And he'd said *she* had looked smug! Joel Davenport was obviously delighted that his work had put a stop to her going out with Philip.

When she reached her flat that night Chesnie felt too exhausted to do anything but flop into bed. Almost a whole week had gone by and she had done nothing about buying herself a car—perhaps she'd find a minute next week in which to go car-hunting.

After a good night's sleep she felt recovered, and drove to her old home with Joel taking over her thoughts.

The weekend went pretty much as expected. Her parents were as tetchy with each other as ever, and Chesnie wasn't sorry to see Sunday morning arrive. On her way home she called in on her sister Robina—now back with her husband—and still had Robina's complaints about her philandering husband ringing in her ears when, because her sister Tonia would never forgive her if she didn't call on her too, she stopped in to have a cup of tea. Nerissa phoned her shortly after Chesnie reached her apartment, to chat and enquire about her latest 'doings'. But to neither her parents nor any of her sisters did she mention her 'nine-day wonder' of an engagement, or the fact that—quite ridiculously, she owned—she had fallen hopelessly in love with her non-fiancé.

Philip also telephoned her that evening, and her thoughts on not seeing him again caused her to want to tell him as much. 'Shall I see you on Saturday?' he asked, and the words to explain her decision hovered on her lips.

The only man she wanted to see on Saturday was Joel, and… Suddenly her pride gave her a sharp nudge. What the blazes did she think Joel would be doing on Saturday? Sitting at home thinking of her? Get real!

'I'd like that,' she told Philip before she could think further.

Chesnie spent some time on Monday morning reorganising Joel's already fully scheduled diary when he needed to find an extra hour to see someone in connection with one of their subsidiaries. He also needed to fit in an unexpected invitation to lunch with Edward King the following day. Edward King was a fellow senior director who had married a Yeatman. Chesnie knew Joel valued Edward's opinion, but as yet was uncertain if he had Edward's vote. Joel was already working under pressure—admittedly he seemed to enjoy it—and Chesnie saw it as her role to ease that tension whenever and wherever she could.

He had just gone off to his lunch with Edward King the next day when she received a phone call that caused her to realise Joel now had pressure of a different kind. Though she was sure it was nothing which he couldn't handle. His father rang.

'How's my daughter-in-law to be?' he asked cheerfully—and Chesnie knew panic. Instinctively she wanted to tell him that there was not the remotest possibility that she would be his daughter-in-law, and that she and his son were not engaged, and never had been.

'Magnus—' she even began, then, homing in to cause her to check was her knowledge of what a gossipy chatterbox he was—and he was on friendly terms with Arlene Enderby. Chesnie changed her mind to ask, 'How are you?'

'Extremely happy!' he replied. 'But I'd be even happier if you agreed to take your poor old near dad-in-law to lunch.'

She winced. She liked him. He was a bit of a rogue, a bit of a love, but while everything in her urged her to tell him the truth, and to tell him now, loyalty to Joel kept her silent. She would have to clear it with Joel first.

'I can't make lunch today,' she told Magnus, feeling relief that, because Joel was probably going to take an extended lunch hour, she needed to be back in the office 'holding the fort' by two.

'Oh.' He sounded disappointed. 'I was looking forward to seeing you.' He attempted to persuade. 'I'm happy, but still a bit lonely.'

He piled it on. And she fell for it. 'How would tomorrow suit? I could have lunch with you tomorrow,' she offered.

'I'll call for you,' he promptly accepted.

Which, as they said goodbye, caused Chesnie to know that Magnus would have to be told the truth before tomorrow. He was part of Joel's family, for goodness' sake. Joel's father. And Joel would obviously see that it was only right his father should be told.

So why was she feeling so churned up inside? she wondered when at three-fifteen she heard Joel enter his office. Come on, don't be absurd, do it. Do it now.

Chesnie took a deep breath, got to her feet, dithered for a split second and then, repeating, 'Absurd', she walked quickly across the carpet. With her chin up, her cool persona firmly to the fore, she opened the door and went in.

Oh, how she loved him—a chink appeared in her cool persona. 'Good lunch?' she enquired pleasantly.

He looked back at her. 'Thought-provoking,' he answered, his eyes on her still, a touch speculatively, she rather thought. Instead of enquiring, Any messages? which was what he sometimes did, and which would give her a lead to say that his father had telephoned, Joel invited, 'Take a seat.'

Drat. He sat one side of the desk; she took a seat across from him. She was interested in the 'thought-provoking' lunch he'd had with Edward King, but at the same time there were priorities here and, having built herself up to say what she had to say, suddenly it wouldn't wait.

'Your father rang,' she stated crisply.

'He upset you?' Joel asked, perhaps taking from her manner, for all she was trying to cover it, that she was in a tiny bit of a stew about something.

'Not at all!' she replied quickly. 'That is, he invited me to lunch, and though I couldn't go today, because I didn't want to leave the office, I—' She broke off. *Get it said, do.* 'I'm having lunch with him tomorrow and I think he should be told, before then, that you and I—that w-we are not engaged.' There. It was out. But Joel was already shaking his head—and that annoyed her. It was *his* problem, for heaven's sake, not hers! 'In fact,' she continued, spurred on because she didn't seem to be getting through to him, 'I think it would be very much better all round if you told everyone, right now, that we were never engaged in the first place.'

Joel looked at her for long moments, then, 'Oh, Chesnie,' he said. And while her 'cool' was shot, his was there by the bucketload. 'I'm afraid I can't do that.'

Taken aback, she stared at him. She knew that his work came first, but surely just a whisper in the right ear would start a counter-rumour going. 'You—can't?' she questioned, somehow starting to feel that there was more going on here than Joel just trying to politely get rid of the predatory Arlene. 'Why can't you?' Chesnie demanded, but, looking at him, saw in his expression something that hinted she might not like what she was about to hear.

'I cannot,' he began, his eyes nowhere but on her, 'because, point one, you won't be lunching with my father tomorrow.'

'I—won't?' she queried, mystified.

Joel shook his head. 'I have to go to Glasgow tomorrow. I want you with me. Point two,' he went on as she took on board that she would again be rearranging his diary, 'far from wanting to be released from my engagement...' *His* engagement! '...I'm being pressured to get married.'

Staggered, Chesnie stared at him. 'Why?' She asked the one question her intelligence had managed to bring her.

Joel shrugged, but staggered her further when he openly explained, 'Over lunch Edward confirmed what you and I already know, that Russell Yeatman intends to put himself up for the chairmanship. What we—I—didn't know until lunchtime, when Edward revealed his hand, is that Edward is going to vote for me, and that Winslow, our present chairman, has confided his belief that I'm the best man for the job.'

Chesnie's eyes never left Joel's face. She was truly delighted that Edward King had revealed his colours and was going to vote for Joel. And, casting her mind over the other candidates, she knew—her love for Joel aside—that, as Winslow Yeatman had said, Joel really was the best man for the job.

'But?' she questioned, knowing that there had to be more to it than that—what on earth did this have to do with Joel being pressured to get married?

'But, as you rightly ask, should it come to a split vote—and bearing in mind that out of eight available directors' votes, excluding my own, I have a guarantee of only three votes so far—with Winslow having the casting vote, he has confided in Edward that because of his love of family Winslow will only vote for a man who is married.'

Chesnie was staggered anew, and was fighting to see this matter objectively. Russell Yeatman, while being childless, was, she knew, married. She almost asked Joel if he wanted the chairman's job so badly he'd be prepared to marry to get it. But she knew that he did. Joel was ambitious, she had known that. He wanted the chairman's job and now looked to have an excellent chance of getting it. Particularly since—subject to him being married—he would have the present chairman's backing.

Chesnie felt quite ill at the thought of Joel being married, but she did not want his astute brain picking up so much as a glimmer of how she felt about him. Which left her with little option but to suggest, 'It sounds to me as though you'd better start looking in your little black book.'

'I don't need to,' he answered, his blue-eyed gaze holding her eyes.

'Y-you've found someone to marry?' she queried, hardly

knowing how she managed to keep her voice level. She was hurting and, love her job as she did, didn't know how she would be able to take working for him when he married.

His eyes were still holding hers when, staggeringly, he calmly replied, 'I'm looking at her.'

Which left Chesnie staring at him dumbstruck. 'You're…!' she gasped. Then, like a lightning bolt, what he was saying suddenly hit her—and she woke up with a bang. 'Oh, no!' she bluntly, angrily replied, and was on her feet.

'Why not?' he asked calmly, getting to his feet too and watching her across his desk.

'*Why not?*' She could hardly believe her hearing. How could he say what he had just said and remain so calm, so cool? 'I'm your PA and nothing else!' she exploded, slowly getting over the shock. 'What you've just suggested comes under the heading "Beyond the call of duty"!'

'Think about it,' he suggested. 'We—'

'There's nothing to think about!' she interrupted hotly.

'What are you getting so stewed up about?' he wanted to know.

'You don't consider what you've just said anything to get *stewed up* about? You know perfectly well that I'm not remotely interested in being married.'

'Which is all to the good, surely?'

Chesnie was about to flare up again, but his question halted her. 'How?' she asked.

'You don't want marriage because you've seen too many marriages end in disaster. But we would know in advance how our marriage would end—no hurt on either side.'

She felt too churned up inside to cope with whatever logic that was supposed to be, so asked hostilely instead, 'Why should I marry you?'

'Because you know I'm the right man for the chairman's job. From comments you've made I've seen that you recognise I'm the more likely candidate to move this company forward than any of the others.' She couldn't argue against any of what he said. 'I think you'd enjoy being the chairman's PA too,' he added with a small smile.

Emotion started to get to her. The fact that she too would take that top rung of the promotion ladder passed her by. Joel *was* the right man, the best man for the job, for the company and its employees; she knew that. But marriage? No! Definitely no!

She gathered he had seen from her expression that she wasn't to be swayed when he took another tack and questioned, 'Apart from not wanting a husband, do you have some other reason? Your affair with Pomeroy?' he prompted.

'I'm not having an affair with him!' she denied hotly.

Whether Joel believed her or not she couldn't tell, but, whatever, he used her reply to his advantage. 'There you are, then—there's nothing to stop you.'

Confound him! Where did he get his nerve? 'Why should I?'

'Why shouldn't you?' he answered, managing to make what he proposed sound quite reasonable as he added, 'practically live with me now.'

'I'm not goi[ng to live with you!' she erupted]and saw him sl[ ]but as if live with him, s[ ]'I'm not!' she re[ ]getting through[ ]

She was espec[ially]then his phone ra[ng]Glasgow tomorro[w]evening.'

She opened her[ ]to discuss. But wh[en]to ignore the pho[ne]better of her, and,[ ]to her own office—

Back at her desk[ ]

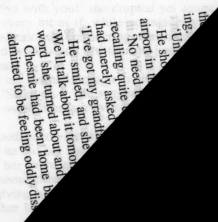

been said; she wasn't having lunch with Magnus tomorrow, she was flying unexpectedly up to Scotland, and she was having dinner with Joel tomorrow, where they would discuss getting married!

She seemed to be working on autopilot as she made the flight arrangements, made their hotel reservation and took sundry phone calls. Later that afternoon she telephoned Joel's father to tell him that she couldn't lunch with him tomorrow after all.

'I know,' he answered, sounding quite cheerful about it. 'Joel gave me a ring and said he was heading north tomorrow. Naturally he wanted you with him.' Grief!

Chesnie felt she was sinking deeper into the quagmire. She was glad to be busy, but felt she just couldn't cope with all Joel had given her to 'sleep on' and run his office efficiently as well. She gave up thinking about the fusillade of shock he had showered her with, and concentrated on that which she was paid to do.

Why, when at six-fifteen she had cleared her desk and was ready to go home, she should feel awkward about going in to see him, she didn't know. If anyone should feel awkward it should be him.

Adopting a cool, calm outer being, she went quickly into ␣e next-door office. Joel looked up from what he was do-
␣'Off home?' he enquired affably.
␣less there's anything…?'
␣ok his head. 'Are you all right for transport to the
␣␣e morning? I could pick you up and—'
␣␣␣o get carried away!' she interrupted crisply,
␣␣␣clearly how, on their last Scottish trip, he
␣␣␣her if she knew the way to the airport.
␣␣␣␣ther's car—and the answer's still no.'
␣␣␣␣had one of her 'hating' moments.
␣␣␣␣row,' he decreed. Without another
␣␣␣␣left him.
␣␣␣␣rely half an hour when she
␣␣␣␣atisfied with her lot. It was

all Joel's fault—it had to be; he'd unsettled her. She glanced around her sitting room. She had been happy here. And would continue to be happy here, she decided firmly. Yet somehow she felt in need of a change. Something, perhaps, to take her out of this rut.

This rut! She hadn't felt in a rut until today! Unsettled, yes. Falling in love with Joel had truly unsettled her. She'd tried not to think of him, but so much for trying. He was in her head the whole of the time.

How dared he create such havoc in her well-ordered life by suggesting they marry? Oh, she could quite well see why he was prepared to marry. Without question ambitious, and given he worked like a Trojan, Joel would let little stand in the way of his getting to the top. If he had to take a wife to achieve his ambition to get there, so be it.

But why would she want to marry him? In general— well, that was before today, she qualified—she had been quite happy with her lot. True, she loved him, and wanted to help him get what he had worked so hard towards. And it was also true that she didn't know anyone better to do the chairman's job—but to *marry* him!

She went to bed. Sleep on it, he had suggested. Who could sleep with that buzzing around in her head?

Though quite when she started to fear that if she did not marry him then Russell Yeatman, or even his cousin, Aubrey Yeatman, might get the chairmanship, neither having the drive and energy Joel had, she was unsure.

She thought about the family closing ranks against Joel, and did not like it. He deserved this job; she knew he did. Yes, but—to marry him? For heaven's sake, don't even consider it. The man was Romeo personified—well, he'd have to stop that for a start! At that point Chesnie just had to laugh. Grief, she wasn't going to marry him and that was that—even if it were true that there had been fewer females phoning him just lately.

A couple of hours later and Chesnie was still wide awake, having gone around and around in circles, and was still striving hard to convince herself not to get involved. If only she didn't love the wretched man, there wouldn't *be* any problem.

But she did love him, and she did want to help him. But she didn't want a husband. Her sisters had been along that route, and look what a disaster area their marriages were.

Yes, but, as Joel had said, she would know in advance how their marriage would end. So, plainly he was only thinking in terms of a brief marriage, while he got himself firmly secure in the role of chairman, and then—no hurt on either side, so he'd said—presumably they would divorce.

Given that her emotions were involved, Chesnie tried her hardest to look at the matter logically. It was a fact that she had no intention of ever marrying. So, given that she had nothing planned to do with her life for the next year— other than to prove herself the best PA going—would it hurt her to go through a ceremony of marriage with him?

What, precisely, would be different in her life, say in a year or so's time, from what was happening in her life now? Presumably she would still be working for Joel. The only difference being that they had been married, but were now divorced.

On that thought her eyelids started to droop. She didn't fool herself that Joel would ever fall in love with her. She sighed as sleep came to claim her. Joel wasn't interested in any long-term relationship. But then, neither was she.

CHAPTER SIX

CHESNIE was relieved on Wednesday to be too busy to think of personal matters. She flew to Glasgow with Joel and spent the morning in his office there, then attended a very involved and protracted meeting with him in the afternoon, where she took the minutes.

They eventually returned to their hotel some time after seven. She felt pretty drained, so had a fair idea how Joel, who'd led the discussions, must be feeling.

'I've a few matters to go through with you before I leave you in the morning,' he said, as they stepped out of the lift and walked along the corridor to where she had her room and he had his suite. 'Would you mind if we had dinner sent up?'

Her heart warmed to him. Clearly he needed space to unwind, and since he wasn't home, where better than his suite? 'I could do with relaxing a little myself,' she answered lightly.

And felt adrenalin start to pump when he looked down into her eyes and commented, 'We're so in tune.'

Chesnie parted from him and went to freshen up, beginning to feel a little churned up inside. As single-minded as ever, Joel had not said a word all day about his proposal. In fact, so single-minded had he been about the work they were there to do, she felt she could be forgiven for believing no such proposal had ever been voiced.

But, he *had* suggested what he had, just as he had said they would discuss it over dinner tonight—and she was starting to feel anxious. Yesterday she had dismissed the idea out of hand. Today, having 'slept on it', having thought and thought *and* thought, she had gone from a

'Couldn't possibly. It was unthinkable' to be tripped up by her love for him. She still had no wish to marry—but Joel was far more worthy of that job than anyone. And he wanted it badly. Did she love him enough to marry him to help him get it?

She reckoned she had done a fair bit of 'in depth' thinking, not to mention enough thinking 'round in circles' to last her the next decade. She did not want to think any more, and as soon as she was ready, having changed into black trousers and a crisp white shirt, she left her room.

Joel had taken a quick shower too, she observed from his damp hair. 'What do you fancy to eat?' he asked courteously, inviting her into the sitting room of his suite. He had soon phoned down their order, and while they were waiting for it he went over some complicated work detail which, as well as typing back the minutes, she would be doing the next morning while he went off on other work pursuits.

Their meal arrived and, with work out of the way, Joel kept the conversational ball rolling—on any subject except the one which Chesnie was beginning to think he had changed his mind about.

She started to really relax then, and began to talk freely, conversationally, herself, delighting in his company. She savoured those moments, and sipped the last of her coffee knowing that very shortly, nothing said, she would return to her room.

And then it was that Joel, glancing from her lips, which were showing a natural smile rather than the more guarded smile she allowed, commented, 'We've had a hectic and tiring day, Chesnie. But before I let you go...' his glance was now steady on her green eyes '...have you an answer for me?'

On that instant her throat went dry. 'An an-answer?' she stammered chokily.

'I suggested we marry,' he reminded her, when she needed no reminding at all.

'Oh,' she mumbled, and, looking at him, loved him so much. 'Er—for how long would it be?'

'Two years at the most,' Joel replied promptly. 'I'd need time once I've won the chairmanship to show what I can do. Once I've done that, my position should be secure.'

Two years was a long time! 'I wouldn't want to be married for any longer,' she said.

'Does that mean you've just said yes?'

Oh, help. 'You could be celibate for two years?' she asked, instinctively feeling then that in the circumstances she should marry him, but unable to help feeling a touch panicky all the same.

'Celibate?' Joel enquired in surprise, to her ears sounding as though he had never heard the word before.

Chesnie felt herself going a little pink. She strove hard for something of her cooler image, and needed it as she explained, 'Well, obviously you and I...I mean, our marriage—if we do get married,' she inserted hurriedly, 'will end at the—um—bedroom door.' Joel looked interested, but didn't comment or interrupt, allowing her to struggle on to the very end. 'While, of course, ours will be a marriage of convenience only, I couldn't put up with a m-man who...' her voice was fading, but she made herself go on, '...who took his pl-pleasures elsewhere.'

'Two years?' Joel queried. This was clearly something he had not given a moment's thought. But, 'Very well,' he agreed, after some careful consideration. And in turn surprised her by asking, 'And you?'

'Me?' Chesnie queried, not at all with him.

'While I accept that any marriage between us would be for my benefit alone, I hope you'd allow me the same pride.'

She stared at him, mystified. 'I've lost you,' she confessed.

'Your pride precludes me from having affairs outside of our marriage. May I take it that you intend to be celibate too?'

Oh, grief, she could feel herself going pink again. But she had started this, so she swallowed and answered, 'Er— that seems only fair.' And knew it was crunch-time when his expression went deadly serious.

'You'll marry me, Chesnie?' he asked.

As she saw it, it was too late to back out now. Already she felt committed. 'I've nothing else planned for the next couple of years,' she answered, as evenly as just then she was capable.

He smiled then. 'Thank you,' he said quietly. 'I truly appreciate you doing this for me. Given that we have to give the register office a clear fifteen days' notice of our intention to marry, you've no objection if we get on with it straight away?'

'You don't want a long engagement?'

'That's not my way.'

That was true. See it, do it Davenport. She realised then that, the die cast, she was starting to feel less strung up. 'The sooner we marry, the sooner we can divorce,' she said with a smile. Strangely, Joel did not smile back.

'Right,' he said after some moments. 'Let's get down to practicalities.'

'Right,' she agreed.

But was more than a little taken aback when he said, 'I suppose we'll have to invite our families to the wedding.'

'We can't just get married and then explain it's a convenience thing?' she asked.

'Not a chance!' He blocked that notion before it could go any further. 'We have to keep that between our two selves,' he informed her, but did explain. 'I don't know about your folks, but can you see my father keeping something like that to himself for even two weeks, let alone two years?'

'That's a point,' she had to agree.

But was little short of amazed when Joel revealed; 'Only last night I had a phone call from my mother—she wants to meet you.'

'Your *mother* wants to meet me?' Chesnie echoed disbelievingly.

'She returned home yesterday from holidaying abroad. My father lost no time in contacting her to tell her I'd got myself engaged.'

'I take your point. We can't tell our families the real reason for our marrying,' she agreed. Her family was larger than his, from what she could make out. Who was to say that one of her family, one of her brothers-in-law, wouldn't say something in the wrong ear? 'Did you want me to make the arrangements, or shall I leave it with you?'

'You'll have to come to the register office with me to give notice of our intention to marry, but I think, brilliant though you are at organisation, the rest of the details you can leave to me,' Joel decided. And, all work done, nothing else to discuss, Chesnie thought she would return to her room.

'If there's nothing else?' she queried, but was already getting up to leave.

'I don't think so,' Joel answered, escorting her to the door. 'Naturally I shall see you have somewhere pleasant to live when we split up. So...'

Chesnie halted in her tracks. 'Sorry?' she questioned, staring up at him. 'I've already got somewhere pleasant to live.'

'You enjoy living there?'

It was small, but she liked it well enough. 'It has everything I need,' she replied.

Joel did not argue, but, while accepting her answer, *his* answer shook her to her roots. 'If that's what you want,' he replied. 'Let me have your landlord's details and I'll see that he gets a cheque.'

'Am I being a little slow here?'

'It goes without saying that your rent for the next two years is down to me,' he enlightened her.

'I beg your pardon?' Chesnie queried, her pride starting

to bristle—though she saw Joel was the one puzzled this time.

'You've just said you'd like to move back to your present address afterwards,' he reminded her.

'I wasn't thinking of moving out *before*!' she let him know in quick time. His response was equally quick.

'Oh, come on! You can't expect everybody to believe we have a normal marriage if we live at separate addresses!'

'I...' she faltered. She should have thought of this; she should have. 'By "everybody" you mean the board?'

He didn't answer; he didn't have to. He just stood there, looking set and determined, and she began to realise that if she wasn't prepared to move into his home with him then they might as well call if off right now. But—she had already said yes, and, while the thought of living in his home with him made her feel more nervous than ever, she loved him. And he deserved that job.

'I hope you've got plenty of room,' she remarked coolly, and turned to face the door.

'Ample,' he replied. He opened the door, but had one last comment to make. 'Chesnie?' he said. She looked up and would have sworn she saw a hint of devilment in his eyes. 'I'll leave you to tell Pomeroy—that the best man won.'

She thought that perhaps she should give Joel a hint of a frosty look. But how in the world could she find any frost when he must see that her lips were twitching at his comment?

'Goodnight,' she bade him, and try as she might she couldn't keep the laughter out of her voice.

His eyes lingered on her unguarded expression. 'Goodnight,' he returned, and Chesnie walked away, knowing then that she loved him more than enough to marry him.

Work went on as usual, with neither of them referring to their impending marriage. Since Joel had said she could safely leave the arrangements to him, she supposed he would organise everything within the next month or two.

It crossed her mind to wonder what would happen in the event that Joel did not get the chairmanship. But that was unthinkable. He was thinking positive; she must think that way too. Anyhow, she had no need to think what the outcome of their marriage would be should the worst happen. Instant divorce was the answer to that one.

'I'm off home now,' she stated, when on Friday evening she had a clear desk and went in to see him.

'Have a good weekend,' he bade her, but then, leaving what he was doing for a few minutes, 'Have you told your family about—us?' he asked, getting up and coming round to her side of the desk.

'Should I?'

He smiled, and she fell deeper in love with him. 'I think you should.'

She smiled back. 'Then I will.'

'This weekend?' he suggested.

It was his way, she knew, not to delay. 'There are some things you can't do over the telephone—I'll take a drive to Cambridge on Sunday,' she said.

And felt her heartbeats go into overdrive when Joel thought for a moment and then offered, 'I can make myself available Sunday afternoon, if you'd like me to come with you.'

'I...' Oh, yes, she'd love to spend a few hours with him away from the office on Sunday. 'That's all right. Thank you anyway.' She denied herself that pleasure. Goodness, this wasn't going to be your normal kind of marriage. Besides, he had better things to do than spend his time listening to her parents looking for an opening to have a go at one another.

He accepted her decision without comment, but while she was already regretting having deprived herself of his company he was going on, 'I take it you've informed Pomeroy of our marriage plans?'

'I'm having dinner with him tomorrow,' she answered openly—and was quite unprepared for the look of instant displeasure that came over Joel's face.

'The devil you are!' he grated harshly, and, in the same fierce tone, 'You haven't told him yet?'

'I haven't had much chance!' she erupted. And, beating him to it when he looked meaningfully to the telephone, 'As I have already said, there are some things you can't do over the phone.'

'He means that much to you?'

'We're—friends.'

Joel stared down at her. 'And he's in love with you—and has asked you to marry him.'

What could she answer? Love Joel she might, but to her way of thinking it didn't seem right to discuss Philip's emotions this way. Chesnie recognised that her normal cool exterior had a very large dent in it, but she did her very best to show Joel an unflustered façade.

'I'll see you on Monday,' she said, and started to turn away.

'Goodnight,' Joel replied, accepting that she didn't wish to discuss Philip, but giving her a hard look that seemed to say that *he* did the dismissing here.

Chesnie spent Saturday morning doing her usual household chores and not looking forward to seeing Philip that night. She knew it would be the last time she would see him, and that he would be hurt. And she liked him and did not want to hurt him. But there was no alternative.

Philip was due to call at seven, and at four she decided to have a wallow in her bath and try and think up the most tactful and painless way of telling him what she must. She shampooed her hair while she was about it, rinsing off the shampoo with the shower attachment.

Barely had she stepped out of the bath, though, when the outer buzzer went. Who? Nerissa? Hastily Chesnie pulled on her cotton wrap and mopped at her wet hair with a towel as she went. She had wanted to tell Nerissa of her marriage plans first, but realised her parents would feel slighted if they weren't the first to know. But if it were Nerissa at the door, then what would be more natural than that she wouldn't be able to keep her news to herself?

'Hello?' she said into the intercom, her voice welcoming.

'Who were you expecting?' Joel asked bluntly.

Joel? A few weeks ago she might have answered, Obviously not you—but she loved the man. 'I thought it might be one of my sisters,' she answered truthfully, and had nothing more to add.

'Can I see you?' Joel asked when a few seconds had ticked by and she had done nothing about releasing the door catch.

'I—er—I've only just got out of the bath,' she answered in a rush. For goodness' sake—what had happened to sophisticated? Chesnie struggled hard to recapture her image. 'I'm not fit to be seen.'

'I don't believe that for a minute,' Joel replied, and added, 'I know you've an appointment this evening. I won't stay long.'

She wished he would state what he wanted from where he was, on her doorstep, but she had seen his tenacity in action. If he wanted to see her about some small matter then see her he would, though she hadn't a clue what that matter could possibly be.

Without saying another word she activated the door release button, then hared back to the bathroom. She wasted valuable time trying to dry her hair, then realised she had other priorities and wound a towel around it. She was in the middle of making her thin wrap more secure when Joel rang the doorbell.

She would at least have liked to put some underwear on, but there was no time. Joel had said he wouldn't stay long. He was right there. She was going to send him on his way the minute he'd told her the reason for his call.

'Come in,' she greeted him on opening the door, her

heart going all wobbly again. He seemed taller somehow in his casual clothes.

He followed her in to her sitting room, but when she might have suggested he take a seat she bit it back. She was aware of his eyes going over her, just knew that he knew she hadn't a stitch on beneath her thin wrap, and wished, quite desperately, that she had kept him waiting while she put some clothes on. Her light garment was doing little to conceal her curvy contours.

'I really should be getting dressed,' she mumbled, half in apology for the sketch she knew she must look, half as a hint that he should spit out what he'd come to say and leave.

'You look beautiful as you are,' he observed. And, to her astonishment, he seemed to be teasing her, or maybe noticing that she felt awkward and attempting to make her feel more at ease. 'You should wear a pastel-shaded towel around your head more often.'

He was charming her! That was all he had to say and she was ready to wilt! But this would never do. 'As you know, I'm out this evening. But if you've brought me some work you urgently require, I could probably manage it when I come home,' she offered, her tone coolly professional.

Only he did it again. He smiled. And her insides acted all giddy again. 'Am I such a hard task master?' he asked in surprise. Then realised that he probably was. 'Don't answer that,' he ordered, and, putting a hand in his pocket, said, 'I brought you this,' and pulled out a ring box.

'What…?'

'I thought, with everybody knowing we're engaged, you'd better have a ring,' he remarked matter-of-factly, and opened the box to reveal the most exquisite single-stoned engagement ring.

'Joel, I…!' she gasped.

'An emerald, to match your eyes,' he stated, just as matter-of-factly.

'You've...' She was still in shock. He was trying to sound as though he hadn't given it any thought. But surely to have purchased an emerald because of the colour of her eyes must mean he had given it a little thought?

'If it fits you could wear it when you go to Cambridge tomorrow,' he suggested. 'Come to think of it, you might as well start wearing it now.'

'It's lovely,' she murmured, but felt too shy to take it from its box and put it on.

Which made her glad when Joel took the ring out of the box for her. 'Which finger?' he asked, when she was certain he full well knew. She gave him a speaking look, but felt all trembly inside when he caught a hold of her left hand and slid the ring home on the correct finger.

'It fits perfectly!' she whispered, and glanced up to see that he was looking gently at her.

'I'd give you a kiss in the time-honoured manner, only I'm terrified you'd resign.'

Was he teasing again, to get her over any stray touch of awkwardness? She rather thought he was. And liked him more with each new and kind facet she learned of him. 'I'm glad you remembered,' she murmured, but suddenly became conscious that her cotton wrap had stated to gape, revealing more of her right breast than she cared to have on public view. 'Ooh!' she cried on a faint strangled sound, and saw as she went to hurriedly cover herself up that all she had succeeded in doing was drawing Joel's attention to her person. Being taller, he had quite a good view, she knew.

She saw him grin as he dragged his gaze back from the creamy silken swell of her breast. 'Er—don't catch cold,' he commented humorously, and was still grinning as he added, 'I'll see myself out.'

Chesnie was left staring after him. She heard the door close, and collapsed into a chair. Then found she was gazing at the ring on her finger. It was absolutely gorgeous, but she could hardly believe how it had got there. Or indeed, for that matter, that Joel had purchased it and had brought it to her at all.

How long she sat there just looking at the engagement ring, just looking and thinking of how Joel had adopted a teasing manner when he had seen that she felt awkward, Chesnie could not have said. Only when it came to her that she had better start doing something about her hair if she didn't want to look a sight when Philip called for her did she move.

She couldn't resist another glance to her ring, though. But it was then, as she recalled Joel's 'you might as well start wearing it now' that she realised she could not. She had to tell Philip first, and it just seemed a bit—well, not quite nice to be sporting Joel's ring when she told Philip.

Suddenly, thinking of that remark Joel had made, she found she was wondering if Joel had *wanted* her to wear his ring that night. Was he in fact—staking his claim, so to speak? Rot, said her head. As if.

Philip seemed in a serious frame of mind when, just before seven that evening, he called for her. She didn't invite him up to her flat but went straight down, wanting to get said what she had to say while at the same time not wanting to hurt Philip.

But, as things turned out, he already knew. She went with him to his car, but instead of setting the car in motion, as she expected, Philip turned to her and said in a rush, 'I've heard that you and Davenport are an item.'

Chesnie was amazed. 'How did...?' she gasped. Even with the evidence she had that business news travelled fast, she was absolutely stunned that this personal matter had reached him.

'It's true, then?' he questioned, hope fading from his eyes.

'I'm sorry, Philip. I really am,' she apologised. 'I wanted to tell you myself. I intended to...'

'You were going to tell me tonight that this is our last

date?' he asked, and Chesnie could see no way of easing what seemed painful for him.

She offered to cancel their dinner date, but Philip would not hear of it. But the evening was not a success, and when Philip took her home she did not resist when he took her in his arms and held her close for some moments before at last he kissed her.

'Goodbye, darling,' he said.

And Chesnie went up to her flat, feeling near to tears that she had hurt him but aware that she and Philip would never be anything more than the friends she had told Joel they were. When Philip had held her in his arms just now she had felt only sorrow. Joel had only to touch her hand, as he had that afternoon when he had put his ring on her finger, and she tingled all over, felt alive and aware.

Her parents were staggered when, the next day, she told them that she was engaged to be married. 'Why isn't he with you?' her mother asked, getting over her shock.

'Joel wanted to come,' Chesnie began to explain— though 'wanted' was putting it a bit strongly, she knew. 'But he's extremely busy.' That didn't go down too well, and Chesnie found herself inventing. 'We've decided to marry quite soon, so he's rushing to clear away as much as he can so we can spend more time together.'

'I hope you're going to give me enough notice so I can get myself a new outfit!' was her mother's only comment, and Chesnie saw that Joel had been right when he had said they would have to invite their two families to the wedding. Her mother was talking about what she would wear and she hadn't been invited yet!

Chesnie phoned her sisters from her parents' home, and found it little short of amazing that, when her sisters' marriages were such strife-torn disasters, they should be overjoyed at her news. 'Oh, how wonderful!' Nerissa sighed.

Robina was in raptures. 'You dark horse—you said you'd never marry. I couldn't be more pleased!' she enthused.

'Where have you been hiding him?' squealed Tonia excitedly. 'I'm so happy for you.'

Chesnie went into work on Monday still feeling bemused by her family's reaction. 'Good morning,' she bade her fiancé formally, and went all squashy inside when he did her the courtesy of leaving his desk and coming through to her office to see her.

'Any problems?' he enquired, his eyes taking in her neat, trim shape in the sage-green suit.

By 'any problems' she guessed he meant had she told her parents and Philip? 'I've told everyone who needs to be told,' she answered.

He nodded, then said pleasantly, 'I'm glad you're wearing your engagement ring,' and returned to his office. Did the man miss nothing?

Chesnie worked late on Monday, and was busy preparing data on Tuesday morning for a meeting Joel had the next day when he came in to see her. She discovered he had been busy making telephone calls and needed her to go out with him within the next hour.

'I'll have my notepad ready,' she answered, thinking they must be going out on some business matter.

'You won't need it,' he answered, and, when she stared at him uncomprehendingly, 'Have you any plans for two weeks next Saturday?'

'You need me to work?' she asked, ready, willing and able.

'I thought we might get married,' he suggested casually—and she went hot all over. She hadn't been expecting it this soon.

'I—er—I'd better ring my mother. She wants to buy a new outfit,' Chesnie said on a rush of breath, only just holding back a gulp.

But nearly fell off her chair when Joel remarked softly, 'You really are wonderful, aren't you?'

Because she wasn't having forty fits! Thank goodness he didn't know the sudden mass of panic going on inside her.

'I wouldn't dream of arguing with you,' she replied as coolly as she was able.

He gave her a half-smile and then, as practical as ever, 'We need to go to the register office to give notice. We'll need to call at your place first, for either your birth certificate or your passport,' he stated. 'I'm afraid we've a busy time ahead, but I'll find some free time to give you a hand carting your gear over to my place,' he volunteered, and as it struck Chesnie that soon she would be sleeping every night under his roof, so the reality of what was happening hit her with full force.

She was incapable of replying to his offer, so said the only thing she could think of, 'You don't think you should spend what free time you have—living it up?'

'Living it up?'

Oh, crumbs! He was forcing her to explain! 'In view of the fact that very soon you'll be saying goodbye to your—er...'

He was quick on the uptake, and amused with it. 'Loose-living ways?' he supplied.

'Exactly!' she said, and was sinking fast when he laughed.

'Oh, Chezzie Cosgrove,' he said lightly, 'I think you and I will fare very well together.'

Chezzie! She liked it—but then, she was falling apart. She loved him with all her heart, and—oh, help—their wedding day established, that day was coming nearer!

CHAPTER SEVEN

WHAT with a heavy workload, and going to spend one weekend with her grandfather and the next weekend at her parents' home—to shop with her mother on the Saturday for the new outfit her mother insisted on having—there didn't seem to be a moment spare for Chesnie to pack up her belongings. It was the Monday before her wedding when she found some spare time in which to start filling her suitcases.

She was glad to be busy—even if it did sometimes seem to her that from the moment she had consented to marry Joel this coming Saturday she had not had a second to draw fresh breath. She did not want to have time to spare, time in which to think about what she was doing.

As well as coping with an overloaded work schedule, and after speaking to her mother on the phone that night, who asked pertinent questions about what her youngest daughter would be wearing, Chesnie decided that if her mother could have a new outfit then so could she.

A hurried lunchtime trawl of the shops on Tuesday and Wednesday produced just the right cream-coloured silk dress and three-quarter-length matching coat. A hunt for hat, bag, shoes and gloves caused her to be late getting back to her office.

'Have a good time?' Joel asked when she eventually made it back, spying through the open door the expensive-looking large carriers and other large parcels she came in with.

Chesnie put her shopping down and went into his office, and had to smile as she asked, 'What are you getting married in?'

'Heaven help us!' he exclaimed. 'You're not expecting me to do the morning suit bit, are you?'

Chesnie savoured the moment, an imp of mischief unexpectedly taking her. 'Would you?' she asked.

Joel stared into her lovely green eyes which, for all she was straight-faced, could not hide their mischievous sparkle. For long moments he just studied her, before confirming, 'If I have to.'

She laughed lightly, was unable to suppress it. 'An everyday kind of suit will do,' she said, and, aware of his eyes on her, decided enough of this levity—she was going to be working late again tonight, and there were more things to pack when she finally got home.

On Thursday Joel paused in the middle of dictating a letter to enquire, 'Everything going smoothly your end?' which surprised her. Work was work; personal was personal—and never the twain should meet.

'You mean the wedding?'

He paused, staring at her for some moments—a habit he seemed to have got into just recently, she suddenly realised. 'Our wedding,' he said succinctly.

'Oh, well, if you're going to be personal about it,' she said—and, spontaneously, they both burst out laughing.

It was a good moment, the memory of which Chesnie knew she would keep with her for some time. Then Joel was serious as he remarked, 'In the unlikely event there is a problem you need help with—what are fiancés for?'

Her heart did a little flip and she acknowledged that she loved it that he should term himself her fiancé. Her heart did another little flip when, on the heels of that, it came to her that from Saturday on he would be able to term himself her husband.

She had envisaged no such problems. Then on Friday, when she took a breather from work to ring her grandfather to double-check that he would be there at her wedding, one unforeseen problem cropped up. 'I—um—may be a little late,' he confessed.

He was never late! He could not bear unpunctuality in any shape! 'What's wrong?' Chesnie was just asking, when Joel came in, saw she was on the phone—but decided to wait.

'Nothing's wrong,' Rufus Cosgrove assured her.

'Yes, there is,' Chesnie responded quietly. 'Come on, Gramps,' she prised gently, but determinedly, 'tell me what's happened.'

Reluctantly, over the next minute or so, he revealed that he had only just heard that there were going to be weekend rail disruptions while track maintenance was being carried out, which would affect the route he intended to travel on. 'But I'll get there as soon as I can,' he ended cheerfully.

Chesnie said goodbye to him and put the phone down, her mind busy. 'A trouble shared?' Joel interrupted her thoughts.

She smiled at him. She'd been rushed off her feet, but for all that she had just spent a most pleasant week working with him. 'It's not trouble, exactly,' she answered. 'Though, on thinking about it, I'll have to put off bringing my stuff over to you until—er—tomorrow.'

'Tomorrow?' He seemed surprised. 'You *have* remembered you're getting married tomorrow?'

'Of course I have,' she replied, starting to feel heated. For pity's sake! On account of tomorrow she'd chased around like a scalded cat all this week!

Joel was still looking. 'So why are we altering our plans for this evening?' he wanted to know.

'I need to drive to Herefordshire tonight,' she answered.

'Because?'

Chesnie looked back at him, then had to concede that, albeit this was nothing to do with work, it was possibly a little something to do with Joel after all. 'Because there's weekend disruption of the rail service on my grandfather's route, and I'm afraid he might not be able to make it to the register office in time for the ceremony tomorrow, and—' She broke off—and started to feel angry with Joel

Davenport and his dogged tenacity when he wanted more than that.

'And?' he insisted.

'And,' she erupted, feeling self-conscious and blaming him for it, 'I want him to be there. I know it's irrational, that ours will not be the usual kind of marriage, but—but he's special to me, and—and,' she ended stubbornly, 'and I want him there.'

She felt stupid, but wouldn't back down, and stared solemnly, stubbornly, at Joel. He stared back, then quietly assured her, 'Then you shall have him there.' With which he strolled back to his office and closed the door. A few minutes later he was coming back to suggest, 'You might like to let your grandfather know that one of our drivers will pick him up at nine tomorrow morning.'

Chesnie looked at him open-mouthed. 'B...'

'That should get him here in ample time to see you married,' Joel stated. 'The same driver will take him back when your grandfather's ready.' And, when she continued to look at him absolutely dumbfounded, 'What's the matter?' he asked. 'You think you're the only one who can solve problems?'

She didn't, of course, but had to smile, and felt the need to explain. 'I'm sorry to have to bother anyone. Normally my grandfather would drive himself, only...'

'Only you've got his car.'

This man she was marrying forgot nothing! 'I'll be giving it back to him as soon as he moves into the cottage he's just bought,' she said. Then, realising Joel probably had more work to do than she had, she felt she had said enough on the subject, and added simply, 'Thank you, Joel.'

He paused only to instruct, 'Don't forget to let the motor section have your grandfather's present address.' And on his way to his own office tossed over his shoulder, 'Your favourite baggage-handler will call at your place tonight— as planned.'

Chesnie carried on working but suddenly became aware that she was working with a ridiculous smile on her face. Good heavens! Though, on thinking about it, for all she had been working in overdrive for most of the time, that smile had had a great number of airings recently. And, come to think of it, having worked for Joel for around five months now, never had she known him so light-hearted as he had been all this week either. Though in his case he was light-hearted because after tomorrow his battle for the chairmanship would be a little more cemented in his favour. So why was she smiling? Perish the thought that it was because she was marrying the man.

At half past four the door opened and Joel came into her office. The present chairman was with him and was carrying the most wonderful bouquet of flowers.

'Joel tells me you both wish to marry without any fuss, but I couldn't let this occasion pass without coming to wish you the very best of everything.' Winslow Yeatman beamed.

Chesnie had been standing, about to do some filing. She put down her papers and came away from the filing cabinet. 'Thank you,' she said as she smiled and accepted the bouquet.

'I've told Winslow our wedding is to be a family-only affair. But we'll be having a party to celebrate later in the year—won't we, darling?' Joel commented, coming over and setting her pulses jumping by placing an arm about her shoulders.

'Be sure Flora and I get an invite.' Winslow beamed again, and Chesnie, finding the idea of entertaining him and who knew who else quite terrifying, continued to smile too.

'Of course,' she assured him, and chatted with him for a few minutes before he and Joel went into Joel's office.

Chesnie got on with her filing, and only then, her filing requiring no great feat of brain-power, did it start to dawn on her that there was likely to be more to this marriage than merely speaking her vows tomorrow.

Though as she began to get used to the notion of being hostess at a party to which all of the 'big-wigs' of Yeatman Trading would be invited, so her initial reaction of being terrified at the very idea began to fade. Should Joel have been serious then, nerve-racking though it would probably be, Chesnie knew—perhaps with a few tips from Nerissa, who was used to entertaining big-time—that she would cope.

She left her office as Miss Cosgrove at six-thirty, and drove home finding she was again smiling as she mused that on Monday she would return as Mrs Davenport. She abruptly stopped smiling. She didn't want to marry—ever. Well, that was— Oh, hang it—roll on tomorrow. Let's get it over and done with.

Strangely, when Chesnie was forever going in to Joel's office to see him, and had only parted from him a couple of hours ago, she experienced a feeling of shyness when he called at her flat that night. She covered her shyness with her calm, efficient PA manner as she invited him in.

'What happened in between our last goodbye and now?' Joel wanted to know, clearly remembering, as did she, their amicable parting when she'd left the office.

'I'm sorry,' she apologised, and wanted to leave it there—but then found that when you loved someone it wasn't that easy to be detached, and that there was a tendency to want to meet them halfway. 'I...' She hesitated, then plumped for the truth. 'I can hardly believe it—and you'll think I'm being ridiculous—but I think I'm feeling shy.'

Joel stared at her. 'Of me?' he asked, and then his mouth, his superb mouth, started to curve upwards. 'It's a new situation for both of us,' he said softly. 'But as long as you're not about to change your mind we'll be fine,' he promised and, making her heart thunder, he ran the back of his hand down the side of her face. Then, his manner changing to his usual one of 'let's get things done', 'Shall we get your belongings over to my place?'

His place was a very different place from hers. It was in a better area, for a start. It was modern and in a relatively new building. The rooms were large and had carpets you could hide your ankles in, and beautiful furniture with clean-cut lines.

Joel showed her over the whole of the apartment, opening the door to his bedroom to show her the layout of everywhere, as though to endorse that she would not be any casual visitor. Saying, in effect, she realised with a glow of warmth, that she must feel that his home was her home too.

'I thought you'd like to have this bedroom,' he said, leading the way to a bedroom with its own adjoining bathroom, which was just across the hall from his. 'Feel free to change anything that doesn't please your eye. If you'd prefer a different set of furniture...'

'It's lovely as it is,' she said, and couldn't fault the spacious room and its abundant wardrobe space.

They went into the kitchen, where he offered to make her coffee, but she had started to feel shy again—though didn't make the mistake of adopting her PA cover this time.

'I think I'd better go home,' she said lightly, beginning to feel a little churned up when she thought of how, from tomorrow and for the next two years, her home would be here—with Joel. 'Er—who keeps your home looking so lovely?' she asked, to cover her shaky feelings.

'A very kind fairy by the name of Mrs Attwood. She arrives several times a week, cleans, sometimes cooks, shops. I just leave her a note. Very often I don't see her for months on end.' He looked pleasantly over to Chesnie and she somehow knew that he had seen her shyness and was answering her question in detail to help her get over her shy moment. She fell yet deeper in love with him.

It was getting on for eleven when he drew his car up outside of her flat. She was feeling all right with him again. Indeed she felt comfortable with him, and, not wanting to be left alone to have last-minute doubts about the wisdom of what she was doing, would have liked to invite him up for coffee. But, regardless of the fact that she was marrying him tomorrow, theirs wasn't that sort of casual relationship. So she got out of the car without a word, and Joel came to the outside door with her.

'Your sister's driving you to the register office, isn't she?' he asked before he let her go, confirming there were no last-minute snags.

'Nerissa insists,' Chesnie replied.

'Until tomorrow, then,' he said, and went. And Chesnie wanted him back. Suddenly there were a dozen or more matters she wanted to discuss with him.

What did they do after the ceremony, for instance, after they'd finished eating and their families had gone their separate ways? Did she go back to his apartment, change and take herself off to the cinema? Go go-cart racing? Shopping? Did he shrug his shoulders and shut himself away somewhere with a good book? And what about meal times? She should have asked. Did she make herself a sandwich and eat it in the kitchen while he dined on some delicacy Mrs Attwood had cooked?

Chesnie did not sleep well, and was wide awake long before her alarm clock sounded. Nerissa rang at eight. 'Are you in a stew?' she asked lightly.

Chesnie had thought her years of training herself to be composed would see her scorning any such idea. But, 'In a word, yes,' she replied. She knew that she would go through with it, she had promised, but oh, how she wished it all over and done with.

'I'll come round early,' Nerissa promised. She had previously blithely stated that her husband was big enough to find his own way to the register office, and that she would meet him there.

True to her word, Nerissa arrived with ample time to spare. 'Coffee?' Chesnie offered.

'I'll make it. You're supposed to be waited on today.'

They were sitting sipping coffee when Nerissa enquired, 'Anything in particular bothering you?'

Where to start? Chesnie shook her head. 'I just didn't expect to feel this—jittery.'

'Par for the course,' Nerissa said with a smile. 'You'll be fine once you see Joel again.'

She was right, Chesnie discovered when she and Nerissa entered the register office. Joel was already there, and was in conversation with her family, a tall, aristocratic woman whom Chesnie took to be his mother, and Magnus. Joel was wearing a smart suit she hadn't seen before, and immediately he saw her he excused himself and came over. Nerissa wandered over to her husband.

'You're not keeping me waiting!' Joel greeted her with a smile, and, taking both her hands in his, he bent and kissed her cheek. She should have been ready for it—it would have looked more odd if he *hadn't* saluted her that way—but she jerked away.

'Sorry,' she immediately whispered.

He bent close to her ear. 'Don't be nervous,' he instructed softly. 'Everything's going to work out well.' He pulled back, an admiring look in his eyes as he surveyed her in her cream silk outfit. 'And you look totally exquisite.' He smiled at her—and suddenly she was feeling better. 'I've introduced myself to your family. When you've said hello to them you must come and say hello to mine.'

Chesnie *knew* she was a bride, but only when one by one her family embraced and kissed her did she actually begin to feel like one. She had been afraid that perhaps she had gone over the top with her outfit. But seeing not only her family but Joel's mother arrayed in wedding finery made her realise she would have looked very much the poor relation had she not bothered.

She introduced Joel to Nerissa and, since her grandfather wasn't one to push himself forwards, Chesnie went and gave him a special hug. In turn she was given a big hug by Magnus Davenport. 'I've always wanted a daughter,' he asserted, with a sly look at his ex-wife. She ignored him.

'Chesnie,' Dorothea Davenport greeted her warmly when Joel introduced her. 'I'm so glad to meet you at last.' She did not embrace or kiss Chesnie, as everyone else had, and shortly afterwards Chesnie and Joel were called to see the registrar.

The ceremony passed in something of a haze for Chesnie. She made her responses when called upon to do so, felt Joel take a hold of her hand to slide a gold band on her wedding finger, and knew that her inner trembling had communicated itself to him when, for the briefest moment, he paused. Then he looked into her eyes and smiled the most wonderful smile.

She was his wife! For someone who had never wanted to be married, Chesnie had to admit, she didn't feel so bad. And Joel didn't look too upset to have given up his freedom either, she noted, as briefly he touched his lips to hers. 'Thank you,' he said quietly—and she was drowning!

'Any time,' she replied, and they looked into each other's eyes—and laughed.

Then, while his parents were congratulating him, her family were crowding round to add their good wishes. As they went on to congratulate Joel, Chesnie had a moment or two alone with her grandfather.

'Promise me you'll be happy,' he said, and Chesnie knew then why, apart from her love for him, it had been important to her that her grandfather was there. Of all her family, his was the only marriage that had been wonderful. She had somehow needed to know on this day that not all the Cosgrove marriages ended in disaster.

'I will be, Gramps,' she assured him.

'I couldn't bear it if I thought you'd end up like your sisters.'

Oh, Gramps. Guilt smote her. His marriage to her grandmother had been near perfect. Gramps wanted the same for her. She loved him so much she felt then that she wanted to confess everything to him. But, conversely, she loved him too much to want to cause him a moment's distress. So she smiled and kissed his worn cheek and laughed as she replied, 'Didn't you know? I'm different.'

'I'm banking on it,' he laughed back. Then Dorothea Davenport had come to stand ready to offer her good wishes. And over the next few minutes, when Dorothea Davenport did give her a kiss of congratulation, Chesnie started to like Joel's mother.

Especially when, with a quick look to check that her ex-husband wasn't within earshot, she confided, 'Don't tell Magnus, but I've always wanted a daughter too,' adding, 'Where is Magnus, by the way? The last time I saw him he was conning your sister—Nerissa, isn't it?—into taking him to lunch one day next week.'

They were having a quiet smile about it when Joel came over to them, closely followed by Magnus. 'I know you and Joel are going to be happy together,' Magnus said, kissing Chesnie's cheek. 'You're not like any of those other women he—'

'Thank you, Father,' Joel interrupted him. 'I'm not sure Chesnie is interested.'

'Sorry,' Magnus apologised with a grin. 'Though you can't expect to have any secrets where families are concerned. Have 'em all together and somebody's bound to end up embarrassed.'

As was proved when, after adjourning to a smart hotel where Joel had organised a private luncheon, they were mid-way through the celebratory meal and Chesnie's mother, after recharging her bickering batteries by having a stab at her husband, turned to Magnus to impart, 'I always knew Chesnie would marry someone she works with. She's always been much too busy to go out looking for someone.'

And if that wasn't embarrassing enough—'go out looking for someone'—as if ensnaring some man was the be-all and end-all of existence—Chesnie's sister Tonia, probably trying to make things better, chimed in with, 'You're the only one of us who ever thought Chesnie would marry at all, Mother. She's always sworn that she would never say "I do" to any man.'

'That was before the love-bug crept up on her unexpectedly.' Her sister Robina chipped in with her two pennyworth—and Chesnie was aware that Joel, sitting next to her, was looking at her.

'You've gone a touch pink,' he murmured in an undertone.

'Your father was right!' she replied, glancing at him, and felt quite spell-bound when he grinned handsomely.

Had she imagined that she might feel awkward once the wedding party ended and she was left alone with Joel, she soon realised that she need not have worried. Following tradition, and after more hugs and kisses to speed them on their way, she and Joel were the first to leave.

'Anything in particular you'd like to do this afternoon?' he surprised her by asking as they drove away from the hotel.

'I—er—thought, as soon as I've changed, that I'd better get on with my unpacking,' she replied, the notion to sort out her belongings only then coming to her.

'We can eat in or out—whichever you prefer,' he suggested, laying to rest any idea she might have nursed that it might be 'I do solemnly declare...' at the register office and then, I'll see you at the office come Monday.

'In, I think,' Chesnie opted. 'Though I don't think I shall be ready for another meal for a while.'

Chesnie wasn't at all sure how they would fare living under the same roof, and she suddenly realised that Joel might initially be experiencing similar slightly awkward feelings as she was, in the circumstance of their starting to live together under the same roof. That realisation tempered her own anxious feelings, so that by the time he had garaged his car and they were inside his apartment she was more than ready to meet him halfway.

With the intention of going straight to her room, she set

off along the hall. Only to halt and to turn when Joel called, 'Chesnie!' She took a couple of steps back towards him. Joel came nearer, and stopped to look down into her eyes. 'Thank you for today,' he said quietly. 'It means a great deal to me.'

'I know,' she answered softly, her mood all-giving.

'Is there anything I can do for you in return?' he asked, and she knew, proud man that he was, that she would only have to mention it, whatever 'it' might be, and it would be done. But then he said something that caused *her* pride to shoot off into orbit. 'Naturally I'll arrange for an allowance to be paid into your bank acc—'

'I don't want an allowance!' she exploded, offended on the instant.

'Don't be ridiculous!' he retorted crisply, his easy manner gone. 'You're married now. You're my wife. Of course you—'

'I didn't marry you for your money!' she erupted hotly.

'I know *that*!' he stated tersely. Then caused her anger to depart as swiftly as it had arrived, panic taking its place, when he paused and, his stern expression fading, asked, 'Just why *did* you marry me, Chesnie?'

Oh, heaven help us! Suddenly she was desperate to keep this sharp and clever man from guessing that, had she not fallen heart and soul in love with him, it was very doubtful she would have married him at all. 'Given that you must have caught me at a weak moment, what PA worthy of the name could resist the chance to be PA to the chairman?' she found from a barren nowhere.

He must have accepted that, she realised, because though she had seen him question, question and question that which he needed to know, he did not pursue it, and suddenly the corners of his mouth were turning upwards. Then his glance went to her mouth and, unhurriedly, his hands were reaching for her and he was giving her heart failure by drawing her to him. 'I really do think, Mrs Davenport,' he began as, unresisting, slightly mesmerised, she went into the circle of his arms, 'that we should seal today's events with a kiss of marriage.'

She stared at him, but as his lips met hers she closed her eyes. With her heart banging against her ribs she thrilled to the feel of his firm arms about her as warmly he kissed her. As kisses went, it started as a fairly chaste kiss, but his arms tightened about her and his kiss deepened, and Chesnie was quite unprepared for the less than chaste re-action of her body. She had never been up this close to him before, but the feel of the hard muscles of his arms about her, the feel of his body against hers, the feel of his body warmth, was staggering. She loved the feel of him, loved his touch, and held on to him—because she had to. She was under the spell of him, mindless of anything save him and his wonderful mouth over hers as she responded to his kiss.

Only when he broke his kiss and took a step back, his body no longer touching her, was Chesnie able to regain a little brain-power. 'Oh, by the way,' she said, from a cool, off-hand heaven-alone-knew-where, considering that her legs were about to buckle, 'I think I left my gloves in your car.'

Joel stared at her in astonishment, and she rather gathered he was used to a very different reaction to his kisses. Then, unexpectedly, he burst out laughing, his eyes alight with amusement, and commented, 'Do you know, Chesnie? I believe I could get to quite enjoy living with you.'

Inside she was smiling. But without a word she turned and walked towards her bedroom. She only hoped her legs would hold up until she got there!

CHAPTER EIGHT

THEY had been married for two weeks when Chesnie became aware that, while not husband and wife except on paper, their relationship seemed to have changed in some subtle way. That change, she realised on thinking about it, had begun when Joel had claimed that kiss of marriage on their wedding day.

She could not have explained what exactly was different, but, while she still performed her duties as his PA in her usual efficient manner, away from the office PA and boss just didn't come into it. Though what their relationship was, apart from on their marriage certificate, she was unsure.

Were they friends? She supposed they might be. Joel was always friendly to her, considerate to her, even, as if believing that her having moved from her own home and into his had been a big adjustment to make.

Not that she saw a great deal of him out of the office. In her view Joel, having lived on his own for a number of years, must also have had to adjust to someone living in his space. To give him as much space as possible she would often take herself off to her room—when her preference would have been to stay where he was.

'You don't have to go, you know,' he'd said only last night when, after a gruelling kind of day, he'd had to attend a business dinner but had then come home earlier than she had expected.

'I—er...' That abominable shyness she had become acquainted with recently arrived again to trip her up. 'I—er—quite enjoy my own company,' she'd answered.

'In other words, you've seen quite enough of me for one day?' he'd suggested.

126

He had sounded a touch put out—was he looking for a fight? She loved him. She didn't want to fight with him. So she had smiled. 'Goodnight,' she'd said, and had gone to bed.

Now, this bright Saturday morning, she was going to do what she could delay doing no longer. Gramps was moving into his new home on Monday—she really must go looking for a car. Joel always left for the office ages before she did, but in any case, what with him sometimes working away or going off for some business conference or other at the end of the day, cadging a lift with him on a daily basis was a non-starter. She needed her own car.

Chesnie went in to the kitchen to make her breakfast, and found Joel there, just finishing his. 'Good morning,' she bade him cheerfully, so truly pleased to see him she forgot all about the cool demeanour she usually showed him. Though, come to think of it, that cool demeanour had slipped quite a bit just lately. But, she excused, why not? He was, after all, family.

'You sound as if you slept well,' he observed lightly.

'That bed is bliss.' Her heart was acting the giddy-goat again. 'Would you like some more coffee?' she asked, going over to the percolator.

'I'll take a cup to my study,' he accepted.

And so the day began. She supposed she could say that they coped with living under the same roof quite well. She went off looking for a new-second-hand car and saw one within her price range but which she was undecided about. She decided to think it over and go and take another look in her lunch hour on Monday.

'Want to do anything in particular tonight?' Joel asked when she returned to the apartment and went into the drawing room.

She looked at him. 'Was I wrong?' she asked.

'Enlighten me?'

'To stipulate no girlfriends?'

He grinned; her heart bumped. 'You're suggesting I must be bored because I want to take my wife out?'

Want to? Wife! She was crazy about him. She laughed. 'I've got this boss who keeps my nose to the grindstone. At weekends all I want to do is just curl up with a book,' she lied, declining his offer to take her somewhere.

She went to her room, already mentally kicking herself for refusing his invitation. Would it have hurt to have enjoyed some more of his company, for goodness' sake? Had she resigned herself to staying in alone reading every weekend for the next two years? Honestly!

Yes, but, if possible, she was falling even deeper in love with him day by day. How would they fare if he saw her love for him? He'd be embarrassed—she'd be *mortified.* Already her guard had slipped so much as to be almost permanently down. In the office she could mask her feelings—at home, witnessing at first hand a less businesslike, more lenient side to Joel, she greatly feared lest he gained an inkling of her caring for him.

On Sunday morning the phone rang while Joel was in his study. When he didn't answer the phone straight away she presumed he was tied up with work, so took the call. It was Magnus. He said he hadn't rung to speak with Joel especially, but said he was lonely.

Joel was just emerging from his study when she got back from the supermarket. 'We ran out of something?' he enquired, his glance on the three plastic carriers in her hands.

'I—um—invited your father to lunch,' she said in a rush—and saw Joel's look of amusement.

'You mean he rang, gave you some sob story, and you fell for it.' He immediately saw how it had been.

'You're invited too, if you like,' she offered in a take-it-or-leave-it fashion.

'A home-cooked meal that didn't come out of the freezer—try to keep me away.'

It was a good time that Sunday lunchtime. One Chesnie knew she would ever remember. For all Joel had no illusions about his father, he treated him with all the respect due not only to his parent, but also to someone whom his wife had invited into their home—and she loved Joel for it.

But Monday was work again and busy, busy, busy, with an unexpected need arising for her to make arrangements to fly with Joel tomorrow to their offices in Glasgow. Chesnie was so absorbed she didn't even have time to think of going to take a second look at the car she was considering buying, much less take a lunch hour to go and look at it.

On Tuesday she went to the airport with Joel in his car. They talked about work some of the way, and shared some business papers during the flight, and she felt so much part and parcel of the whole venture that she never wanted to work anywhere else.

Though, having been calm when they arrived at their hotel, Chesnie's composure was shattered when, in relation to the booking she had made, the male receptionist smilingly went to hand her the key to her room—and Joel stopped him.

Both Chesnie and the receptionist shot him a startled look. Joel was not one whit put out of countenance. 'Miss Cosgrove must have forgotten,' he said, turning to her but addressing the desk clerk. 'We were married two weeks ago.' And, turning back to the clerk, 'Mrs Davenport will be sharing the suite with me.'

Instantly Chesnie called on her reserves to hide her inner feelings, and smiled her guarded smile while the man congratulated Joel. But she wasn't feeling at all kindly disposed towards the man she had married when she rode up in the lift with him. Other people being in the lift prevented her from letting Joel know exactly how she did feel.

'Why did you do that?' she demanded, once they were in the suite and the door was closed on the outside world.

'What's your problem?' Joel enquired, not a glimmer of a smile about him.

'I'd have been quite comfortable in a room on my own.'

'You'll have a room on your own. There are two bed-rooms with this suite,' he explained patiently, as one would to a child. She did not thank him for it. His apartment was large, this suite was largish—but to go away together, to share it, to let the staff know that they were married, made it all seem too intimate somehow. 'And,' Joel went on when she just stared stubbornly at him, 'I don't want word getting back to the board that we don't share.'

'How could it get back?' she demanded to know.

'All it takes is for you to accidentally leave something behind in your single room and the hotel to ring our London office and say where they found it.'

He had her there. She could think of half a dozen sce-narios where word could get back to London. 'You think of everything!' she complained in disgust.

'True,' he accepted, and she had to laugh. And, seeing the way her lovely face lit up, he placed an arm about her shoulders, gave her a squeeze and said, 'Come on, flower, we're going to be late.'

She dropped her overnight bag where she stood and went with him to the meeting, the short car ride giving her very little time in which to get her accustomed composure back together. Flower? That squeeze of her shoulders which, if she hadn't know better, she might have confused with a hug of affection?

From the moment they entered the meeting it was note-pad out and concentrate, so that Chesnie didn't have a mo-ment in which to think her own thoughts. They had a sand-wich at lunchtime, and worked on. But when at five Joel suggested that, because of some data he wanted typed back for the morning, she might like to return to the hotel, she took her leave. Joel stayed behind, and the drive back to the hotel gave her a chance to savour again the more pleas-ant part of their spat that morning.

She didn't really think that had been a hug of affection, and a squeeze about her shoulders was a million miles away from Joel being even a tiny bit in love with her. But she reckoned, and hoped, that he must at least like her. He trusted her, she knew that—had to. Trust was all part of the sometimes highly confidential work she did for him. Trust? Like? Both, she realised. For, from what she knew of him, she could not see Joel, even for the expediency of getting that chairman's job, marrying himself to someone he didn't like.

On that fairly satisfying thought she reached their hotel, went up to their suite and set up her makeshift office and got on with some work. She had been typing for about an hour when her mind wandered to consider that the first thing Joel would want when he got back would be either a drink or a shower. She wanted a shower too, but there was only one bathroom. If she showered now, it would leave the bathroom free for Joel when he came in.

Abandoning her typing for a short while, Chesnie, using the smaller of the two bedrooms, exchanged the clothes she had worn all day for her cotton wrap and, armed with her bag of toiletries, headed for the shower.

Her hair got wet, so she thought she might as well shampoo it.

Fifteen minutes later she was back in her room and was busy with the hairdryer. She thought that rather than get back into her business gear she might as well change into the smart but casual long skirt and top she had packed.

A dab of moisturiser, a touch of face powder and a smear of lipstick, and she was ready to resume her typing. She was tidy-minded, however, and was putting her room to rights when she realised she had left her toilet bag in the bathroom. She didn't want her belongings cluttering up the bathroom when Joel came in, so went quickly to retrieve it.

It was a fairly large walk-in bathroom and she went boldly in—only to stop dead in her tracks. Joel was already in! In fact he had just stepped out of the bath!

By no chance was she able to adopt a cool front. Stark

naked, Joel turned at the strangled cry that broke from her.
And Chesnie, stunned, her face a furious red, started to
back away from him, her eyes fixed on his face.

From what her scrambled brain could make out, Joel had
not the slightest hang-up about his nakedness, so she could
only gather that it was for her benefit that, on seeing her
scarlet face, he stretched a hand out for a towel and
wrapped it around his waist.

'You're blushing!' he observed, and, a startled look coming to his face, 'You *have* seen a naked man before?'

'I usually close my eyes!' she replied on a hoarse note
and, from being too transfixed to move, had never moved
so quickly when she did a snappy about-turn and got out
of there.

By the time a fully clothed Joel had joined her she had
recovered a little of her equilibrium. It was so embarrassing. Well, he hadn't seemed at all flustered, she qualified,
but she still felt scarlet right to the tips of her toes.

To his credit he gave her the chance to recover, and
didn't mention the incident, but looked over her shoulder
at the work she was completing. In silence they worked on.
It was a little after eight when Joel announced, 'If I don't
get something to eat soon my stomach will think my
mouth's on strike.'

He did not suggest that they eat in the suite, as he had
before, and she was glad he didn't. While she knew she
would have to learn to live with her unfortunate intrusion
into his privacy, it was still too fresh—still too intimate.

'I have a key,' he informed her when she picked up the
key she had used to gain entry to the suite.

'Fine,' she murmured, realising he must have picked up
a spare at Reception when he'd come in. If only he hadn't,
if only he'd had to knock on the door for her to let him in,
then that bathroom incident never would have happened.
As it was she had gone from blocking everything out of
her mind to recalling every moment in detail.

She was sitting opposite him in the dining room and they

were mid-way thought their meal when she recalled again what a wonderful body he had. She had seen the back of him first, his broad shoulders, perfect behind and straight legs. Then he had turned and on the instant of panic her eyes had first become riveted on his broad manly chest. Then she had raised her eyes and kept them rigidly on his face.

'Penny for them?' Joel offered for her thoughts.

As though he could read her mind, she went pink. 'They're not worth that much,' she answered lightly, and was glad he let her get away with it. She spoke of any other subject, and tried hard not to think about his chest with that smattering of damp, darkened hair.

Then, 'Why?' he suddenly asked.

Chesnie hadn't a clue what he meant, but somehow felt that it had nothing to do with their work. 'Why not?' she bounced back at him, fearing the worst, fearing that, having given her all the time in the world in which to get herself back together again, he was having a tussle with his curiosity and curiosity had just won.

Then she found that he wasn't taking 'Why not?' for any kind of answer, and, had she thought about it, she supposed she knew enough about him to know that what he wanted to know he always found out.

He tried another tack. 'You don't look frigid.'

'I'm not!' she defended.

'But you've never seen a man minus his clothes before. As naked as—'

'Do you mind? You're blowing my cover!' she exclaimed—rather desperately, it had to be admitted.

Bravely, she met his eyes, but felt all kind of trembly inside when his glance on her suddenly softened. 'I'm embarrassing you—again,' he stated gently. 'I'm sorry,' he apologised. 'You just sort of—surprise me at every turn.' He smiled then, that smile turning into a fantastic grin as he added, 'A man could go a touch crazy in the head about you if he wasn't careful.'

She felt about to swoon. His grin alone was playing havoc with her senses, without that last bit. 'Then you'd better be careful!' From somewhere Chesnie managed to sound as if her backbone was rock-solid, when in actual fact it was meltdown time. 'We part in less than two years, remember?'

'You're not leaving me!' Her eyes shot wide that Joel seemed appalled at the very idea. But, before she could get too thrilled that he appeared extremely loath that she should ever leave him, he added, 'You've proved to be a quite sensational PA,' and again Chesnie was having to make desperate attempts to hide her feelings. It wasn't her, his wife, he was appalled at parting from, but her, his 'quite sensational PA,' he didn't want to lose!

'You have remembered that we're going to end up divorced?' she reminded him.

To her chagrin, he looked relieved. 'I'm counting on it!' he said.

Well, there was more than one way of getting slapped down, she mused. She went to bed that night—and again thought of the way she had seen his splendid uncovered body. She loved him so much, and realised that part of that love was a need to be held by him, to be loved by him, to be made love to by him. But it would never be—so she had better forget such thoughts and concentrate on her career.

She was pleased to return to the London office the next afternoon. Unusually, Joel left the office before she did that night, but when she let herself into what she was now adjusted to being her home, Joel came along the hall to meet her.

'I've something to show you,' he greeted her.

'What…?'

He wouldn't say, but before she could utter another word had taken a hold of her by the arm and was guiding her round the set of garages where she had just parked her grandfather's car for the night.

Joel led her over to one of the garages on the opposite side. 'I've borrowed this one for the week while the owner is touring Wales,' he remarked, and, letting go her arm, he unlocked the garage. Mystified, Chesnie stood there while the garage door rose and disappeared into the roof space. 'What do you think?' he asked, taking hold of her arm again and escorting her inside.

'Very nice,' she replied, realising that he was asking her opinion of what looked like a brand-new top-of-the-range sports car.

'I thought a smaller car would be better for you driving around London and trying to find a parking space,' Joel commented.

Chesnie stared at him in some surprise. 'You want me to drive it?'

'I hope you will. It's yours.'

'*Mine?*' she questioned incredulously. 'B-but...' Words failed her.

'Yours,' Joel confirmed.

'But I can't...'

'You're going to argue. I knew you would. I said to myself, She won't like it. She kicked up a fuss when you wanted to make her an allowance. She's bound to create a fuss over this. Then I thought, Yes, but I really can't let her, the future chairman's wife, be seen driving around in her grandfather's car.' Chesnie stared at him. If she knew anything about Joel she knew without a question of a doubt that he didn't have a snobbish bone in his body. Providing the vehicle was roadworthy, he wouldn't give a hoot what kind of down-market car his wife was seen driving around in. She looked at him speechlessly. 'And what about your poor dear grandfather?' Joel pressed his cause. 'He must be desperate to have his car back.'

What could she do? Joel expected her to argue. She swallowed hard on a knot of pride, hoped she wouldn't have fallen too much in love with the car when the time came when she would have to hand it back, and she smiled.

'Thank you, Joel, it's a beautiful car,' she told him. And, when she knew he hadn't been expecting that at all, she gave him something else he hadn't been expecting either— she stretched up and kissed him.

For a moment his hands gripped her waist and he looked into her eyes. Then they were both stepping away from each other. 'Come on, let me see you put it through its paces,' Joel suggested, and handed her the keys to the car.

Two days later and Chesnie had adjusted to her new car, and was loving it. What she was not loving was the fact that, ever since they had returned from Scotland, she had begun to feel overwhelmed by her feelings for Joel. He was generous to her, kind to her—and she did not seem able to get him out of her head. As a consequence it was taking her all her time to make the concentrated effort needed to hide her feelings for him. Which left her feeling tense and knowing that she had to get away, if only for a few hours, to sort herself out.

She met him in the kitchen at breakfast time on Saturday morning, and knew what she was going to do when, teasingly referring to how she had stated last Saturday that all she wanted to do at the weekends was to curl up with a book, Joel enquired, 'Do you have sufficient reading matter? If not there's an art exhibition we could—'

We! Oh, Joel, don't! There was nothing she would like better than to go with him but—self-preservation won the day. 'I think it's time I returned my grandfather's car,' she butted in.

'You're going to Herefordshire?' Joel was standing by one of the work surfaces and glanced across to where she stood making some toast.

'Gramps moved into his new cottage last Monday. He no longer has a garaging problem.'

'How are you getting back?' Joel wanted to know.

Chesnie thought about that, realising that there was every possibility of weekend rail work still being carried out. 'If I can't make it back today, I'll stay overnight and make an early start on Sunday morning.' She smiled at Joel then, and didn't see why he should be the only one allowed to tease. 'Don't worry. I promise I'll be at my desk for nine sharp on Monday.'

Chesnie, with an overnight bag in her car just in case, was driving out of London when, Joel as ever in her thoughts, she reflected that he had seemed a bit put out that she had turned down his offer of a visit to the art exhibition. Then reality gave her a poke—as if! The only reason Joel was likely to be at all put out was in case his mother or someone rang and began to wonder what was going on that, married for only three weeks, they were so soon spending time apart. But, anyway, Joel could handle that; she knew he could.

Though she had to doubt her own ability on that score when, having been hugged and kissed by her delighted grandfather, his first question was, 'Where's Joel?'

'Joel has some work he needs urgently for Monday,' she replied, hating to lie to her grandfather. But Joel was against anyone knowing the real reason they had married, and he was her first consideration now. So not even to her beloved grandfather could she reveal the secret of her marriage.

Her grandfather was still to a large extent living out of packing cases, and finding homes for his belongings as he used them. Chesnie metaphorically rolled up her sleeves and set to.

After a couple of hours she had cleared many boxes and cartons, but she could still barely move without tripping over something or other.

It had soon become obvious that her grandfather had taken all of his furniture out of storage. It was equally obvious that, hating to part with any of the furniture that had been with him throughout his married life, her grandfather had enough furniture to furnish three cottages, let alone one.

'Your grandmother loved that old dresser,' he said fondly

when Chesnie had just knocked her shin on it, trying to get past.

'It is lovely, Gramps,' Chesnie replied. It was his home; he would decide in due time if he wanted to continue to live in the small sitting room with a large three-piece suite and various other padded chairs. That decision was his and, in her view, no one had the right to make that choice for him.

'How are you getting back?' He suddenly seemed to realise that if she was leaving his car behind she was going to have to use public transport.

Chesnie looked at her surroundings. For all her efforts the place still resembled a dumping ground. And while her heart pulled, wanting to be back with Joel, to be back under Joel's roof, there was just no way she could leave her elderly grandparent to wade through this muddle on his own.

'How about we find homes for all your ornaments and then have a bar meal at the Bull? I'll go back to London in the morning.'

'You'll stay the night?' He looked puzzled.

'*I* thought it was a good idea,' she teased.

'Everything *is* all right with you and Joel, isn't it?' he asked, looking worried. And Chesnie knew then, as she recalled how on her wedding day he had said that he couldn't bear it if he thought her marriage would end up like those of her sisters, that she could not let her grandfather in particular know that there was anything different from what it should be about her marriage.

'Everything's fine!' she answered. 'Joel and I are with each other every day and night.' She managed a light laugh as she added, 'Joel's probably glad to have a few minutes to himself.'

Her grandfather did not look convinced, but managed a smile as he told her she had better go and make up a bed for herself. He would make her a nice cup of tea.

There was barely room to move around in the spare bedroom, more of a junk room, which housed a large double bed, two wardrobes, a dressing table with a chair stacked on top of it, two standard lamps, two boxes of books and other assorted impedimenta. Chesnie wanted to go home. Her heart was aching to go home—to Joel

It was getting on for seven that evening when, having made a great deal of difference to the general cluttered look of the place—she could do nothing about minimising the bulky furniture—Chesnie realised that while she toiled so would her grandfather. Poor sweetheart, he must want a rest.

'Ready for the Bull?' she asked. 'I can finish off the remaining boxes before I leave in the morning.'

She ate her meal wondering what Joel was doing. Was he making himself a meal from the supply of pies and casseroles with which Mrs Attwood regularly stocked up the freezer? Perhaps he intended going out for a meal later. Perhaps... Jealousy took a nip. No, not Joel. He had agreed—no women-friends. Still the same, she could not help but wonder what he would do for relaxation that night. Heaven alone knew he worked hard enough.

It was still relatively early when they left the Bull to walk the short distance back to her grandfather's new home. But as they turned the corner so, with the cottage in view, Chesnie's heart started to beat a crazy rhythm. That car standing outside her grandfather's property looked exactly like...

Joel must have been watching from his rearview mirror for, to make her heart dance a jig, the driver's door all at once opened and, tall, good-looking and, oh, so dear, Joel stepped from the car.

'Joel!' she exclaimed as they neared him, and, strive though she did, she could not keep the smile out of her voice.

'I thought you might be needing a lift back home,' he said, for her grandfather's benefit coming over and lightly kissing her mouth. 'Mr Cosgrove,' he said, turning to hold out his hand to her grandfather.

'You've completed your work earlier than expected,' Rufus Cosgrove commented.

And, still tingling from head to toe from that light kiss, Chesnie could only admire Joel the more that, when he couldn't have a clue what her grandfather was talking about, he smiled as he replied, 'The apartment wasn't the same without Chesnie.'

That pleased her grandfather. 'So you've come to take her home,' he noted, and seemed very happy with that. But he caused Chesnie a few moments' consternation when he suddenly said, 'Chesnie was going to stay the night. Why don't you both stay? Have you anything pressing to get back to London for?'

'Well, no,' Joel admitted, but, as if thinking that Chesnie might want to spend more time with her grandfather, 'I wouldn't want to put you out. I'll check into a hotel somewhere near.'

'Wouldn't hear of it!' Rufus Cosgrove declared stoutly. 'Would we, Chesnie?' He enlisted her support.

She couldn't! Not possibly! It was out of the quest… But—she'd have to! 'Of course Joel must stay with us!' She backed her grandfather firmly—if her insides had just gone to jelly then only she was going to know about it. But, oh, what had she done? But what else could she have done? Gramps mustn't know the truth—he would be devastated! 'Have you eaten?' she asked Joel nicely, as any loving spouse would, her initial panic easing as she pinned her hopes on Joel's brain being sharper than hers just then in this fine mess they were in. He'd find a way of getting them both out of this situation without her grandfather being in the least aware that theirs was not a normal marriage, of that she started to feel certain.

But—no. 'I had something to eat on the way here.' Joel smiled—and had nothing more to add. And while Chesnie had started to panic frantically again—hadn't he realised that this was only a two-bedroomed cottage?—her grandfather was heading for the garden gate.

Once inside the cottage her grandfather was setting about finding Joel a new toothbrush and a pair of pyjamas, while Chesnie was realising that, even if the cottage had boasted three bedrooms, there was no way she and Joel could have occupied separate bedrooms without her grandfather thinking it peculiar.

'The place is a bit of a jumble at the moment,' her grandfather was explaining to Joel, while Chesnie smiled and hid her feeling of going under for the third time.

'You only moved in on Monday,' Joel answered. 'It takes a while to know just where you want to put everything.'

How could he talk so easily, so without stress, so as if the prospect of having to spend a night sleeping in the same room with his platonic wife was neither here nor there to him? She couldn't yet begin to think of him having to sleep in the same bed, let alone the same room. Yet in that over-cluttered room there was barely six inches of floor space free anywhere, and there was nowhere else for him *to* sleep—but in the same bed!

With Joel and her grandfather conversing comfortably, Chesnie began to feel the only stranger here, and went into the kitchen to make a night-time drink. For herself, she'd stay exactly where she was until daylight tomorrow morning, but she doubted her grandfather had ceased his habit of getting up in the middle of the night. No way, Chesnie realised, could she stay down and risk her grandfather coming down to make himself a cup of tea at three tomorrow morning.

'It's been a long day,' her grandfather announced, draining his cup and getting slowly out of his chair.

'It has,' Joel remarked, on his feet too.

Chesnie was loading cups and saucers on to a tray when her grandfather offered, 'I'll show you the facilities and where you'll be sleeping, if you like.'

'You don't mind if I go up first, dear?' Joel asked pleasantly.

Was he serious? She looked at him. His expression was bland—his eyes told a different story. He thinks it's funny!

'I won't be long,' she promised sweetly. Oh, grief! 'I'll just rinse these few things through...'

Won't be long? She knew she could have washed dishes from a seven-course meal—and still wouldn't be ready to climb those stairs. But—oh—what else could she do? With her insides churning she grabbed her overnight bag from beneath the kitchen table—about the only available free space—and climbed the stairs.

She still wasn't ready to join Joel in that bedroom, though. And by no chance was she going to undress in front of him. She ducked into the bathroom and unzipped her bag. From choice she would sleep in her clothes, but didn't fancy her grandfather's comments on her crumpled appearance tomorrow at breakfast.

She showered and changed into her short cotton nightdress and tried desperately hard to be detached. If only she could find some of that calm composure that had seen her deal with many a difficult business situation in the past.

Chesnie shrugged into her cotton wrap, knowing that the difference here was that this was not a business situation. She, who had never slept with a man in her life, was about to now—and she was having kittens about it! And the fact was she was feeling very far removed from being calm and composed.

Only by telling herself that she was not going to sleep with Joel in *that* sense was she able to leave the bathroom. Only by telling herself that Joel was not just anybody, but was someone she knew and liked, was she able to go to the room where she knew he was.

She pushed the door inwards, and her heart sank. She had been hopeful that the light might be out—but it wasn't. She had been hopeful that Joel might be asleep—but he was definitely awake.

Chesnie went in and had never needed her mask of calm efficiency more. She was inwardly shaking like the proverbial leaf. It didn't help a bit to see in that one swift glance to the bed that Joel had declined the use of her grandfather's pyjamas—the jacket anyway; she didn't want to contemplate his trousers. Joel was sitting up in bed and, daring another glance, she observed he had been reading one of her grandfather's thrillers. But as Joel politely lowered his book she was swamped by the intimacy of spying his broad hair-roughened chest. Thankfully he was over on one side of the bed, leaving her ample room on the other.

'Don't stop reading on my account!' Chesnie remarked as evenly as she was able, and, looking from him and hoping he wasn't looking at her, she quickly disposed of her wrap and as quickly got into bed. 'I never thought to ask...' some kind of welcome automaton was taking over '...do you snore?'

She rather thought the automaton would have carried her through until she went to sleep—had not Joel laughed. She could not believe it, but—as though what she'd said had amused him, as though he found this whole situation funny, more relaxing than stressful as she was feeling—laugh he did.

'I've never had any complaints,' he replied lightly, and she was starting to grow more and more uptight by the second, sitting there with the bedcovers up to her chin; she was a while away from even considering lying down. 'You're a cool one,' he commented.

Cool! If only he knew. She dared a sideways glance at him and, given that he was as near naked as she wanted to know about, and that her covering was not much better, she could detect not the smallest hint that Joel might be feeling inclined to take advantage of the situation.

'I'm sorry,' she apologised, and for the first time since she had stated 'Of course Joel must stay with us' felt herself begin to feel less tense. 'I suppose I could have handled all this differently, only...' She faltered.

'Only?' Joel prompted.

'Only, as I love my grandfather so he loves me, and—

and he sets great store on the institution of marriage. On the day we got married, you and I, he asked me to promise I'd be happy, and said he couldn't bear it if he thought my marriage would turn out to be like those of my sisters.'

'So to protect him, his feelings, you're prepared to sleep the night with me?'

She looked into his eyes to ask, 'Are we friends, Joel?'

He stared into her searching green eyes. And, after long moments of just looking at her, 'I'd like us to be,' he said.

Chesnie smiled a beam of a smile. 'Thank you,' she said simply. 'Gramps will have to know about our divorce, of course, but not for a long time. Eighteen months from now I can start to gently prepare him to hear that you and I will be separating.' With that, she lay down and turned to face the furniture-festooned wall. 'Goodnight,' she said quietly. And waited.

His reply was a long time coming. Then quietly, in return, 'Goodnight, my dear,' he said, and switched off the light.

It took Chesnie an age to get to sleep. My dear? Was that a new habit formed from using an endearment for her grandfather's ears? Did friends share that sort of warm familiarity? Joel had said he would like them to be friends. Her heart leapt. Friends meant he liked her, and, while like wasn't love, she would still want him to be her friend when their marriage was over.

Her thoughts started to become a little woolly. She had an urge to change her position, to turn over, but fear of bumping into Joel made her deny that urge. She started to marvel suddenly that she was sharing a bed with him at all. He could have insisted on going to a hotel, she realised. Though of course this marriage was for Joel's benefit, not hers. Her thoughts became even woollier—but she wouldn't have married him at all had she not loved him. But he was never to know that.

On that thought, sleep claimed her, and in sleep her body gave in to the urge to change her position. In fact, over the following hours she changed her position many times, and each time, as if unconsciously magnet-drawn, Chesnie moved closer to the man she loved.

Dawn was just breaking when Chesnie awakened. She opened her eyes, saw patterned curtains that were not her own, and in split seconds was blasted with memory of where she was, how and why she was there and—whom she was sleeping with! But over and above all that, screaming in, came the realisation that she did not have her head on her pillow. Alarm raking her, she awakened to the fact she had been resting with her head—on Joel's shoulder! Sleeping, incredibly, with his right arm about her.

She gave a small jerk of movement, perhaps intending to leap out of bed—she couldn't be sure—panic taking her that she must have edged towards him during the night and was invading his space.

But—and she was sure she didn't imagine it—that arm about her gave her a small squeeze, as if to say, Stay exactly where you are, and whether or not it *was* her imagination after all, she obeyed.

Joel might be awake, he might be asleep; she couldn't tell. But as she relaxed against him so those few moments of lying there, close to Joel, closer to him than she had ever been, just seemed—beautiful. So beautiful she did not want to move and spoil it.

She felt safe, secure in his hold. She even felt a little loved when, if her imagination wasn't playing dastardly tricks on her, she felt a light pressure on her head—as if Joel had kissed her hair.

Kissed her hair! Don't be ridiculous! Chesnie decided, exquisite though it was to be held so close to him, that she ought to get up. End it now before her imagination got worse.

She went to move—and felt a slight tensing in that arm around her, almost as if Joel too felt that these moments were beautiful and did not want them to end. And, even though a second later she was discounting any such wild fantasy, she no longer seemed to have the will-power to move.

'I...' she murmured on a breathless sound, then found more vocal power, albeit keeping her voice low, just in case Joel was asleep, as she confessed, 'I've never slept with a man before.'

Joel's body seemed to still, and she became certain that he was awake. And knew it for the truth when he quietly asked, 'In—any sense?'

She wanted to look at him, to see his dear face, but was afraid to disturb this wonderful time with him. 'Does that make me odd?'

'It makes me wish you hadn't told me.'

'Why?'

She was sure she could hear laughter in his voice when he answered, 'It makes you—untouchable.'

She felt like laughing too. She loved lying here with him like this—it was like being married. 'That's a rotten thing to say to a wife on a fine Sunday morning,' she replied, quite without thinking—but was relieved when his chest shook and she heard him laugh.

'What is it about you, Chesnie Davenport?' he asked, and when, feeling slightly bemused, she couldn't give him an answer, went on, explaining, 'Half my time I expect you to jump one way—and you constantly surprise me by jumping the other.'

'What did I say?' she wanted to know, and felt him move. All at once he was lying on his side, resting on his forearm and looking down into her still delicately sleep-flushed face.

'How can you look so lovely?' he asked.

There was a tender light in her eyes, and as her pulses started to zip along so her brain started seizing up fast. 'Wh-what did I say?' she repeated, as she strove hard to pull herself together.

'This time?' He smiled gently. 'This time, almost in the same breath that you tell me you're a virgin, you...' his head started to come down '…invite me…' He paused, and his mouth was almost against hers when he breathed, 'To…' and said no more, but kissed her.

It was a wonderful kiss. Tender, yet seeking. A kiss like none they had shared before. Joel raised his head and looked into her eyes, as if expecting that she would raise some objection—but then hadn't he just stated that she never did what he expected half the time?

'That was—nice,' she said, and smiled.

'You and your invitations,' he grumbled, but was smiling too when he drew her close up to him.

'Oh, Joel,' she cried—a little shakily, it was true.

'Am I alarming you?'

She shook her head, and, wanting quite desperately that he should kiss her again, replied openly, 'I—er—wouldn't mind—er—knowing more, actually,' and was rewarded with a kiss that left her feeling quite breathless.

Then Joel was pulling back to look into her lovely green eyes—and, as if satisfied that she wasn't put off, that she still wanted to know more, 'You're so sweet,' he breathed, and the next moment she was being kissed in a way that made her realise she had never truly been kissed before. His tongue caressed her lips and her whole being seemed to tremble in his arms.

She loved him, and loved the sensations he was creating in her body. She had no power to push him away, and as she felt his hands caressing her spine, drawing her yet closer to him, she did not want to push him from her.

But even as he was kissing her suddenly it was Joel who was doing the pushing away. Unexpectedly, abruptly, he was suddenly wrenching his mouth from hers. 'No,' he groaned on a strangled kind of sound.

'No?' she echoed, utterly confused.

'We—have to stop.' The words seemed to be dragged from him.

'Stop?' Her wits had flown. But Joel was breaking from

her, moving swiftly to the side of the bed, grabbing up his trousers.

Chesnie was staring at him dumbfounded when, 'Here endeth the first lesson!' he ground out, and in one movement seemed to be in his trousers, and snaking on his shirt as he went, and was out through the door.

CHAPTER NINE

PRIDE was her only friend on that drive back to London. Chesnie knew full well from his terse silence that Joel was very much regretting having stepped through the platonic barrier—even if he did seem to think she had invited him over that particular threshold. To her chagrin, she could not say that she hadn't.

But by the time they arrived in London she had started to grow a little bit annoyed. Her sisters had the sort of marriages where they and their husbands went for days without speaking to each other. So, fine, the marriage she had with Joel was a vastly different affair—but, still the same, she had no intention of going down that same tortuous, less than monosyllabic road.

They were in the apartment and Joel was just about to go to his study when the steam valve on her temper blew. Though somehow she made herself sound calm as she called his name.

'Joel!' He turned, stony-expressioned, and her heart quailed—but she still wasn't having it. 'Apropos—er—sex and stuff—' she introduced the root evil of what this was all about '—I wonder if we can come to an agreement whereby if I promise to keep out of your bed, you promise not to show me lesson two?'

He didn't laugh, but his lips definitely twitched, she would swear. 'You're doing it again,' he said, and, at her look of enquiry, 'The unexpected. I was sure you'd want to avoid that subject like the plague!'

It was she who laughed, her temper gone, and they were friends again. Without another word she turned and, aware that he was watching her, breezed away and went to her room.

She did not see very much of him that day, but he came into her office the following day to discuss some business and to tell her that he was flying up to Glasgow that afternoon.

'I haven't any note of it in your diary,' she replied, her heart sinking; he had said nothing about her going with him.

'I'll probably be away a few days,' Joel replied, and went on to talk about other matters, and so obviously didn't care tuppence that he wouldn't see her for several days that Chesnie was sure that she didn't care either.

And, oh, what a liar pride had made of her. The evening stretched on and on endlessly without him. Even though she made a point of never being in the same room with him over-long, just to know he was under the same roof was a comfort to the love she had for him.

Chesnie had a vision of life without him in two years' time, and didn't like it. She gave herself a talking to. Subject: Don't get attached to him, you knew in advance that it wasn't going to last.

She finally went to bed, to lie awake determining that she was going to be more impersonal about this—she remembered his kisses, and for ageless minutes was lost in the wonder of the joy of those kisses. But, of course, those kisses were a 'one-off', never again to be repeated. So, yes, they had got personal, but they were both human and had said goodbye to a strictly business relationship on the day they had married.

But clearly Joel regretted those intimate moments they had shared, so from now on she would keep herself as aloof as possible away from the office. Which, since she had barely seen Joel since they had returned from Herefordshire, and was obviously the way Joel liked it, didn't look as though it would be any great problem.

Chesnie was still thinking 'aloof' when she drove to the

office the next day. Around eleven the phone rang, and as she recognised Joel's voice so 'aloof' started to slip.

'I—need you here,' he said. He didn't sound very inviting, but still the same her heart began to race. 'By the time you've briefed Eileen Gray to take over for you it will be too late to catch an earlier flight. You'd better take the one-fifteen from Heathrow,' he commanded. 'Today,' he added, and hung up. Chesnie made a face at the phone. Then she burst into smiles. So much for 'aloof'; she was going to see Joel!

She made Heathrow with little time to spare, and had just taken her seat aboard the aircraft when a late arrival came and took the seat next to her. He did a double-take and then beamed. 'Chesnie Cosgrove!'

'Philip!' She was surprised and pleased to see him, and smiled back.

'Had I known you were making the Glasgow trip I'd have sprinted twice as fast!' he exclaimed, then caught sight of her wedding band. 'Chesnie Davenport,' he corrected. 'I don't suppose you'd consider divorcing him?'

'I've only just married him! How's your new PA?'

'You'd have been better,' he said. 'Still working?'

'I'm on my way to assist Joel now.'

'Lucky devil!' Philip exclaimed, but went on, 'Of course. I've a meeting with Joel in the morning—I should have expected you'd be in Glasgow if he's there. You must know all about Yeatman's sniffing around after Symington Technology.'

She hadn't! Why hadn't Joel told her? She kept her composure to enquire lightly, 'How do you feel about it?' Didn't Joel trust her?

'My feelings are very mixed. Part of me says no; the other—'

'Philip, I'm sorry. I shouldn't have asked.' She stopped him right there. 'It was unfair of me.'

He turned his head and smiled at her. 'Because you're working for the other side?' She nodded, feeling guilty, but blaming her intrusion on the fact that, had she known in advance about Yeatman Trading 'sniffing around' with a view to taking over Symington Technology, she'd not have felt so shocked, and would have been more watchful of her tongue. Why would Joel keep something like that from her? 'You're lovely,' Philip said, and impulsively caught a hold of her hand. Bringing it to his mouth, he kissed the back of it. 'Your husband can't object to that,' he said, and Chesnie doubted that he would.

Throughout the rest of the journey she and Philip spoke of matters other than work, but Chesnie owned to feeling a touch hurt that Joel had not told her what, in her view—married to him or not—a confidential PA, a trusted PA, should know.

So much so that when Philip stated that, once his meeting was over that afternoon, it looked as though he was in for a solitary boring evening, she almost invited him to dine at her hotel. She was sorely tempted, she had to admit, and not entirely on account of Philip being alone and bored. She'd love to see Joel's face when he realised that as far as she was concerned he could keep his secrets—she knew about his proposed takeover anyway.

She did not invite Philip to dine with her because for one thing she was unsure, depending on how much work Joel had for her, if she would be having a 'working' dinner. For another, she didn't know if Joel would expect her to dine with him, and, since he had a meeting with Philip tomorrow, if to entertain him to dinner that night might pre-empt their business.

'Will you be at the meeting tomorrow?' Philip asked when, he going on to a different hotel, they shared a taxi from Glasgow airport.

'I'm not sure,' she replied. 'I'll be busy one way or another, I'm sure of that,' she added lightly.

Philip saluted her cheek with a kiss as they parted. 'Bye, Chesnie,' he bade her, and she almost wished it was him that she loved, but she didn't love him—and the man she did love didn't trust her.

She was expected at the hotel and went up in the lift to the same suite she and Joel had occupied before. While knowing that he would be either at his desk or round some conference table working, she still felt a little breathless in case Joel had already returned from his labours.

Illogical? Call it love. She sighed. She had the suite to herself for a while, by the look of it. Yet, even while she wasn't very sure that she felt too friendly towards Joel, she still the same went to the mirror, ran a comb through her hair and renewed her lipstick.

Chesnie glanced at her watch. There was still a large part of the afternoon left—hours before she could expect to see Joel. What was she supposed to do? He knew what time she was arriving. He'd been the one to tell her which flight to catch. Did he expect her to sit and twiddle her thumbs for the rest of the afternoon?

She half decided to take a taxi to the company offices, then thought that if Joel had wanted her to go to Yeatman House he'd have said so. Which meant he didn't need her there so urgently that she'd had to catch that lunchtime flight after all.

Why hadn't he told her that he was looking into a deal with Symington's? If he had a meeting with Philip tomorrow, then obviously negotiations were either under way or about to happen. Presumably Glasgow had been chosen for the negotiations to limit any possible hint to the press at this early stage.

Feeling hurt at her exclusion, Chesnie was half minded to leave the hotel and go and take a look at the shops. Then she realised that, since Joel seldom did anything without a purpose, he would probably telephone with some work instruction. He knew what time her flight got in.

Chesnie waited a half-hour. No call. A half-hour later, leaving the bathroom door ajar just in case, she went and had a bath. An hour after that she changed into an outfit which would suffice should she have dinner at her work table or in the hotel's dining room.

Joel arrived at a little after seven. Chesnie pinned a smile on her face. He did not smile—she wondered why she had bothered. 'Long day?' she asked sweetly.

'I've had longer,' he grunted, and, loosening his tie as he went, he made for his bedroom.

Chesnie disappeared into her room. If he wanted her he knew where she was. She heard him taking a shower, and her feeling of mutiny began to weaken. Poor love, he'd most likely slaved away all day. What he didn't need at the end of it was a sulky assistant.

She went into the sitting room. A short while later he joined her. 'Are we eating here, or downstairs?' she enquired pleasantly.

He looked at her, seemed to look at her long and hard, and then he smiled. 'Thank you for coming.'

She wanted to say something casual such as, It's my job, but she'd have flown to him without that. 'Anything for you,' she said, and offered him a cheeky grin so he'd know she didn't mean it.

'That impudent mouth of yours will get you into trouble one of these days,' he commented, his glance automatically finding her lips—but he seemed to have recovered his good humour.

Impudent mouth? How could he say that? She'd thought she was the very soul of discretion and sobriety. However, it appeared there were matters buzzing in Joel's head, so they worked for an hour, then had dinner sent up, and worked some more. But at no time did Joel mention what all the time she had been expecting, hoping, he would mention—the Symington Technology negotiations.

By the time they had finished their work for the evening Chesnie was having to work hard in another direction—to hide her feelings. 'Time for a little relaxation, I think,' Joel remarked. 'You can finish that lot tomorrow. I've an appointment at eight, so I'll be out of your way until some time in the late afternoon.'

'You want me to stay here in Glasgow?'

'You need to go back tomorrow?' he asked sharply.

He annoyed her. 'Not particularly,' she answered—and was faintly amazed to see Joel take what appeared to be a controlling breath.

'Can I get you a drink?' he asked evenly.

'No, thank you. I think I'll go to bed.'

She didn't look at him, but left him and went to her room. Then hated that she had to leave her room to go to the bathroom for her habitual shower before she got into bed.

He was seated on the sofa when she went through. She rather thought he seemed a shade fed-up about something, but she wasn't looking at him long enough to be certain. Not that she cared anyhow. She stood beneath the shower, not bothered a button that he might be fed-up.

That made two of them that were fed-up. So he'd had a bad day—her day hadn't been too brilliant either. From where she was viewing it, it didn't seem very nice at all to discover in a roundabout way—even if those talks were secret—that her boss didn't trust her enough to let her into that secret. That her husband didn't trust her enough—

Abruptly she broke off such thought. He wasn't her husband—except on paper. She… Chesnie blanked off more thoughts and stepped out of the shower. She dried herself and got into her nightdress and cotton wrap, still trying to keep weakening thoughts at bay.

'Goodnight!' she offered crisply as, with her bundle of clothes under one arm, she went quickly through the sitting room.

Joel stood up, as though he perhaps wanted to have a word with her, but she wasn't stopping to listen. He had not returned her goodnight when she went into her room and closed the door on him.

And that was when she thought, Dammit, I'm not having

this, and, dropping her bundle of clothes down on a chair, stormed back to the door and wrenched it open—and came face to face with Joel.

'I was just coming to see you,' he stated calmly.

'Snap!' she retorted hostilely.

He studied her angry expression. 'By the look of you, you'd better go first.'

She waited for no further invitation, but, having stewed for long enough over the issue, exploded, 'You have a meeting with Philip Pomeroy tomorrow!' and saw straight away from the look of fury on Joel's face at the mention of Philip's name that she was correct in her thinking that Joel did not want her to know anything about it.

'He told you that, did he?' Joel charged tersely.

'*You* didn't!' she answered angrily, and waited for him to tell her why he hadn't.

But to her amazement he declined to make any explanation whatsoever, and questioned instead, 'You flew up with him?'

What had that got to do with anything? 'Philip was on the same plane.'

'Cosy!' Joel snarled. Then, sharply, 'By prior arrangement?' he demanded.

'What?' Chesnie wasn't with him.

'You and Pomeroy—you've been in touch with him all along? You never—'

'Don't be…' She began to fire, then erupted in fury. 'You don't trust me!' she raged. 'If you did you'd have told me you were interested in Symington's, and not left me to find out from—'

'Pomeroy told you!'

'Why wouldn't he? *He* trusts me!'

'You're that close?' Joel snarled.

What the Dickens was he getting at? 'Close enough for me to consider inviting him here to dinner tonight!' she flew, refusing to back down.

'The devil you did!' Joel roared, his jaw jutting furiously.

'You're married *to me*, remember!' he barked, his hands coming to her upper arms, biting into her flesh.

But she still wasn't having it. 'Only for the next two years!' she retaliated, sparks flashing in her lovely green eyes.

'He'll wait?' Joel thundered. She shrugged, and let him think what he would. He apparently didn't like the answer his thoughts had brought him, for angrily he drew her hard up against him, his arms coming round her, and the next she knew Joel was punishing her mouth with a kiss of unrestrained fury.

And Chesnie hated it. And she fought him. She wanted his kisses, but not like this. But his grip on her was unbreakable, and that punishing kiss deepened until at last she managed to drag her mouth away from his. *'No!'* she cried on a half-sob, but for a while she was still fastened to him in his rock-hard hold.

Until suddenly, abruptly, he let her go, all tension and fury seeming to melt from him. 'I'm—sorry,' he apologised on a hoarse breath of sound. His face appearing to have lost some of its colour, he groaned, 'Oh, my dear, I've frightened you half to death,' and while Chesnie, her anger and fury gone too, stared into his remorse-filled expression, 'I don't want to hurt you,' Joel murmured.

And this—his remorse, *his* obvious hurt—she could not take. 'It's all right,' she whispered. 'Oh, Joel, it's all right.' And, her heart his, her love all his, she stretched up and gently kissed him. 'I'm not frightened,' she tried to gently assure him. And, smiling, hoping to elicit a smile from him, 'I just don't care much for being kissed like that.'

'My dear,' he said softly, and as she had gently kissed him so he gently kissed her. 'Is that better?'

Her heart was beating nineteen to the dozen. 'Much,' she answered softly, and somehow they were kissing again.

Tender, gentle kisses. Kisses that wiped away all anger and pain. Kisses that Chesnie never wanted to stop. She loved him, was in love with him, and just then could think of nothing but the joy of being in his arms.

'We should stop,' Joel breathed against her ear.

He had said something similar before—and she had felt bereft when he'd taken his arms away from her. 'Why?' she whispered.

'Why? Because… Because you're making it difficult for me to think clearly.'

She smiled. 'This is no time for thinking clearly,' she laughed.

'Oh, Chesnie,' he breathed helplessly, and gathered her more closely in his arms.

Quite when they had moved away from the door and further into her room Chesnie had no idea, but suddenly she became aware that they were nearer to her bed than to the door. She saw Joel follow her glance.

'This is where you say, "It's been nice knowing you, but…"' he teased softly.

And Chesnie kissed him. 'You know I seldom say what you expect me to say,' she answered dreamily, and as his brow lifted in surprised comprehension she didn't care that she had just given him full permission to kiss her again and again. She heard him groan, as if he were fighting a battle within himself. Then she felt the pressure of his arms about her increase. But, fearing that was a prelude to him removing his arms from her completely, she kissed him, and held him, and then to her joy felt him returning her kiss. And all at once, as he parted her lips with his own, he was arousing in her such a vortex of feeling that she could barely think.

Joel's kisses to her throat and shoulders thrilled her anew. She was vaguely aware that he was removing her cotton wrap, vaguely aware that she stood before him in nothing but her thin cotton nightdress, vaguely aware that he was shirt and trouser-clad, but nothing mattered as he gathered her to him, his hands caressing over her back, down to her hips, and caressing until his hand captured her pert behind, holding her, drawing her against him.

Willingly, if a little unsure, she pressed into him, her arms up and over his shoulders, and felt near to collapsing against him when his hands caressed over her body until tenderly he captured one breast in a gentle hold.

She supposed she must have made some small sound for he asked softly, albeit his warm hand stayed at her breast, 'Is this all right with you, Chesnie?'

She smiled up at him. 'It's—er—a bit wonderful,' she answered shyly, and asked, 'May I do the same to you?'

He laughed lightly; it was a lovely sound in her ears. 'Come here,' he said, and kissed her, caressed her, and, her nightdress a hindrance, he slipped it from her shoulders. Then he kissed her again before, pulling back, he bent his head to her naked breasts.

She swallowed hard, her insides a riot of emotion as he raised his head, and while caressing the hardened peaks of her breasts he kissed her.

Her nightdress fell to the floor. 'You're blushing,' he teased tenderly. What could she do? She raised her hands and began to unfasten his shirt, and he smiled, his eyes steady on hers until, as bare-chested as her breasts were, he drew her against him and she entered a world of pure delight.

More enchantment was hers when, unhurriedly, without haste, he moved with her to the bed. They kissed again, and again, and a fever of wanting started to mount in her. That fever wanted only one kind of release when she found she was lying with Joel, their legs mingling, and realisation came to her that he was no longer wearing trousers.

He gently moved her until she was lying with her back against the mattress. Then, lying on his side but keeping some daylight between their two bodies, Joel looked deeply into her eyes. 'Help me here, Chesnie,' he requested.

'How?' she asked huskily, feeling too bemused just then to be able to decipher what he meant.

'I want, quite desperately, to make love to you—but I'm unsure…'

'Oh, Joel.' Her heart was leaping about like nobody's business. 'I—I think I want to make love with you too.'

'Think?' he queried, and, when she was desperate to feel him close again, not coming any nearer.

She gave him a tremulous smile, then told him honestly, 'I think I'm a bit nervous about—about—close intimacy, but I've never felt like this before, and I don't think I could bear it if you left me without—' She broke off, that shyness she had spoken of causing her to be unable to finish.

But Joel seemed to know, and to understand, and suddenly she had her wish and he came closer and began creating such a fire in her she could barely breathe from the emotion of it. She felt his hands caressing over her back, staying there, allowing her to get used to his touch, to feel comfortable with his touch. Then, causing that fire in her to blast off anew, his hands caressed down to the delicious naked curves of her behind. She moaned a sigh of bliss, of wanting, and he seemed to understand, and came closer to her, body half over hers. And she wanted to feel more of him, and her hands instinctively found the back of the only item of clothing he wore. She thrilled anew as she placed her hands inside and, with fingers caressing his well-shaped buttocks, pulled him to her.

There was no going back then. She knew it as he rolled from her to remove that article of clothing and then feast his eyes on her body, to stroke and to caress, to take her breasts in turn into his mouth, while at the same time, in gradual sensitive seeking, one hand caressed tenderly down over her body to make her gasp in shyness and rapture.

'Oh, Joel!' she cried, her voice all kind of wobbly.

But he seemed to know of both her shyness and her need, and what her cry had been all about, for he kissed her, rousing her to arch herself to him and, his touch becoming yet more intimate, causing her to gasp. Joel took time for her to make that big adjustment to such private intimacy and, as a sigh whispered from her, 'Soon, my love,' he murmured. 'Soon.'

Chesnie slept but briefly after she and Joel, because of her untried body, had made slow-tempered, wonderful love. 'Sleep now,' he'd said softly, and to her delight had made no move to go to his own bed but, as naked as she, their passion spent, had tenderly kissed her, holding her against him. She had gone to sleep in his arms.

She was still in his arms about an hour later, but had moved to be lying on her side, with Joel's body fitting to the curve of hers. His hand was on her naked belly, and she wanted to turn and kiss him, marvelling at the tenderness he had shown her, the unsuspected gentleness of this man whom she knew could be quite hard in some of the tough business decisions he was called upon to make.

She did not turn to kiss him but lay still, her heart full as she recalled the tenderness of his touch, his gentleness and understanding, his utter unselfishness when she'd experienced a few difficulties at the outset. He had instantly stilled, and had oh, so tenderly kissed her. 'There's no hurry, my darling, no hurry at all,' he had breathed, and kissed her again. And she had wanted him so much, and had so much wanted to give him pleasure that she had moved first—to offer him her body—with love. And Joel had tenderly, and as slowly as her virginal body would allow, accepted.

Chesnie fell asleep again, thinking of the wonder of his lovemaking, thinking of that heady closeness they had shared. The next time she awakened—Joel had gone!

Instantly she missed him—and wanted him back with her. Why hadn't he wakened her? Why had he left—just like that, without a word? While she found it fairly incredible that Joel should have removed himself from the bed they had been sharing without her waking, she found it even more incredible that she—a light sleeper, for goodness' sake—had overslept that morning!

Her cheeks flushed with pink when the answer to that hit her full square—she and Joel had been making slow, unhurried love well into the night. Was it any wonder she had slept soundly? The only wonder was that Joel had been able to surface so early.

But then, he was probably used to this sort of thing. Suddenly, abruptly, that was when, in the cold light of day, thoughts began to surface which she did not want to surface. And she hurriedly got out of bed and headed for the shower before spiteful darts of jealousy could throw more unwanted spears.

Under the shower she tried her hardest to think logically. Joel had a meeting at eight, for goodness' sake! For all she knew his meeting could be on the other side of the city. Given that most cities had a traffic problem at that hour in the morning, was it likely, since he was probably hosting that meeting, that he would hang around the hotel until five minutes before the meeting was due to start? He had probably left just after seven...

Chesnie got out of the shower, dried and dressed, and was still trying to think logically when she went into the sitting room. She tried hard to convince herself that it was out of consideration for her that Joel hadn't wakened her—then found that she was looking for a note, looking for some sign that it hadn't been purely just sex for him.

There was no note—and that was when she came to with a bump. What else did she think it was other than purely sex, for heaven's sake? So, yes, Joel had used a few endearments, a few encouraging kisses when she'd had a few initial problems, but the words had meant nothing to him. Oh, what a fool she would be to dwell on that encouraging 'my darling'—or any of it, for that matter.

She didn't want breakfast and sat down at her work table striving hard for some kind of professionalism to cope with the work she had to do.

But in her endeavours to pin her thoughts on something else she failed miserably. She wanted Joel to love her, and he didn't. She wanted him to have made love to her with love for her in his heart—fate cackled with mirth at such a ridiculous notion. Chesnie had to face the truth—that Joel's lovemaking had started from his fury with her, and that, quite plainly, all their lovemaking had meant to him was a release from his anger.

She forced herself to make a start on some work, but at nine o'clock she knew it was decision-time. She could not work. To sit there and to try and concentrate on complicated matter which yesterday she had been able to decipher with ease, today seemed totally beyond her. In fact, the way she felt then, Chesnie was of the opinion she would never have that capability again.

And it was Joel's fault. He had last night lifted her up to the heights, and this morning—she had come crashing down. She wished that she could hate him for it, but she could not. Because, basically, it was *not* his fault but hers. She, after all, in all of her actions, had given him the go-ahead all the way. Oh, the shame of it! Chesnie leapt up from her chair, her thoughts unsustainable. She knew then, without having to think about it, what she must do.

It was time to get out. Time to leave Joel, and her job with him. It was her only option; she saw that now if she could see nothing else. To stay, to carry on working for him, to go away with him again, to risk some point of disagreement cropping up—heaven knew what—she was too panic-stricken to know—and the same thing could happen if Joel kissed her again. She would be lost; she knew that she would.

A half-hour later and she was on her way to the airport. She had resigned. She did not have to put her resignation into writing. Joel would know that she did not intend to work for him again when he returned to the hotel—late that afternoon, he'd said—and discovered she had walked out on the job. Left without completing the work in hand. Not that the work was work which Eileen Gray could not take over, anyhow. From what Chesnie could make out it was not all that confidential. It was nothing to do with Symington Technology anyway.

Chesnie caught the ten-thirty flight and landed in London at midday. Her thoughts during that flight were tortuous. She drove to the home she shared with Joel plagued by doubts now that she had thought of Symington Technology—Joel had only made love to her on account of his fury that she might be 'playing around' with Philip Pomeroy. Joel's fury that, while married to him, she might be intending perhaps to break their 'no indulgence with the opposite sex while married' agreement. Joel was a man of his word; he wouldn't think very much of her breaking hers.

Chesnie sighed as she let herself into their home. Joel wouldn't want her under his roof now. She had better go and pack her belongings. It would be less painful if she did it now, while Joel was out of the way in Scotland.

She supposed if Joel were returning to London that night he would catch either the six-thirty or the seven-thirty flight. Whatever time he arrived home, though, she was sure he would certainly not expect to find her there when he got in.

Just the same, Chesnie found she had a need to take a final look around his home before she went to pack. She wandered from room to room, trying to clear her head of the memory of Joel's tenderness with her last night. But in remembering his tenderness she began to grow confused. Recalling Joel's considerate lovemaking, she began to wonder had he really made love to her on account of her 'relationship' with Philip? Joel's lovemaking had been sweet and gentle, not harsh and vengeful.

But—what did she know? Chesnie cogitated that, inexperienced as she had been, would she have known the difference? With demons of doubt chasing her, she went and got out her cases.

She was halfway through her packing, and was hurting so much she could barely think straight, when she began to realise that, should Joel come home tonight, then tonight or possibly first thing tomorrow morning she was going to have to have some sort of conversation with him. She'd have to do that by telephone. She wasn't ready to speak with Joel face to face yet—she had no idea if she ever would be. But when she was back in her old flat, when she felt calmer, she would ring him and explain that she had realised she didn't want to stay living with him—oh, what a lie that was—and that while he was at liberty to make up whatever he wished to explain her leaving Yeatman Trading she was perfectly willing, in the interests of him securing the chairmanship, to attend any function with him that he deemed necessary.

Having reached that conclusion, Chesnie felt very much like bursting into tears, and heartily wished she had never flown up to Glasgow yesterday. Though, if she had not, if that situation had never got out of hand, she would never have known the exquisite joy of Joel's lovemaking.

Cackling fate must be having a wonderful time at her expense, she mused unhappily. She had never wanted marriage. A year ago, six months ago, even three months ago, she would have run like blazes in the opposite direction. Now here she was married—well and truly married, thanks to last night—and when she and Joel had always been going to be divorced anyway, here she was—wanting to stay married.

She bit her lip to stop herself from crying—then heard a sound that made her spin round. A gasp of shock left her, and scarlet colour rioted through her skin.

She had thought she was not yet ready to speak face to face with Joel—but it didn't look as if she had very much choice in the matter. So taken up with her thoughts had she been, she had not heard him come in!

'H-how...?' she stammered, then grabbed at a passing snatch of her former calm. 'What time did you get in?' she asked, her racing heartbeats thundering in her ears.

Joel looked steadily back at her, not a smile about his

features. 'At a guess I'd say my plane touched down forty-five minutes after yours,' he answered evenly. Then, his glance going from her scarlet face to her almost full suitcase, his expression grew tough. 'What, would you mind telling me, do you think you're doing?' he demanded curtly.

CHAPTER TEN

WHAT did she think she was doing? She'd have thought that was fairly obvious. 'I—thought I'd leave—if that's all right with you,' Chesnie answered, never knowing from where she found such a cool, controlled tone.

She saw a muscle jerk in his temple. 'Actually, it isn't all right with me,' he responded, and sounded as tough as he looked. 'It's very far from all right with me!'

'I'm s-sorry you feel that way,' Chesnie replied, her controlled tone starting to fracture. 'Naturally I'll attend any function with you that you'd—'

'All this because we made love?' Joel cut her off harshly, causing colour to rush to her face again. Scarlet which Joel observed. 'Oh, Chesnie,' he said, his tough tone at once evaporating. 'Was it so very dreadful for you that—?'

'No!' She stopped him abruptly. Their lovemaking had been beautiful; she had been enraptured by his tenderness and sensitivity. Whatever else he believed she just could not let him believe it had been dreadful for her. But, not wanting him to read any kind of emotion in her face, she turned her back on him. 'It wasn't dreadful at all,' she denied huskily.

She heard him move and knew he was right behind her when he said close by, 'If it's not that, then something else has upset you. Something equally major—you are meaning to leave me *and* your job, aren't you?'

Dumbly, she nodded, and felt more churned up than ever inside when Joel gently took a hold of her shoulders and turned her to face him. She didn't want to look at him, but after long seconds of silence she couldn't bear it and raised her head, and found herself looking into a pair of extremely serious steady blue eyes.

Hot colour flared in her face again as, while looking into his eyes, she recalled their lovemaking, that ultimate intimacy they had shared. But as she looked at him so Joel looked back at her, and observed the waves of colour ebbing and flowing to her face. 'Poor love, you're in one almighty emotional whirlpool, aren't you?' he said softly.

'I'm n—' She would have attempted to deny it.

'And that's entirely understandable.' Joel gently cut through her denial. 'You have shared with me a most precious and special time,' he stated with a smile, 'and it's rather shaken you.' His smile faded. 'But, since I'm obviously the root cause of why you want to go, and that special time is obviously the trigger, don't you think that maybe we should talk about it first?'

Chesnie looked at him in alarm. 'That's the last thing I want to talk about!' she retorted swiftly—he was being too understanding; it was unnerving. 'I j-just want to pack my cases and be gone.'

'And to blazes with what I want?'

'I've already said I'm willing to attend any functions with you in regard to you getting the chairmanship!' she retaliated.

And was left staring at him dumbstruck when, as clear as anything, so she knew she hadn't misheard him, he retorted, 'To hell with the chairmanship—I'm talking about you and me!' Chesnie was still staring at him open-mouthed when he caught hold of her arm. 'We need to talk this through, Chesnie. We'll go into the drawing room.'

She didn't want to talk at all, and could only think that she must still be stunned by his declared 'To hell with the chairmanship', because she allowed him to guide her from the bedroom to the drawing room. To be chairman was what he had wanted above all else.

Chesnie realised she was still not functioning properly in that she discovered she was seated on one end of the sofa,

Joel at the other, without quite knowing how she had got there.

But this would never do. She sought and found some backbone and turned in her seat to look at Joel—he was already turned facing her, she discovered, and went all weak inside again. How dear he was, how tender his caresses... 'It's better this way!' she gabbled in a rush.

'Why?' Joel asked, and she supposed she should have seen that coming. She had worked for him long enough to know that, if it interested him, what he didn't know he always dug at until he found out. She had no answer. None that she was prepared to give him anyway. 'I'm assuming here,' he went on, when he obviously thought he had waited long enough, 'that your decision to go has nothing to do with Philip Pomeroy.'

'Philip Pomeroy!' she exclaimed, her look of amazement that Joel could think such a thing enough of a denial.

'And, since you've intimated you didn't find our lovemaking offensive—'

'I honestly don't want to talk about this,' Chesnie interrupted him, going pink again.

Joel smiled gently, but was determined, nevertheless, and reminded her, 'We had an understanding, you and I, that you would stay married to me for two years. That you would live with me for two years—'

'We can still stay married,' she butted in. 'I have no problem with that,' she added hurriedly—and could have groaned out loud.

As she had immediately realised, Joel wasn't likely to miss the implication of that last hastily added bit. 'But you have a problem living with me?' he questioned.

'I...' she answered helplessly. Then made desperate attempts to get herself more of one piece. 'I'm going,' she said, but her attempt to get to her feet didn't get very far. She had moved fast, but Joel had moved faster, and before she knew it she was again sitting on the sofa, only this time she was blocked in by the sofa arm on one side and Joel on the other.

She admitted she felt shaken, but she was even more shaken when Joel, an angry Joel, suddenly rounded on her, accusing harshly, 'You walk in, disrupt my life, and then, entirely without explanation, calmly think you can walk out again?' He shook his head. 'It's not on, Chesnie.'

She stared at him, opening her mouth to protest—disrupt his life!—then gained her second wind. 'What about me?' she challenged. *Calmly* think? She couldn't just then remember the last time she had thought calmly when she thought of Joel.

'What about you?' Joel asked, not letting up on the determined stance he was taking. 'Tell me about you. Tell me what this is all about,' he demanded.

She didn't want to answer, but saw no let-up in his determined manner. 'I don't want meaningless sex!' she blurted out, at once wished she hadn't, and strove hard to discover if she had revealed too much.

'Who—?' Joel broke off. He had appeared ready to argue but seemed to swiftly change his mind—as though, having got her to start talking, he wanted to hear more. 'Go on,' he encouraged.

She didn't want to go on, but she was still wedged in, she could feel his thigh warm up against her thigh—it didn't help very much. 'I...' She hesitated, but by his very silence he was making her go on. 'If I st-stay working for you, then at some time or other I'll have to go away with you again. I—don't know what happens. That is to say, I'm unsure what— Anyhow, if we erupt into an argument again—if you kiss me again—' She broke off helplessly, wishing so much that she had never got started—but still Joel's very silence was goading her on. 'Well...' she was floundering '...you know what could happen.'

'It could just as well happen here,' he pointed out quietly, his eyes on her face, studying, assessing.

'No,' Chesnie denied. 'It wouldn't. Here you allow me

my own space. Your ethics wouldn't allow you to violate that—'

'You feel I *violated* you?' Joel broke in, looking and sounding absolutely appalled.

'*No!*' she denied, outraged at the very thought. 'Of course I don't! What we... Our... You were wonderful with me,' she admitted, her face on fire again, but loving him too much to ever let him hate himself for those moments they had shared. 'You were so patient, so understanding. You made that time beautiful for me,' she said. But, knowing she was crimson, she began to fear that in her earnestness to assure him she didn't feel in the least violated, she might have said too much. 'I'd better go,' she decided urgently.

'No!' Joel denied her, putting out a hand to restrain her.

His touch unnerved her. 'You'll get the chairmanship without any—'

'Did you not hear me? I'm not bothered about the chairmanship.'

'Yes, you are!' she argued. 'You're ambitious and—'

'Let me qualify that,' Joel cut in, then strangely he paused and seemed to take a deep breath. 'Chesnie Davenport,' he resumed, looking nowhere but into her lovely green eyes, 'I have lately come to realise that if you are not in my life, then nothing else matters.' And, when Chesnie, her eyes huge, just stared at him dumbstruck, 'I don't give a damn about being chairman if you're not there with me,' he ended.

'B-but it *is* your life!' she stammered—and was left dizzy with emotion at his answer.

'Chesnie, *you're* my life,' he told her. She swallowed hard and just continued to stare at him, wide-eyed. 'Everything I've achieved or want in life is worthless if you're not there to share it with me,' he went on, taking her breath away and causing her to be for the moment incapable of speech. 'And as for making love with you being meaningless, you couldn't have it more wrong.'

'I—c-couldn't?' Was that husky squeak of a voice hers? Her heart was beating so fast she felt she would faint. Happiness, incredible joy, was pushing to break through, caution holding it back.

'You have high values, Chesnie, and I like that. But don't sell me short.'

'I—um…'

'My dear,' Joel murmured, 'don't you know your sweet response to me last night made my heart rejoice? I couldn't believe we were going to make love, that you…'

'I didn't want you to stop,' she whispered involuntarily.

'Oh, sweet darling,' Joel breathed, and, as if he truly had to know, 'Tell me you care for me a little,' he urged. 'Tell me you'll stay.'

Chesnie was such a bundle of nerves by then, still uncertain for all she had never seen him look so sincere, that nothing would get that sort of confession from her. 'Which one would you like to hear first?' she prevaricated.

'The one follows the other.' He looked into her eyes, and waited. Then, placing an arm about her shoulders, he lightly kissed the corner of her mouth. 'You're not going to tell me, are you?' he questioned. She would not answer. But, since she wasn't attempting to leap up again and leave, he seemed to grow a fraction less tense than he had been, and took time to explain, 'I didn't want to leave at all this morning. You looked so adorable lying there.'

'You didn't—wake me.'

'I was afraid to,' he confessed softly. 'I wanted to kiss you awake, but had to go quickly. I feared, had I kissed you, you might be as welcoming as you had been a few hours earlier. Then—' He broke off as a tide of pink crept under her skin.

He seemed unable to resist the allure of her lips, and bent his head and kissed her—and at the feel of his lips on hers everything in Chesnie started to go haywire. She pushed at his chest. He broke his kiss and pulled back, his expression grave.

'I've read the situation wrong!' he exclaimed shakenly.

'I need to think,' Chesnie replied. 'And—and you're making thinking very difficult.'

A slow smile started to spread across his features. 'Because I kissed you, dare I hope?'

'I don't know what it is—I've never been like this.'

'I understand,' he said softly.

'I've been kissed before, b-but I've never gone so wildly out of control before.'

'I know,' he repeated with a tender smile. He looked as though he might kiss her again, but suggested, 'If I've worked this out correctly—and what you've just said seems to confirm it—you, my darling, are just a little bit in love with me.'

Chesnie jerked away from him, but was still held firmly in the curve of his arm. She was just a very great deal in love with him, she would have said, but was feeling so jumpy inside that there was no way she was going to admit it. 'How did you come to that conclusion?' she enquired, while wondering if she was being wise or foolish. She had countless times seen him work through the most complicated of issues, casting aside irrelevant parts until he came up with the answer—was she leaving herself totally without cover? But, to a certain extent, she had that methodical ability too, and all at once her confused thoughts were clearing and she was doing some analysing of her own. Taking into account what she knew of him, she was then adding it to the memory of having lain in his sensitive and caring embrace—and all of a sudden she was starting to believe the unbelievable; that perhaps, just perhaps, Joel's caring might extend beyond the warm glow of their intimacy together. She jerked a look at him—but still wasn't ready to tell him what he wanted to know.

As if he understood, he smiled down at her and answered her question first. 'I've had a plane journey of one and a quarter hours in which to concentrate my thoughts solely on why, when we had been so at one with each other, you would take flight—not only leaving me, but, when your pride in your work is second to none, feeling you had to decamp leaving your work unfinished. Not to say barely touched. You weren't angry with me like the time before, when you went home—the reverse, in fact.'

'I—er… You weren't expecting to return to the hotel until late this afternoon,' Chesnie reminded him quickly.

'How could I concentrate on a meeting when thoughts of you were filling my head?' he asked.

'Really?' she questioned in wonder.

'Really,' Joel confirmed. 'Throughout that first tedious meeting with Pomeroy all I could think of was you, how you had been, how you had looked as I left, with your hair all loose and soft about your lovely head. I wanted to be back with you. That meeting finished at ten, for Pomeroy to go into discussions with his team and me to mine. I decided to delegate—we have a first-class team in Glasgow, as you know. I dashed back to the hotel—only to be informed, when I couldn't find a trace of you, that you'd taken a taxi to the airport. I couldn't believe it!'

'Oh, Joel,' she mourned, guilt swamping her. He did care for her! He must!

'You can be quite wicked when you put your mind to it,' he accused, but didn't seem to hold it against her. For he favoured her with a heart-melting tender look and told her, 'I hared after you, knowing in advance I wasn't going to make the same flight anyway.'

'You caught the next plane?'

'And,' he took up carefully, 'had time on the flight to recall again how lovely you had been—how shy, how innocent, but how wholly giving you had been with me. Giving as you had been with no man. And then all at once, my darling, my heart started to pound away as I thought about you, thought of the self-contained person you normally are, and I suddenly started to realise that there was no way, *absolutely no way*, you would have made love with me—unless you loved me a little.'

'You're—um—too clever by half,' Chesnie mumbled, feelings of joy refusing to be denied and starting to push through. As Joel seemed to have learned a lot about her, she too, she realised, had learned a lot about him. By the same token it seemed to her, then, that there was no way Joel would have told her of his findings—no way, since he did not want her to leave, he would have told her any of this—if he...did not love her a little in return!

'I don't know about clever,' he answered. 'Just tell me, am I accurate? Do you have any love for me?'

He was tense again, she noted, that arm about her taut as he waited. She gave in—partially. 'I suppose you could say that I—um—care as much for you as you appear to care for me.' She shyly understated the depth of her love for him, and saw that muscle jerk a beat in his temple again.

'You're saying, then, that I'm in your head night and day? That you can't eat or sleep for thinking of me? That you get up in the morning with me in your head, are restless and have taken to prowling about your bedroom, have known wild, unreasoning jealousy—and yet have stubbornly been refusing to acknowledge what is wrong with you?'

'You—care for me like that?' Chesnie asked on a whisper of sound.

'I love you like that—and more,' Joel corrected, and, while her heart raced, drew her into both his arms and gently kissed her. When he pulled back it was to look long and lingeringly into her face, and to ask, 'Would the extent of your caring begin with the letter "L"?'

Chesnie smiled. She loved him, and while it seemed incredible that he should return her love, she knew that as she trusted him, so she could trust his word. 'My caring for you begins with a very large capital "L",' she replied shyly.

'You love me?' It amazed her that he seemed to need to have it confirmed.

'Do you think I married you just to be the new chairman's PA?'

He was watching her, his clever intelligence reading every blink, every nuance. 'Why *did* you marry me, Chesnie?' he asked quietly.

She kissed him. 'Because I fell in love with you,' she answered simply—and was held, crushed up against his heart.

'Oh, Chesnie,' he breathed against her ear, and drew back to look into her face. 'You've loved me all these weeks? I can't believe it.' He kissed her, held her, and tenderly kissed her again. 'I need to know more,' he breathed. 'When, exactly?' he urged, and she laughed lightly. But as his tension left him, so her tension seemed to leave her.

'I didn't want to fall in love with you,' she felt she should tell him.

Then found he had worked that out for himself when he too gave a laugh, a loving laugh, and answered, 'Knowing you, I'm sure you kicked against it like the very devil.'

She kissed him, wanted to stay with him like this for ever, but sharing confidences like this was so wonderful she wanted to know more, to know absolutely everything. 'Was it like that for you too—refusing to acknowledge what those feelings were that got to me so many times?'

'The feeling of being irked—irrationally so?' he countered, and placed a light kiss on her mouth. 'You were so different from any other woman I've ever known,' he explained.

That surprised her. 'How?' She just had to know.

Joel settled her more comfortably in his arms. 'For a start, while a few other women I've known have declared they weren't interested in marriage, you were the only one I knew I could believe honestly and truthfully meant it.'

'That made you feel comfortable about it when you decided that to marry would give your chairmanship chances a boost?'

'You've been reading my mind.' He grinned. 'But it's for certain that when the idea came to me the notion to marry didn't panic me the way it would have done at one time—though only if you were my bride.' He paused, then with a self-deprecating smile added, 'The writing must have been on the wall then, only I failed to see it.'

'You decided to risk it?'

'What risk? I thought it all through. You had positively no wish to stay married and would be as keen as I to divorce in a couple of years' time, no harm done, no complications.' He looked into her eyes, his eyes alight with love as he went on, 'Only complications arose when I realised I was in love with you.'

'That upset your plans?'

'Made mincemeat of them,' he admitted, but didn't look too unhappy about it. 'Though I have to confess I had a regard for you that I'd never had for any other PA almost from the beginning.'

'Honestly?' she asked.

'I didn't own up to it—just wasn't ready to face what was happening to me,' he said with a smile that made her backbone melt. 'So why, when in the past I've had female staff who irritated me by batting their eyelashes at me every time I passed, did I feel a touch put out that my present PA was quite totally immune?' Chesnie smiled in love and wonder. 'It was only as it should be,' Joel continued, 'so why did I find that I wouldn't feel at all irritated, in fact wouldn't mind in the least should I spot a spark of interest from you in me.'

'Don't stop. I'm loving this,' Chesnie begged, her confidence in his love for her growing with every word he said.

He did stop, but only to place a loving kiss on her mouth. 'Then,' he resumed, 'in no time I'm seeing, and getting to know, a vastly different person from the cool and controlled woman I saw at interview.'

'You—um—saw through my cover?'

'I sussed that out quite quickly,' he agreed. 'At our first

meeting you were cool, sophisticated, elegant. Inside weeks of working with you I was discovering a woman who is sensitive and kind to the most junior members of staff—your kindness not confined to the post boy, but extended to my father. The goodness in you that you went to see him in your lunch-hour because you were worried about him…' Joel paused, and then confessed, 'I think love really started to hit me hard on our wedding day, when I saw another side of you—your gentle manner with your grandfather, your loyalty to your squabbling family. But,' he went on, giving her a look of mock severity, 'I kissed you—and all you could think about was your wretched gloves. Mrs Davenport, I am just not used to such treatment.'

'It—er—didn't seem appropriate to tell you that my knees were about to give way,' she answered, by way of apology.

Joel burst out laughing. 'Oh, you darling, you love!' he exclaimed, and just had to kiss her.

'They're giving way again!' she gasped, when he finally drew back.

'Oh, Chesnie Davenport,' he murmured. 'I'm trying with all I have to keep my head here, to content myself to enjoy these first precious moments of heart's-ease since last Saturday, when you put me in trauma by calmly getting into bed with me. And, as calmly and as cool as you please, asking me if I snore.'

'Cool! Calm!' She shook her head to disclaim any such suggestion, and then quickly picked up on what else he had just said. 'Trauma? You were in trauma?'

'I don't know what else you'd call it,' he replied, smiling tenderly at her. 'I was determined to keep to my side of the bed. No way, I told myself, did I want the complication of a consummated marriage. Then somehow during the night I felt you near—and for a brief while a wonderful tranquillity crept over me. I carefully gathered you in my arms and for the first time ever knew enchantment. I couldn't believe I should get such pleasure from just holding you quiet against me like that.'

Chesnie sighed blissfully. 'You knew—when I woke up, you knew I was awake?'

'I knew,' he replied, and kissed her hair as he had done then. 'I wanted us to stay like that, but...'

'But then I started issuing what you saw as an invitation,' she teased.

'Well, I wanted to kiss you anyway,' he laughed, and kissed her. But he pulled back to continue, 'Then my head started to have one gigantic battle with what I wanted to do, against what I should do. What was best for you, best for me...'

'You—um—got out of bed in a hurry.'

'Impudent madam,' he said lovingly. 'What else could I do? One of us had to be sensible— And you can blush.' He broke off to tease her, reminding her that she hadn't looked likely to be the one to put a stop to their lovemaking. 'I confess I wasn't thinking too clearly just then. But with what woolly-thinking capability I had, it seemed to me that if I took your innocence, as I wanted to, I would be causing us a whole heap of problems. Not least that I would have deemed our marriage permanent.'

'Oh,' she said, trying to keep up.

'Indeed,' he commented with a smile. 'So, as you rightly said, I got out of bed in a hurry—and that day went on to be the worst day of my life. I wanted to see you, needed to see you—and for my trouble felt I was going crazy because of you.'

'Joel!' she gasped on a whisper of breath.

'I was going to pieces over you,' he admitted. 'And on Monday, at the office, I found that to try and concentrate with your own good self in the next office was an impossibility. It was a great relief when all the preliminary skirmishing with Symington's culminated in a series of meetings being arranged at short notice. I was glad to be able to get away.'

'You—wanted to get away—from me?'

'I needed to think, my darling,' Joel explained tenderly. 'How could I think with you so near?'

'You needed to think about…?'

'About us. About you and me. I knew by then that I was head over heels in love with you. But what about you?'

'You had no idea?'

He shook his head. 'Not then. I couldn't even begin to reach any conclusion then. All I knew that Monday night in Glasgow was that I was there and you were in London—when what I wanted was that you should be with me. My love for you, sweet, beautiful Chesnie, was driving me crazy. I desperately needed to talk to you—to gauge, to try and work out if you loved me. So I decided that when I returned to London I'd casually suggest we have dinner somewhere, and I would fish to see how you felt. But that was when I realised—never having forgotten your nerve in turning down my first dinner invitation that day you lunched with my father—that you were just as likely to turn down my next one. I was in a complete stew about you, Chesnie,' he told her, to her delight and surprise. 'So on to plan B. If I could get you up to Glasgow…'

'It wasn't strictly necessary for me to go to Glasgow?' Chesnie exclaimed.

'I'm a swine,' he happily accepted. 'But, in my defence, I was suffering. Trust me, my darling, I wasn't thinking in terms of our sleeping together when I rang to ask you to catch that flight. All that was in my mind was that I couldn't bear being apart from you any longer and that once you were in Glasgow then, since we both had to eat, you could hardly turn down my dinner invitation. That would be when, rather than jump straight in and make a complete fool of myself, I might be able to test the water first. That was the plan—only by the time I saw you it had all started to get away from me.'

Never had she expected to hear that Joel had felt so vulnerable. 'Oh, my darling Joel,' she whispered softly, and warmly, tenderly, she kissed him.

'Chesnie.' He breathed her name, and close up to her informed her, 'I'm still trying desperately hard to keep my head here.'

She laughed—a light, never more happy laugh. 'Forgive me,' she apologised naughtily, and urged, 'And so?'

It took Joel a moment or two to recall where they had been. Then he was telling her, 'And so there was I, having given in to the desperate urge to see you, having formed my plan, having sent a car to the airport for you—which, incidentally, got stuck in traffic—but finding I'm unable to wait to see you. So unable to wait, in fact, that I ducked out of a meeting and grabbed a taxi at about the time I calculated you might have arrived at the hotel.'

'Your calculations were out by a good few hours,' she reminded him, recalling it had been early evening when he had returned to the hotel.

He shook his head, his handsome mouth picking up at the corners. 'They weren't,' he denied. 'I was in the taxi that pulled up behind yours. I saw Pomeroy kiss you—and managed to hang on to my sanity long enough to tell my driver to get us out of there.'

'You were at the hotel when...!' she exclaimed on a gasp, wonder taking her anew when it suddenly hit her that it wasn't so much the confidentiality of her work that made Joel dislike her going out with Philip, but... 'You were jealous!' she accused, barely believing what her intelligence had belatedly brought her. 'You were jealous of Philip!'

'I was as surprised as you—when I eventually owned up to the truth,' Joel admitted, and went on to explain, 'It was because I didn't want you having anything to do with Pomeroy that I didn't tell you we were putting out feelers for Symington's. Which,' he went on with a wry grin, 'makes rather a nonsense of me trying to convince myself, ever since he rang you at the office, that my dislike of you dating him was only because he was the opposition.'

'But it wasn't?' she pressed in delight.

'How could it be? I didn't care at all for the idea of him proposing to you. And in fact couldn't purchase an engagement ring fast enough so you might wear it on the night you told him we were to be married.'

'I didn't wear it that night,' Chesnie felt obliged to own.

'I realised, when I thought of your fine sensitivity, that you probably wouldn't,' he answered with a smile. 'I should have faced up to the fact that there was a great green-eyed monster sitting on my shoulder when it wasn't only Pomeroy I objected to asking you out but any other male who came into your office to ask you for a date.'

'Fergus Ingles?'

'The lot of them—him included.'

'Oh, Joel,' Chesnie sighed, and felt honour-bound to confess, 'I was not a little green-eyed myself, over Arlene Enderby.'

'Truly?' Joel enquired, seeming surprised.

'Truly,' Chesnie confirmed, and Joel borrowed some of her delight.

'I should have seen what was happening to me when, with thoughts of you somehow starting to occupy a lot of space in my head, I found I became quite evasive if any of my female acquaintances rang me. I should have realised I was in trouble way back, when you told me you'd no intention of becoming my stepmother! I discovered I didn't want you to be anybody's stepmother—in fact I didn't want you marrying anyone.'

Chesnie looked back at him wide-eyed. Then she laughed, a joy-filled laugh. 'You told yourself it was because, married, I—'

'Might give up your job and I would lose a terrific PA,' he finished for her. But his expression suddenly became so serious that Chesnie's own expression sobered. Her heart, which had been racing, leaping and generally beating out all sorts of rhythms since she had turned round to see him there with her in her bedroom, and not in Scotland, where he should be, suddenly gave a lurch of dread.

'What? What's wrong?' she asked urgently.

'I hope nothing,' Joel replied. 'With all my heart I'm hoping nothing's wrong. The reason I've taken time to explain a few things about how it is with me, the depth of my love for you, my darling, is so you'll know and trust that I will never harm you. And I hope that you'll...' he paused, as if searching for just the right words '...that you'll agree to a few changes in our lifestyle.'

She wasn't sure what he was asking, but to hear him say that he loved her deeply made her feel a whole lot better—what else mattered? 'I'm not sure what you're saying—what you're asking,' she had to confess.

'I'm saying, my darling,' Joel began, with that serious, not to say stern look still about him, 'that I don't want a home-life where the minute I come into a room you go out from it. I'm saying that I don't want a home-life where you go and visit your grandfather at the weekend and leave me wanting you back here so badly that I have to come after you.'

'Oh, Joel!' she cried. 'Was that how it was?'

'I couldn't believe that in so short a time the apartment felt alien without you in it,' he answered. 'I'm saying that, without being aware of why, I had never felt happier than when you finally agreed to marry me, and that I know now the reason for that has nothing whatsoever to do with the chairmanship. I'm almost certain that I've secured the position, but it's insignificant without you. And, while I know that you have a true and ingrained aversion to anything resembling a permanent marriage, I'm saying, my true love, that I just cannot endure living through the next twenty-three months expecting at the end of that time to receive some notification telling me that you have instigated divorce proceedings.'

'Joel!' She cried his name in surprise—only he misread her surprise and took it for alarm.

'I know we agreed only two years—I know it, I know it,' he said hurriedly. 'But I love you so desperately I just cannot bear the thought of having to part from you. I can't promise you a life without upsets, but I promise here and now that never will I allow anything to harm you or put our marriage in jeopardy.' He looked deeply into her serious large green eyes. 'I love you, Chesnie Cosgrove Davenport. With all of my heart I love you. Would you,' he began, 'do me the honour of being my wife—permanently?'

'Oh, Joel,' she cried tremulously—she loved him, he loved her; what else mattered? 'I'd like nothing better,' she whispered huskily.

'You will? You'll stay married to me?' he insisted.

'Willingly,' she answered, and as a look of supreme joy at once came over his expression Joel hauled her close up against him.

'Oh, my dear, darling,' he breathed. 'Thank you,' he added on a heartfelt sound, and kissed her.

MARRIAGE ON THE AGENDA

by

Lee Wilkinson

Lee Wilkinson lives with her husband in a three-hundred-year-old stone cottage in a Derbyshire village, which most winters gets cut off by snow. They both enjoy travelling and recently, joining forces with their daughter and son-in-law, spent a year going round the world 'on a shoestring' while their son looked after Kelly, their much loved German shepherd dog. Her hobbies are reading and gardening and holding impromptu barbecues for her long-suffering family and friends.

CHAPTER ONE

THE taxi skirted Hyde Park and dropped Loris Bergman outside the Landseer Hotel. Having paid the driver, she hurried inside and crossed the plush lobby to the Ladies' Cloakroom.

When she had shaken the raindrops from her hooded cloak she gave that, and the small weekend case she was carrying, to the attendant, before glancing quickly in the mirror to check her image.

It was a bad enough crime to be so late for Bergman Longton's St Valentine's party, without her appearance being found wanting.

A small oval face with a pure bone structure, a wide, passionate mouth and almond-shaped eyes the colour of pale sherry, looked back at her. To others, her beauty was startling, but to Loris, with her total lack of vanity, familiarity had made her looks commonplace.

Satisfied that her long black hair and wispy fringe were tidy, and she looked cool and collected, she headed for the chandelier-lit ballroom.

The party was in full swing, with music and laughter and conversation. Some of the guests were dancing to a good-sized band, others milling about or gathered, glass in hand, in little groups.

A fair-haired, slimly built man, just under six feet tall and wearing impeccable evening dress, was standing alone in the background. His very stillness amongst the lively throng drew Loris's attention. She had a fleeting sense of familiarity, a feeling that a long time ago she might have known him.

A second look convinced her she was mistaken.

If she had ever met this man, with his look of maturity and quiet strength, his unmistakable air of self-assurance, she would have remembered.

His stance was easy, relaxed, back straight, feet a little apart. A slightly cynical expression on his good-looking face, he was watching the other guests.

She was wondering who he was, and what he was doing at the gathering, when his brilliant, heavy-lidded eyes met hers.

Suddenly meeting that cool, ironic regard had the same impact as walking into an invisible plate-glass window. A sense of shock made her stop in her tracks while her heart began to beat in slow, heavy thuds.

As she stood, momentarily held in thrall, her mother's voice said, 'So there you are, at last...'

Tearing her gaze away from the stranger's with an effort, Loris turned to the petite, dark-haired woman, whose still-beautiful face was marred by an irritable expression.

'We were beginning to wonder where on earth you'd got to. Your father's certainly not pleased.'

'I told you I had a six-thirty appointment and would no doubt be late,' Loris said patiently.

'It's utterly ridiculous on a Saturday night! And you didn't say you'd be *this* late. The party's more than half-over.'

Although her parents knew quite well that as an interior designer Loris frequently had to work unsociable hours, they always kicked up the same kind of fuss, treating her like a recalcitrant teenager rather than a confident, talented woman with a blossoming career.

'Unfortunately Mrs Chedwyne who is a client I can't afford to lose, wouldn't be hurried, and when I did manage to get away I still had to go back to the flat to change.'

Refusing to let the subject drop, Isobel Bergman complained, 'I don't know why you don't insist on people consulting you during normal business hours.'

Loris sighed. 'It doesn't work like that. I have to visit my clients' homes at *their* convenience. Quite a number of them are out during the day. Some only have weekends or evenings free.'

'Well, don't be surprised if Mark's furious. After all, it is a special party to celebrate the Cosby takeover, and it was your place to be by his side. He's missed you.'

Spotting her fiancé on the dance floor entangled with a tall, vivacious blonde, Loris remarked tartly, 'He doesn't appear to be missing me at the moment.'

'When you're this late what can you expect? You should have been here to keep an eye on him. If you're not careful some scheming little gold-digger will steal him from under your nose.'

Though Loris was well aware of Mark Longton's tendency to be attracted by a pretty face, the notion that she needed to 'keep an eye' on him wasn't a particularly pleasant one.

'Don't forget Mark Longton's quite a catch,' Isobel persisted. 'A handsome, sexy man, still in his thirties, who runs a company and has money, isn't to be sneezed at.'

'I'm not interested in his money,' Loris said flatly.

'Well, you ought to be. Your father's turned sixty, and if I can't get him to change his will when he dies your stepbrother will get the lot and you'll be left out in the cold...'

Simon, extrovert and loaded with charm, had always held pride of place in Peter Bergman's affections and, knowing what she did know, Loris hadn't been at all surprised by her father's decision. But well aware that it had been a bitter blow to Isobel to learn that her husband's son from his first marriage was to inherit everything, Loris said soothingly, 'I really don't mind if Simon does get the lot. I have a career I enjoy and—'

'It shouldn't be *necessary* for you to work. Your father could easily afford to give you an allowance—'

'I'm twenty-four, not fourteen.'

Ignoring her daughter's protest, Isobel rushed on, 'Seriously, I'd never have married him if I'd known he'd turn out to be such an old skinflint.'

It was a familiar complaint, and one that Loris had learned to studiously ignore.

'He's even talking about giving up the London flat and semi-retiring to Monkswood.'

'A lot of people work from home these days, and it would make it a lot easier to run the estate.'

'Well, I don't want to be stuck in the country the whole week. I'd go mad. But your father only thinks of himself, never of me. Weekends are bad enough—' Isobel continued to complain '—unless we're having a house party... By the way, I hope you remembered to bring some things?'

Loris and Mark were joining the weekend house party at Monkswood, the Bergmans' country estate which bordered on the village of Paddleham.

'Yes, I remembered.'

As the dance ended and the floor cleared, both women looked for Mark's tall, thickset figure, but he was nowhere to be seen.

'There's still plenty of food on the buffet if you want to eat?' Isobel suggested.

Loris shook her head. 'I had a sandwich before I went to keep my appointment.'

'Well, I could do with something. This latest diet is much too severe...'

At forty-seven, Isobel waged a continuous, and mainly losing, battle against the extra pounds that middle-age had piled onto her once-slim figure.

'And I'm convinced the pills they gave me with it are making my migraines worse,' she grumbled, as she disappeared in the direction of the buffet.

A waiter approached with a tray of champagne and, accepting a glass with a word of thanks, Loris sipped the well-chilled wine while her gaze travelled over the assembled company.

As she scanned the crowd, instead of Mark's heavy, slightly florid face, with its thick black brows and dark eyes, she found herself looking for a stranger's lean, tanned face, with clear-cut features and light, penetrating eyes.

A sudden fanfare called for the assembled company's attention, and Loris watched as her father, her fiancé, and a thin, balding man, went up onto the dais in front of the band. Sir Peter Bergman, stocky and tough-looking, with shrewd blue eyes and iron-grey hair, stepped forward and held up his hand for silence.

'Most of you already know that Bergman Longton and the American giant, Cosby, have been planning to amalgamate. I'm delighted to announce that that has now taken place, and William Grant—' he drew the thin, balding man forward '—one of Cosby's top executives, is here with us tonight to celebrate the event.'

There was a burst of applause.

'This merger will make us one of the largest and, we confidently expect, one of the most successful companies in our particular field. We have decided to rename the UK part of our combined companies BLC Electronics.' He raised his glass. 'May BLC go from strength to strength.'

There was more enthusiastic applause, and the toast was drunk.

As the three men left the dais they were momentarily swallowed up by a surge of people wanting to shake their hands and offer congratulations.

When the excitement had died down and the crowd began to disperse, Peter Bergman and William Grant walked away together, talking earnestly.

Mark glanced towards where Loris was standing, striking in an aquamarine dress that clung to her slender figure. She smiled and moved in his direction, but his face was cold, and he turned away to join the woman he'd been dancing with earlier.

Stunned by the rebuff, Loris stopped in her tracks. Admittedly she was very late, but she had warned Mark in advance that she might be.

Still, she felt a certain amount of guilt, and if it hadn't been for the blonde, who was laughing up at him, she would have gone over and apologised.

But uncertain of his reaction—Mark could be very unforgiving when something displeased him—she hesitated, having no wish to be humiliated in front of the other woman.

As she stood wondering how to retrieve the situation, a special St Valentine's waltz was announced. '...at the conclusion of which, gentlemen, you may kiss your partner.'

Surely Mark would come over to her now?

But without hesitation he offered his hand to the blonde.

Biting her lip, Loris was about to walk away, when a low, attractive voice, with just a trace of an American accent, asked, 'Will you dance with me?'

Turning, she found herself looking into a lean tanned face, with a straight nose, a cleft chin, and a mouth that was firm, yet sensitive. A very masculine mouth that sent tingles through her, a mouth she could only describe as beautiful.

Again she got that illusory feeling of having once known him, a haunting sense of *recognition*, without being able to place him.

His thickly lashed eyes, she saw at close quarters, were sea-green rather than the silvery-grey she had thought them to be. Their impact was just as devastating, making her pulses start to race and her breath come faster, so that it took a moment or two to steady herself.

Though part of her *wanted* to dance with this fascinating stranger, Loris was well aware that accepting his invitation would only serve to exacerbate things.

Despite the fact that Mark had a roving eye himself, since she'd agreed to marry him he'd proved to be both jealous and possessive, hating her to so much as look at any other male.

Bearing that in mind, she was seeking a polite way to refuse when, noting her hesitation, the man by her side asked sardonically, 'Scared that Longton won't approve?'

So he knew who they both were.

'Not at all,' Loris denied crisply. 'I...' She broke off as Mark and his partner circled past, close as Siamese twins.

Catching her companion's eyes, she saw the unspoken derision in their clear, green depths.

To hell with it! she thought with a spurt of anger. Why should she refuse? Mark had chosen to dance with someone else, and what was sauce for the gander...

She knew by now that if anyone failed to stand up to him he simply walked all over them and, though she hated any kind of discord, she had no intention of being a doormat when they were married.

'I'd love to dance with you,' she finished firmly.

He smiled at her, a smile that lit his eyes and made little creases at each corner of his mouth. His teeth were excellent, white and healthy and gleaming.

She judged him to be around thirty years old and, wondering why such a relatively young, attractive man appeared to be here alone, she moved into his arms.

His hold light, but far from tentative, he steered her smoothly onto the floor. He was a good dancer, and they danced well together, their bodies fitting.

Mark, heavily built and well over six feet tall, dwarfed her slight five feet four inch frame, but this man was about six inches taller than herself, and her high heels brought their eyes almost on a level.

Meeting those brilliant eyes made her strangely breathless and, needing to say something, she remarked, 'You're aware that I'm engaged to Mark, so you must know who I am?'

'I do indeed. You're Loris Bergman.'

Something about the way he spoke made her say coolly, 'As I don't know your name, you have the advantage of me.'

'I'm Jonathan Drummond.' He volunteered no further information.

The name was unfamiliar. Though she was almost convinced they hadn't, she felt compelled to ask, 'Have we ever met before?'

'If we had, I would have remembered,' he replied.

'So how do you know me?' she asked curiously.

'Who doesn't?'

'Most of the people here, I imagine.'

He shook his head. 'I'm sure they all know the lucky woman who has one of the big bosses for a father and the other for a future husband.'

'You sound as if you disapprove?'

'It seems like an eminently suitable arrangement to keep all the money and power in the same family.'

'Money and power have nothing to do with it.'

'Really?'

'Yes, really.'

'Then why are you marrying Longton? Apart from the fact that he's a divorcé and much too old for you, he's not a particularly nice character.'

'Being a divorcé isn't a crime, and he's only thirty-nine.'

'I notice you haven't defended his character.'

'As that's only *your* opinion, it didn't seem necessary.'

'Neither have you answered my question.'

'We happen to love each other.'

At that moment Mark came into view. His partner's arms were round his neck, and he was saying something in her ear.

'He has a strange way of showing it.'

'I'm afraid he's angry with me for being late.'

'Has he any right to be?'

'Some, I suppose,' she answered honestly.

In response to Jonathan Drummond's raised brow, she briefly explained the circumstances.

Coolly, he said, 'As Longton was pre-warned, I don't see any justification for him behaving like a spoilt child. Do you?'

Challenged, without thinking how it might sound, she spoke the truth. 'Not really. That's why I'm dancing with you.'

'I see. Tit for tat. I guess it was too much to hope that you actually *wanted* to.'

As he finished speaking the dance ended, leaving Mark and his partner standing close by.

As couples began to kiss, Jonathan Drummond waited quietly, making no move.

Mark glanced in Loris's direction and, seeing that she was watching him, bent to kiss the blonde, who responded with enthusiasm.

Vexed by such deliberate provocation, Loris slid her palms beneath the lapels of her companion's dinner jacket and raised her face invitingly.

For a moment he stood perfectly still, then, taking her wrists, he lifted her hands away. 'I don't care to be *used*,' he said coldly.

'I-I'm sorry,' she stammered, feeling cheap and foolish. 'I didn't mean—'

'Oh, I think you did. Goodnight, Miss Bergman.'

As she stood unhappily and watched him walk away, Isobel appeared by her side. 'Your father and I are leaving now.'

Loris pulled herself together and, knowing how her mother loved social occasions, asked, 'I thought the party went on until twelve?'

'It does, but it's almost eleven now, and with such heavy rain your father thought we should get started. Most of our guests came to Monkswood last night and are settled in, but one couple weren't due to arrive until this evening.'

Fretfully, she added, 'It's all a bit of a mess. If I'd realised earlier that this company party coincided with our house party I'd have done something about it. But by the time I discovered the muddle over dates it was too late and I—'

'Is Simon there?' Loris tried to stop the flow.

'No, he's staying in Oxford with some friends. I presume you'll be driving down with Mark as soon as the party's over?'

'I suppose so,' Loris said uncertainly.

'You mean he's still with that blonde creature? Yes, I see he is. She's probably after his money... Well, you've only got yourself to blame. All in all you've managed to make a real mess of the evening.'

'It's not entirely my fault,' Loris protested. 'If Mark had been a little more understanding...'

'When have men ever been understanding?'

'I'm sure *some* are.'

'Well, not the macho ones like Mark and your father.' Obviously wondering if she'd said too much, Isobel added hastily, 'Though who wants to be married to a wimp?'

'Not me.' For the first time that night, Loris smiled.

Peter Bergman thrust his way through the crowd and addressed his wife. 'About ready?'

'I only have to get my coat.'

Giving his daughter a look of extreme displeasure, he asked brusquely, 'I suppose you realise you've spoilt the entire evening? Have you any idea just how angry and disappointed Mark is?'

'He's made it quite plain,' she answered wearily.

'Then it's up to you to apologise. And as soon as possible.'

'Do,' Isobel urged as she prepared to follow her husband. 'Otherwise they'll both sulk for the rest of the weekend and it'll be murder.'

Loris was surprised by her mother's caustic observation. Though Isobel frequently criticised her husband, she had never been known to admit to even the slightest imperfection in her future son-in-law.

'You may well be right,' Loris admitted as she kissed the proffered cheek.

'I expect we'll be in bed before you get to Monkswood, so I'll see you in the morning. By the way, you and Mark have your usual rooms.' Isobel hurried away.

Knowing that the only possible chance of saving what was left of the weekend would be to get her apology over as quickly as possible, Loris began to look for her fiancé.

She finally spotted him standing, tall, dark, and powerful-looking, apparently bidding goodnight to some people who were leaving early.

Though he was still what most people would have called 'a fine figure of a man', she noted, with almost a feeling of betrayal, that his black, crinkly hair was showing signs of grey, his jawline had lost its firmness, and he had the beginnings of a paunch.

Relieved to find the blonde was nowhere in sight, she hurried over, and said quickly, 'Mark, I'm terribly sorry I was so late. I know you have every right to be angry with me, but please don't let it spoil the weekend.'

His brown eyes showing no signs of forgiveness, he snapped, 'The party's almost over. Isn't it a bit late for apologies?'

'I would have told you I was sorry straight away if you'd been alone.'

'Pamela's a beautiful woman, don't you think?'

When Loris said nothing, knowing he was just rubbing it in, he added, 'She comes from the States. Her father is Alan Gresham, the American newspaper magnate, which makes her heir to the Gresham millions.'

'How nice.'

So her mother was wrong. It wasn't Mark's money the blonde was after.

'She's made it quite obvious she fancies me.'

Loris's lips tightened in distaste. 'Don't you find her just a bit blatant?'

'She certainly knows her way around,' he said admiringly. 'And she's not the sort to say no, which makes a nice change.'

So it wasn't just her late arrival he was punishing her for. Her refusal to go to bed with him was a good part of it.

In the three months they had been engaged Mark had been fairly pressing, and several times, deciding she was being stupid in holding back, she had almost given in.

He was a handsome, virile man, and she had little doubt that he would make a good lover. Yet each time when it came to the crunch, perhaps still inhibited by the past, she had changed her mind.

Understandably, this had enraged Mark, who had sulked for days. He would be perfectly normal with everyone else, but only address her when he absolutely had to, and then be brief and glacial.

Reading the signs, Isobel had once said seriously, 'I know sleeping together is almost the norm these days, but

I think you're right to hold back until the wedding ring's on your finger.'

It was the first time her mother had ever broached the question of sex and, wondering if she had somehow guessed what had happened with Nigel, Loris had asked, 'Why do you say that?'

'Because Mark's the sort of man who, when he's got what he wants, might well lose interest and start to look elsewhere...'

Like Nigel.

'Of course once you're his wife it won't matter so much. After one divorce, I imagine he'll be fairly discreet.'

Profoundly disturbed by what her mother was suggesting, Loris had said, 'You sound as if you think he'll stray.'

'Don't most men? And I can't imagine a man like Mark being satisfied with one woman.'

Seeing her daughter's expression, Isobel had added, 'After all, what does it matter? You'll have money and position, a good lifestyle. Mark seems generous enough. Unlike your father.'

'I don't happen to want that kind of marriage,' Loris had said quietly.

'Well, of course I could be totally wrong.' Isobel had hastily backed off. 'Mark is getting to the age where he might be ready to settle for the faithful husband bit...'

Becoming aware that Mark was waiting for a response to something she hadn't heard, Loris said, 'Sorry?'

'I merely remarked that if you're jealous of Pamela, you know what to do about it.'

'But I'm not jealous,' Loris denied calmly.

Looking distinctly put out, Mark asked, 'Then why did you rope in that wimp to dance with you?'

'I didn't "rope him in". He asked me.' Remembering Jonathan Drummond's quiet self-assurance, his firm refusal to be used, she said, 'And I certainly wouldn't describe him as a wimp.'

Eyes narrowing, Mark queried, 'Had you met him before?'

'No.'

'Did he know who you were?'

'Yes.' Remembering his comments about Mark, she added, 'I gather you and he know each other.'

Mark looked down his nose. 'I'd hardly say *know*. I've seen him knocking around the offices.'

'Who is he?'

'Just some Johnny-come-lately. He's over from the States with the Cosby crowd.'

Of course. She recalled that his attractive voice had had a slight American accent.

'What does he do exactly?'

'No idea,' Mark said dismissively. 'He's sat in on most of the meetings, but I gather he's there in some minor capacity. Secretary or PA to one of the executives, or something of the sort. Why do you want to know?'

Unwisely, she admitted, 'I found him interesting.'

Looking at her as if she'd lost her senses, Mark echoed, '*Interesting*?'

'He seemed unusually cool and self-possessed. Very much his own man.'

Mark snorted. 'Though he had the infernal cheek to ask you to dance, I noticed he didn't have the nerve to kiss you.'

'I don't think it was lack of nerve.'

'Then he probably remembered his place.'

'Remembered his place?'

'Well, he's definitely not in our league.'

'I wasn't aware we had a league.' Her voice was as brittle as ice.

Sounding human for the first time, Mark said wryly, 'I thought you came over to apologise, not pick a quarrel.'

'I did. I'm sorry, Mark. Let's not talk about Jonathan Drummond.'

'Drummond, that's his name. I'll keep an eye on him from now on.'

'What do you mean by "keep an eye on him"?'

'Just that. It strikes me he could get too big for his boots.'

Well aware that Mark could be quite petty if he took a dislike to anyone, Loris wished she'd said nothing about Jonathan Drummond.

Wanting to change the subject, she asked lightly, 'So, now I've apologised for being late, are we friends again?'

Ignoring the question, he went off at a tangent. 'You do realise that when we're married you're going to have to give up this ridiculous job. I refuse to have my wife working all hours.'

'I won't be working all hours.'

'You are at the moment.'

'Only because I have to pay an exorbitant rent for my flat.'

'You could have gone on living at home.'

'I didn't want to.' Her desire to be independent had made her move as soon as she was able to support herself.

She made an effort to placate him. 'Once we're married the financial pressure will ease and I'll be able to choose just a few special clients.'

'When we're married you won't need *any* clients.'

'But I *want* to work.'

'I flatly refuse to let any wife of mine go about telling other people how to decorate their homes. It reflects badly on me. You must see that.'

'But what will I *do* all day?'

'Whatever it is that other rich men's wives do.'

Loris, who was about to argue, thought better of it. 'Well, I'm sure we don't need to discuss it just at the moment.'

'No, there are more important things to sort out.' He put an arm around her waist.

'Such as what?'

Bending his head, he said in her ear, 'I've had more than enough of your stalling. I want you to sleep with me tonight.'

'But we're at Monkswood.'

'All the rooms have a double bed. Either you come to me, or let me come to you.'

'No. I couldn't. Not in my parents' house.'

'Don't be an idiot, Loris. They need never know if you don't want them to. And even if we shared a room openly I know your father wouldn't mind. After all, we *are* going to be married. Oh, come on! You're living in the twenty-first century, not Victorian times.'

'Yes, I know, but I still don't feel comfortable about it.'

'Then come back to my flat with me now, and we'll go on to Monkswood afterwards.'

About to make the excuse that she wasn't in the right mood, she hesitated. Perhaps it *was* time she cut herself free from the past.

With today's sexual freedom there was little real justification for holding back, and Mark was clearly getting to the end of his patience.

She had opened her mouth to agree when he muttered angrily, 'Look, Loris, I'm warning you. This time I don't intend to take no for an answer.'

Hating to be pressured in this way, she felt her temper flare, and she snapped, 'I'm afraid you'll have to.'

Perhaps if he'd used his not inconsiderable charm, he might have succeeded in talking her round, but, in a mood for confrontation rather than conciliation, he threw down the gauntlet. 'Damn it, if you won't come back to my flat with me, I know someone who will.'

'I suppose you mean Pamela?'

His smile was an unpleasant combination of smugness and threat. 'She'll come like a shot, and I might just ask her.'

'Why don't you?' Loris said coldly, and, chin held high, stalked away.

Going to the Ladies' Cloakroom, she sat on one of the pink velvet chairs, staring blindly into the gilt-edged mirror while a trickle of women began to collect their coats.

The St Valentine's party was almost over, and as far as she was concerned the whole thing had been a total disaster. Had she known what trouble her being late would cause she would have cancelled her appointment, even if it had meant losing a client.

As it was, she'd displeased her father, made Jonathan Drummond think badly of her and, on this special night for lovers, thoroughly upset Mark.

Thinking of the promising moment that had suddenly metamorphosed into an unpleasant flare-up, she gave a deep sigh. Of course he wouldn't do as he'd threatened. The only reason he'd flaunted his conquest of the blonde had been to add weight to his demands, and his ultimatum had been caused by a build-up of anger that had needed to find an outlet.

But it was ironic to think that if it hadn't been for him jumping in too soon they would have been on their way to his flat by now. Perhaps, rather than reacting in the way she had, it would have been better if she'd controlled her temper and agreed to go, regardless.

Once they were lovers the tension between them would ease. They could go back to being happy and enjoying each other's company, rather than Mark, frustrated and resentful, quite often spoiling things by sulking.

She sighed deeply.

But it wasn't too late. She could always find him and apologise yet again. Tell him she'd changed her mind, she would go with him.

Joining a short queue, Loris collected her belongings.

Then, slipping her evening bag into one of the deep pockets of her cloak, she put the cloak over her arm and, case in hand, made her way into the crowded foyer.

She was scanning the throng for Mark when she noticed the blonde. Wearing an expensive-looking fur coat, Pamela was heading for the exit. As she reached it Mark, who had obviously been waiting for her, stepped into view. An arm around her waist, he escorted her through the heavy glass doors.

For a second or two Loris was shocked into stillness, then, a combination of anger and dismay making her heart beat faster, she pushed her way outside.

It was still raining hard, and she was just in time to see, through the downpour, Mark's silver Mercedes spray water from beneath its wheels as it pulled away from the entrance.

A gusty wind was driving icy rain beneath the hotel's brown and gold canopy but, oblivious to the cold and wet, she stood as if stunned, staring after the car.

'Suppose you put this on before you get saturated?'

Taking her cloak, Jonathan Drummond placed it around her shoulders and pulled the big, loose hood over her dark hair.

He himself was bare-headed, wearing only a short car-coat with the collar turned up.

'Let me have this.' He relieved her of the case.

'Thank you,' she mumbled. Then, unencumbered, began to walk towards a line of waiting taxis drawn up on the forecourt.

Reading her intention, he stopped her. 'I'm afraid you'll find they're all prebooked.'

'Oh,' she said blankly.

Putting his free hand beneath her elbow, he urged her towards a modest white Ford saloon. 'Jump in and I'll drive you home.'

CHAPTER TWO

STILL feeling stunned, Loris found herself being helped into the passenger seat. Her case was tossed in the back, and a moment later Jonathan Drummond slid in beside her.

She had made no move to fasten her seat belt, and he leaned over and fastened it for her. His fair hair was darkened by the wet and, feeling curiously detached, she watched a drop of water trickle down his lean cheek.

As they joined a queue of cars and taxis that were leaving the hotel forecourt and slowly filtering into the stream of late-night traffic, he said, 'You live in Chelsea, I believe?'

Loris pushed back her hood and, making an effort to come to grips with the situation, answered, 'That's right. But I wasn't intending to go to my flat.'

'Whose flat *were* you intending to go to?'

She bit her lip, and stayed silent.

Slanting her a glance, he murmured, 'I see. But you were unexpectedly…shall we say…replaced?'

So he'd seen Mark and the blonde driving away.

Gathering together the tatters of her pride, Loris informed him haughtily, 'I was intending to go down to my parents' house.'

'At Paddleham?'

Wondering how he knew so much, she answered, 'Yes.'

'So Longton was supposed to be going too?'

He was too quick by half. Sounding suitably amazed, she asked, 'How on earth did you deduce that, Holmes?'

Grinning, he answered, 'Elementary, my dear Watson. You didn't go with your parents, you don't have a car, and

23

you hadn't ordered a taxi. Which means you were expecting your fiancé to drive you down.'

Then, sounding as though he cared, 'No wonder you looked shattered, being treated so shabbily.'

'It was partly my own fault,' she admitted.

'All the same, it must hurt like hell.'

She said, 'I'm more angry than hurt.' And discovered it was the truth.

'Stay that way. Anger is easier to cope with.'

As they neared the head of the queue, he asked, 'So which is it to be? Chelsea, or Paddleham?'

'I can't ask you to drive me all the way to Paddleham,' she demurred.

'I'll be happy to, if that's where you want to go?'

'It isn't really,' she confessed, dismayed by the thought of having to try and explain Mark's absence. 'But I can't go back to my flat.'

'Gee that's tough, doll.' Sounding like a gangster in a second-rate movie, he asked out of the corner of his mouth, 'So what are the Mob after you for?'

She laughed in spite of herself.

'It's not quite that bad. I agreed to let an old college friend of mine have my flat for tonight and tomorrow night.'

'And there's only one bedroom?'

'Worse. Judy and Paul are on their honeymoon… Monday, they're flying to Oz to go backpacking.'

'Hmm… Well, if you can't go back to your flat and you don't want to go to Paddleham—' he gave her a villainous leer '—what about my place?'

Loris was about to curtly refuse, when she realised he was pulling her leg.

Lightly, she said, 'I'm afraid I'm superstitious about going anywhere new on a wet Saturday.'

'Pity.'

'But thanks all the same.'

'Think nothing of it. We aim to please. So what's it to be?'

Briefly she considered asking him to take her to a hotel, then dismissed the idea. She could well do without the expense. In any case, by breakfast-time next day her parents would require some kind of explanation. Though she dreaded the prospect, her practical streak insisted that it would make sense to be there in person to make it.

Coming to a decision, she said, 'If you really don't mind, I think I'd better go to Paddleham.'

'Paddleham it is.'

A moment or two later they had joined the traffic stream and were heading out of town through gleaming, rain-lashed streets.

Worrying her bottom lip, she wondered how she was going to explain away Mark's absence.

Of course she could simply tell her parents the truth. But if she did she knew it would be *her* they would be blaming, saying she'd brought it on herself.

Which in a way she had. If she hadn't been late for the party in the first place. Though her lateness, she recognised, had only been the catalyst. None of this would have happened if she'd agreed to sleep with Mark when he'd first pressed her to.

But, even after six years, the remembrance of the shame and humiliation she had suffered over Nigel was still a powerful deterrent.

She had been in her first year at art school when she had met him. The son of Sir Denzyl Roberts, one of her father's wealthy friends, Nigel had been five years older, and light years ahead of her in experience. Expecting her to be like most of the women he had known, he had been surprised and intrigued to find she was supremely innocent.

On her part it had never been a conscious decision to

remain a virgin. It had just happened. Since her early teens her unusual beauty had made her a target for every male aged between fifteen and fifty. But, naturally fastidious, she had kept them at bay, disliking their one-track minds and fly-paper hands. Waiting for someone special. Someone she could love.

There had been one boy, different from the rest, a fleeting attraction that might have developed into something deeper if, before she could get to know him, he hadn't vanished from the scene.

At the same time she had met Nigel. Impressed by his looks and maturity, and perhaps falling in love with love, she had fondly imagined *he* was that someone special.

Even so, almost out of force of habit, she had held him off until, rapidly losing patience, he had proposed to her.

Though she had still been very young, the match, from her parents' point of view, had been an advantageous one and, highly delighted, they had encouraged the engagement.

Once the ring was on her finger, Nigel had redoubled his efforts to get her into bed. Certain she loved him, and happy in the knowledge that they were going to be married, she had given in.

Loris had found their lovemaking disappointing, getting little or nothing from it. She had consoled herself with the thought that it was bound to get better when they were used to each other.

It hadn't.

Blaming herself, her inexperience, she had said nothing, merely kept on trying to please him.

They had been sleeping together for almost three months when, turning up unexpectedly at his flat one evening, intending to surprise him, she had found him with another woman.

Though hurt and bewildered, she had been ready to forgive him, until the girl in his bed had taunted her with the fact that this was no one-off, but was, and had been for some time, a regular arrangement for the nights Loris wasn't there.

'He needs a woman who's got some life in her, who knows how to please a man. Not some frigid statue who just lies there and—'

'That's enough!' Nigel had silenced her at that point.

But it had been too late. As far as Loris was concerned, the damage had been done. Nigel had told this brazen slut of a girl intimate details about something she had considered essentially private and sacrosanct.

Badly humiliated, and furious at the way he had treated her, she had thrown his ring at him and walked out.

When her father and mother had learnt of the broken engagement, deploring the fact that she was 'losing her chance to marry well', they had tried to get her to change her mind. But, while refusing to tell them the reason for the break-up, she had made it clear that it was final.

Judy, her friend and room-mate at college, was the only one in whom she had confided her hurt, but down-to-earth as usual, Judy had pulled no punches. 'Think about it. Would you really *want* to marry a two-timing rat like that?'

'No, I suppose not.'

'Then forget him. He's not worth a second thought.'

'I just wish I hadn't been such a fool.'

'Well, we all make mistakes. It isn't the end of the world.'

It had only felt like it.

'I thought he loved me,' Loris had said sadly. 'But he was only *using* me.'

'Surely you got something out of it?'

Loris had shaken her head wordlessly.

Judy had said a rude word. 'Still, it'll be different next time, you'll see.'

But, feeling degraded by the experience, Loris had

vowed there would *be* no next time. Even so, it had taken her a long while to regain her self-respect...

Flashing lights suddenly reflected in a myriad raindrops, and the urgent sound of a siren bearing down on them brought Loris back to the present with a start.

The road they were on was narrow, and there was on-coming traffic. Pulling half-onto the wet, deserted pavement, Jonathan made room, and a second later the ambulance went racing past on its errand of mercy.

Impressed by his presence of mind, she glanced at him. His face was calm, unperturbed.

Intercepting her glance, he gave her a sidelong smile that quickened her pulse-rate and made her feel suddenly breathless.

A moment later they had regained the road and were continuing their journey. By now they were on the outskirts of town, and the downpour was continuing unabated. Rain beat against the windscreen and even at their fastest speed the wipers had a job to keep it clear.

As they reached a crossroads and turned right it occurred to Loris, belatedly, that she had given him no directions and he had asked for none.

Wondering how, being from the States, he knew the way, she queried, 'Are you familiar with this part of the world?'

'I was born and brought up quite near Paddleham.'

'Really? Then your parents were English?'

'My father, a hard-working GP, was English while my mother, who was an airline stewardess until she married, came from Albany.'

'The capital of New York State?'

'That's right. Her parents owned a small business there.'

To Loris, the details of his modest background seemed at odds with his cultured voice.

'Have you lived in the US long?' she asked, wanting to know more about him.

'For several years now.'

She thought he was going to leave it at that, when he added, 'After my father died my mother got homesick for her birthplace and went back to Albany.'

'Do you have any brothers or sisters?'

'One sister. When she left university she married the son of a local landowner. But there was nothing to keep me here, so I spent some time travelling, trying my hand at various jobs, before I made up my mind to settle in the States.'

His answers had been easy enough, but when he volunteered no further information, afraid of sounding nosy, she relapsed into silence.

Once the suburbs had been left behind them, from being unpleasant, the journey became positively hazardous. The country roads were dark and muddy, littered with snapped-off branches and storm debris.

In the bright tunnel made by their headlights Loris could see that a lot of the verges were partially flooded, and though Jonathan drove with care their nearside wheels almost constantly threw up a wave of water.

Just before they reached their destination a swollen stream that had overflowed its banks, and covered the low-lying road to what he estimated was an unnavigable depth, made a detour necessary. Feeling guilty at having dragged him so far on such a terrible night, Loris was seriously wishing she had plumped for a hotel.

'I'm sorry about all this,' she apologised.

Sounding quite unconcerned, he said, 'You mean the conditions? Don't worry—I've driven in a great deal worse.'

A few more minutes and they were passing through the dark and sleeping village of Paddleham. An occasional streetlamp lit up the driving rain, and strung high across the roadway a saturated banner announcing a St Valentine's dance at the village hall flapped dementedly in the wind.

The Yew Tree came into sight, its inn sign swinging on the supporting chains. 'We're almost there,' Loris said, making no attempt to hide her relief. 'Just past the church there's a turning off to the left, then about half a mile down the lane, also on the left, you'll see the entrance to Monkswood. The gates should be open.'

The black and gold wrought-iron gates were open wide, and the Tarmacked drive was well-lit. Several sleek cars were parked on the paved apron in front of the house.

Jonathan drew up beneath the ornate lantern that hung over the porticoed entrance and, leaving the engine running, came round to help Loris out.

She couldn't fail to notice that, parked between a Porsche and a Mercedes, the ordinary little car looked out of place.

Key in hand, she had opened the door by the time he had retrieved her case. A chandelier in the hall, and one at the top of the grand staircase, had been left on, but the rest of the house was dark and still.

'I can't thank you enough for bringing me,' she said, as he handed over her case.

'It was my pleasure.' Briskly, he added, 'Well, everyone seems to be in bed, so I'll say goodnight and let you join them.'

As though her subconscious had already decided, she found herself saying, 'Please, won't you stay? I'd hate to think of you having to drive all the way back to town on a night like this.'

'I wouldn't want to put you to so much trouble.'

'It's the very least I can do. And it really is no trouble. Do stay. You can have Mark's room.'

Though he never moved a muscle, Loris sensed his surprise. Obviously he'd presumed that she and Mark shared a room.

'In that case I'll be happy to.'

Crossing to the car, he switched off the engine and doused the lights before joining her in the hall and relieving her of her case once more.

When she had closed the door behind him, and shot the heavy bolts, she turned and led the way up the richly carpeted stairs and through a decorative archway to the right.

'This is my room.' Taking her case from him, she put it inside before crossing the wide corridor to open a door opposite. 'And this is Mark's.'

Switching on the lights, she led the way into a comfortably furnished bedroom decorated in masculine colours of blue and grey.

'He doesn't leave clothes here, so I'm afraid I can't offer you any pyjamas.'

'That's all right.' Jonathan smiled. 'I don't use them.'

Feeling her colour rise, she said hastily, 'But you should find a new toothbrush and everything else you need in the bathroom cabinet.'

'Thank you.'

A thought struck her, and she added regretfully, 'Except a shaver, that is. I'm sorry.'

He shrugged. 'Don't worry. Though I can't see myself with a beard, in an emergency I have been known to wear designer stubble.'

'Well, goodnight.'

'Goodnight, Loris,' he said gravely.

Feeling curiously restless and unsettled, she went back to her own room and was about to prepare for bed when she thought of her stepbrother.

Though Monkswood was virtually Simon's second home, he wasn't going to be here this weekend. Consequently, in his bathroom, there would almost certainly be a razor that their last-minute guest could borrow.

Without further ado she hastened barefoot along the

darkened corridor to Simon's room and went in quietly. Sure enough, on the bathroom shelf was an electric razor. If Jonathan Drummond hadn't already gone to bed, she could give it to him now, ready for the morning.

As she reached his room she saw through the multicoloured fanlight above the door that his light was still on. Bearing in mind that not too far away people were sleeping, she tapped softly. When there was no answer, she tried again. Still no answer.

Perhaps he was in the bathroom?

She opened the door a crack, and could just make out the sound of the shower running. Deciding to leave the razor where he couldn't fail to notice it, she slipped inside and tiptoed across the room to put it on the bedside cabinet.

Turning back to the door, she gave a half-stifled gasp. Just emerging from the bathroom, Jonathan was in the act of pulling on a short white towelling robe. His hair was wet and rumpled, and drops of water still clung to the fine golden fuzz on his legs.

Without undue haste or self-consciousness, he adjusted the robe and fastened the belt.

Thrown by how irresistibly sexy he looked, and feeling a sudden potent attraction, she stammered, 'I—I did knock, but you must have been in the shower. I've brought you Simon's razor. He won't be wanting it this weekend.'

A well-marked brow rose. 'Simon?'

'My stepbrother.'

'Ah, yes…'

Embarrassed to realise she was still standing goggling at him like a fool, Loris prepared to make her escape. Only to find that, somehow, Jonathan was between her and the door.

'I'll say goodnight again.' She was aware that she sounded breathless.

He took her hand, while green eyes smiled into gold.

Wits scattered, she stood gazing back at him like someone mesmerised, before making an effort to free her hand.

When he failed to release it, she said huskily, 'I must go.'

'Must you?'

Without realising how provocative it looked, she used the tip of her tongue to moisten lips gone suddenly dry.

Using the hand he was holding to draw her closer, he said softly, 'This time I think I'll take you up on the invitation.'

His free hand slid under the fall of dark silky hair to cup the back of her head, and a second later his mouth was covering hers.

Loris found his light kiss both pleasurable and exciting. But though it sent a tingle right down to her toes there was nothing alarming about it, nothing to warn her that she was in any danger.

While part of her mind pointed out that she shouldn't be letting this happen, another part answered that, as kisses went, it was relatively innocent.

She wasn't caught up, wasn't *involved*… She could walk away whenever she pleased.

But she hadn't reckoned on the seductive sweetness that, almost without her realising it, made her want the kiss to go on, made her want to kiss him back.

As her lips parted, his tongue-tip stroked along the velvety-smooth inner skin, making her quiver, before he deepened the kiss.

Mark's kisses were ardent, hot-blooded, sometimes bruising in their intensity. They totally lacked the finesse, the subtlety and imagination of this man's lovemaking.

He explored her mouth with a kind of delicate enjoyment that sent little shudders running through her, while, almost unnoticed, his free hand traced her slender curves.

When it found the soft swell of her breast and his thumb

brushed coaxingly over the nipple, she knew it was time to call a halt.

But the sensations that the thistledown-touch was arousing were so exquisite that every bone in her body seemed to melt, and an awakening hunger that refused to be stilled cried out for more.

Responding to that hunger, his lovemaking gradually became more intense as he added a new and disturbing dimension.

Passion.

But it wasn't a tempestuous, uncontrolled passion that might have swamped any response, or served to scare her. This was a leashed passion that lured her onwards, that enticed and invited an answering passion, until suddenly she was lost. Mindless. Carried away. Caught and held in a web of sensual delight…

Loris stirred and surfaced slowly from a deep and contented sleep, to find grey morning light was filtering into the room.

Though her mind was still enshrouded in a kind of golden haze, she was dimly aware that her body felt relaxed and satisfied.

She was stretching luxuriously when one of her feet brushed against a man's hair-roughened leg.

Shock hit her, and she stiffened as the sharp, cold wind of memory blew in, dispersing the haze.

Oh, dear heaven, what had she done?

After putting off her own fiancé for several months she had gone to bed with a virtual stranger.

She only just stopped herself groaning aloud.

Lying unnaturally still, afraid to move a finger, she listened to Jonathan Drummond's quiet, even breathing.

Satisfied that he wasn't yet awake, she turned her head slowly to look at him.

He was lying facing her, so close that they were almost

touching. His tanned skin was clear and healthy, his breath sweet. There were grooves each side of his mouth, and little laughter-lines radiated from the corners of his eyes. Thick, gold-tipped lashes lay like a fan on his high cheekbones.

It was the face she remembered from the previous night, yet not the same.

The mature self-assurance and the somewhat disturbing irony were gone from it. With his tousled hair and his confident mouth relaxed in sleep he looked endearingly boyish, in spite of the morning stubble adorning his chin.

But there had been nothing remotely boyish about him last night. His lovemaking had proved him to be a skilful and experienced man.

Heat ran through her as she remembered all the things he had made her feel, and her own unexpectedly passionate response. After the fiasco with Nigel, she had started to wonder uneasily if she might be frigid. That had been one of the reasons she had remained celibate for so long. She had been afraid to start another relationship in case the same thing happened.

But last night had proved that she could be warm and responsive and far from frigid. The fault hadn't been hers.

Nigel, she knew now, had been a selfish, uncaring, inept lover who, as well as mangling her self-respect, had almost destroyed her faith in herself as a woman.

Jonathan's skill and generosity, his imaginative lovemaking, had triggered a response that had shaken her to the core. For the first time in her life she had experienced all the joy and delight she had only ever dreamt about.

If it had been Mark she had spent the night with, she would be on top of the world.

Only it hadn't been Mark.

Rather than her own fiancé, it had been a man she had only just met. A man who would no doubt consider her *easy* and, in the cold light of day, feel nothing but contempt for her.

Gathering her wits, and desperate to get away before he awoke, Loris turned carefully onto her side. Her back to him, she was about to ease herself towards the edge of the bed when she felt him stir.

His arm came around her, and with a sleepy murmur of contentment he moved his warm palm to cup her breast.

Like some terrified animal, she froze into utter stillness, her heart pounding. She could feel the heat from his body, and his light breath stirring her hair.

After a moment or two his breathing returned to the evenness of sleep, the arm across her grew heavier, and she felt his hand relax its hold.

Taking a deep breath, she moved cautiously onto her back. Slowly, and with the greatest care, she eased herself from beneath the surprisingly muscular arm and slipped out of bed.

Though on one level she had *known* she was bare, the sight of her nakedness in the full-length mirror made her cringe. She averted her eyes.

The sooner she had put something on and was out of here the better.

Her last night's clothes were lying in an abandoned heap, one silk stocking trailing seductively.

She was reaching for her undies when a movement in the corridor outside brought her heart into her mouth. People were up and stirring, making their way down for breakfast.

Suppose one of the guests saw her creeping from room to room, still wearing what was obviously a party dress?

The towelling robe Jonathan had worn the previous night was tossed over a chair. Snatching it up, she pulled it on and fastened the belt. A quick glance at the bed, meant to reassure herself that he was still fast asleep, gave her a fresh shock. His green eyes brilliant, he was lying quietly watching her.

Gathering up her belongings, she fled without a word. Her timing couldn't have been worse. Just outside the door she ran slap into her father.

'So you did make it.' He didn't sound particularly pleased. 'I thought you might have changed your mind about coming. Our journey here was bad enough, and conditions were deteriorating fast.'

If only she had known how things were going to turn out, Loris thought vainly, she could have used the weather as an excuse for not being there...

Eyeing the tell-tale clothes she was clutching, her father added drily, 'Mark having a lie-in?'

She was saved from having to answer by a female voice cooing, 'Oh, *good morning*, Sir Peter.'

A red-haired overdressed woman she had never seen before was heading towards them.

Always a ladies' man, her father assumed an expression of charm. 'Good morning, Mrs Delacost. So sorry we weren't here to welcome you last night.'

'That's quite all right, Sir Peter. We didn't get back from Monte Carlo until quite late, and your wife *did* explain about the company's party...'

As she spoke, the redhead glanced curiously in Loris's direction.

Noting that look, Peter said without warmth, 'This is my daughter, Loris.'

Seeing her chance, Loris murmured a hasty, 'Good morning,' and bolted into her room.

As the pair moved away she could hear Mrs Delacost gushing, 'It was *so* nice of you to invite us to your lovely home...'

All of a tremble, Loris sank down on the nearest chair

and, twisting the magnificent half-hoop of diamonds she wore round and round her finger, gave a groan of despair.

Her father had been all for the engagement, encouraging it in every way possible, and she sensed that he had been far from displeased to find her leaving Mark's room. But when he discovered that Mark wasn't here it would be a very different story. He was likely to be livid, and that was putting it mildly.

She felt a leaden weight in the pit of her stomach.

Though he had never so much as raised his hand to her, preferring an icy silence or a cold reprimand when she displeased him, Loris had always shrunk from his anger.

But she was a twenty-four-year-old woman and independent, she reminded herself, not some schoolgirl. He had no right to tell her what or what not to do. No right to complain about her actions...

Except that it was his house. The last place she would have chosen to go off the rails and humiliate herself.

And that was exactly what she had done. It had been a stupid mistake. A one-night stand with no feelings on either side. She had been mentally condemning Mark, but she was no better. The only difference was that Mark's decision to sleep with someone else had been premeditated. Whereas hers had been anything but.

So where did that leave her engagement?

In trouble.

With the beginnings of a headache, she longed for a cup of coffee but, resisting the temptation to ring for some and linger over it, she went through to the bathroom to shower.

She would have to show her face and give some kind of explanation sooner or later, so better to get it over with. Though what explanation could she give for spending the night with a virtual stranger? She couldn't even explain to herself what had made her behave so out of character.

But perhaps it was better not to try and explain anything.

Merely give the bare facts and then relieve them of her company, even if it meant staying at a hotel.

Having made the decision, she was starting to feel a shade better when it occurred to her that she couldn't get back to London unless she left with Jonathan Drummond.

No! That wasn't an option. She would sooner call a taxi. The thought of driving all that way with the man who had seduced her was insupportable. Not that she hadn't been a willing victim, honesty forced her to admit. The blame was hers as much as his.

Belatedly it occurred to her to wonder how *he* was feeling. His behaviour hadn't been exactly praiseworthy.

Possibly, depending on what kind of man he was, he would be embarrassed by what had happened? Maybe he'd be as anxious to leave as she was to have him go? He'd been wide awake when she had left his room, so with a bit of luck he would just dress and slip quietly away.

When she had dried herself, she made-up lightly to hide an unusual paleness before dressing in fine wool trousers the colour of tobacco, a cream blouse, and an embroidered waistcoat. Then, summoning up every ounce of composure she could muster, she lifted her chin and sallied forth.

Drawn like a magnet to the door of the room opposite, she stood listening. Not a sound. Did that mean he'd already gone? She fervently hoped so. Shamed and mortified by her own weakness, she dreaded the thought of having to meet him face to face again.

And there was another consideration. An important one. If he'd gone without anyone seeing him she wouldn't have to divulge exactly *who* had slept in Mark's room. That would save trouble all round. Though she had no reason to try and *protect* Jonathan Drummond, if Mark and her father were to learn his identity it could cost him dear. They would, she felt sure, pressure Cosby's into getting rid of him on one pretext or another.

Needing to know for sure, she opened the door quietly and, holding her breath, peered inside. The room was blessedly empty, and the bathroom door, standing ajar, showed that was too.

Going over to the window, which overlooked the apron and the smooth green lawns at the front of the house, she peered out.

The rain had temporarily ceased, though the sky was heavy and overcast, threatening more. The garden looked battered and waterlogged, and shallow pools of water had gathered on the apron.

All the other sleek cars were still standing where they had been the previous night, but she could see no sign of the white saloon that Jonathan had been driving.

He must have gone back to London.

Sighing her relief, she made her way downstairs to the breakfast-room.

CHAPTER THREE

IN THE big, east-facing room all the lights were burning to counteract the dullness of the day. A few of the guests were still eating a late breakfast, while others lingered to converse over coffee, or glance through the Sunday papers.

There was no sign of her father, for which Loris was truly thankful. Though she recognised that it was cowardly, her impulse was to delay any showdown for as long as possible.

With a general, 'Good morning,' to the assembled company, she made her way to the end of the long table, where she froze in her tracks.

Sitting buttering toast and talking to her mother as though it was the most natural thing in the world, was Jonathan Drummond.

Fair hair smoothly brushed and shining under the lights, white teeth gleaming as he smiled in response to something Isobel had said, he looked infuriatingly attractive.

Glancing up, he saw her, and rose to his feet politely. 'Good morning.'

He was dressed in a pair of charcoal trousers, a pale-green shirt and matching tie, and a jacket she recognised as Simon's.

To her chagrin, he appeared cool and assured, every inch master of the situation.

Feeling the hot, embarrassed colour rising in her cheeks, somehow she answered, 'Good morning.' Then raggedly, 'I thought you'd gone.'

'Oh?' He came around the end of the table and pulled out a chair for her.

41

Sinking into it, she said almost accusingly, 'Your car wasn't there.'

'As I'd left it right in front of the entrance, I thought I'd better move it.'

Returning to his seat, and reaching for the marmalade, he added innocently, 'Your mother suggested that as it was a hired car it might be better in one of the garages.'

To get it out of sight, no doubt, as it lowered the tone. The words were unspoken, but the sardonic twist to his lips said it all.

Refilling his coffee cup, Isobel smiled at him, the perfect hostess, making it clear that, though his car might not be up to scratch, she found him very personable.

To Loris, she said expansively, 'Jonathan tells me he's with Cosby's…'

Wondering if her mother knew he was just a lowly PA, and deciding that she obviously didn't, Loris said nothing.

'I thought I remembered him from Ascot or somewhere, but obviously I was wrong…'

Ignoring the dishes keeping warm on the sideboard, Loris poured herself some coffee and drank it gratefully while her mother pursued, 'I've just been saying how very kind it was of him to bring you all the way to Monkswood on such a night.'

Realising she was expected to add something, Loris agreed woodenly, 'Yes, wasn't it?'

Isobel turned to Jonathan and, as though to make up for her daughter's marked lack of sociability, said, 'I'm so pleased Loris managed to persuade you to stay.' Then, without much hope, 'Do you play whist or bridge by any chance?'

'Both. Though not particularly well.'

'At the last minute Colonel Jefferson couldn't come, so anyone who plays cards at all will be a welcome addition to our little party.'

'Oh, but Mr Drummond can't possibly stay for the rest of the weekend,' Loris said with more force than politeness.

Looking surprised by her daughter's vehemence, Isobel pointed out, 'It would make sense. Apparently the Elder has overflowed its banks and quite a few of the local roads are flooded, so the journey back to town could be very difficult.'

'But h-he wasn't prepared to stay.' Loris tried to sound practical rather than panic-stricken. 'I mean, it's a question of clothes and things…'

'Clothes aren't a problem. Luckily Jonathan and Simon are much of a size, and Simon has a whole wardrobe of things he hasn't even worn.'

With a speaking glance at him, Loris said, 'But I'm sure Mr Drummond—'

Face straight, but a wicked gleam in his eyes, he broke in, 'Oh, surely we know each other well enough for you to call me Jonathan.'

Biting her lip, she went on, 'I'm sure *Jonathan* has to get back. We can't expect him to—'

'As I've already told your mother, I'd be delighted to stay,' he broke in smoothly.

Wondering what he was up to, Loris glared at him in helpless fury.

'There! You see, it's all settled,' Isobel said a little testily, 'and has been for the past half-hour. I'm having Simon's bed made up for Jonathan so that if Mark manages to get here after all he can have his usual room. Though he seemed doubtful at first—'

'You've spoken to him?'

'He rang up about twenty minutes ago to apologise for his absence and say he was sorry not to have come down as planned.'

'Does Dad know?'

Isobel shook her head. 'Your father went straight out

after breakfast. He's with Reynolds, checking on reported storm damage to some of the cottages on the estate.'

'When you talked to Mark, did he tell you what had happened last night?' Loris asked cautiously.

'Apparently Alan Gresham's daughter suddenly felt unwell, and because no taxi was immediately available, he offered to drive her home...'

Catching Jonathan's eye, Loris saw a kind of amused contempt there.

'As your father and I had already left, it's just as well that Mark was on hand to do duty as a host.'

Judging by Isobel's insouciance, she hadn't the faintest idea that Alan Gresham's daughter and 'that blonde creature' were one and the same.

'He said he'd get hold of you and, if conditions allowed, possibly bring you down in time for lunch. He seemed very surprised when I told him you were already here...'

I bet he did, Loris thought cynically.

'The whole thing, it seems, was a misunderstanding. He couldn't find you to tell you what was happening, and then when he got back to the hotel you were nowhere to be seen and almost everyone had gone. He thought that, because of the weather, you must have made up your mind to go straight home instead of coming down here.'

Obviously wondering if they'd had a quarrel, her mother asked, 'What made you decide to come without him?'

'My flat was occupied.'

'Occupied?'

'I've lent it to Judy and Paul for last night and tonight.'

'Even so—'

'They're on their honeymoon.'

'Oh. Still, it's worked out quite well. Or rather will have done when Mark gets here.'

'I thought you said he might not be coming?'

'He seemed doubtful at first, but as soon as he knew you

were here he said he was definitely going to try to get down.'

Loris found herself hoping fervently that he wouldn't succeed. The situation would be quite bad enough when her father discovered what had happened, without Mark's presence adding to the problems.

'Though I don't know what his chances are...'

'If he stays on the main road as far as Harefield, and then takes Dewy Lane, which runs along higher ground, he might manage to get through,' Jonathan said with a cheerful optimism that grated on Loris's frayed nerves.

Vexedly, she wondered why he sounded so laid-back, so unconcerned at the prospect of the other man arriving?

Probably he imagined she would keep quiet about what had happened the previous night. And if things had been different, unwilling to broadcast her shame, she no doubt would have done. But what he didn't know, so had failed to take into account, was the unfortunate meeting with her father.

Once Mark and her father had talked, the fat would be in the fire. As well as being furious with *her*, both men would be out for Jonathan's blood, and there was bound to be trouble.

Plainly surprised, Isobel was saying, 'It sounds as if you know this part of the world well?'

'I do.'

'Then you haven't always lived in the States?'

'Only for the past few years. I was born and brought up quite near here.'

'Oh!' She beamed at him. 'Then possibly you know Sir Hugh Drummond?'

Loris sighed. Her mother, who was from a relatively modest background and always tried to hide it, was a down-right snob.

Jonathan raised a fair brow. 'The rich and aristocratic owner of Merriton Hall?'

Oblivious to the irony, she said, 'Yes. Is he any relation—your father, perhaps?'

Watching his hostess's face, he told her calmly, 'My father was a poor GP.'

Looking on, Loris wondered why he'd deliberately added 'poor'. Had he got a chip on his shoulder about not being well off? Or was he making a point of some kind?

Hurriedly changing the subject, Isobel said with forced brightness, 'I'm afraid we've made no real plans for today. Outdoor sporting activities seem to be largely ruled out. Mark, who used to play rugby for his school, was intending to fill in as a forward for the local team, but the game's been cancelled because the pitch is under water. However, we have a squash court and a games room, and there's a billiard table in the library. There's also a late-morning service at St Barnabas that I and some of our guests are planning to go to, if you'd care to join us?'

'Thank you. But I thought I might persuade Loris into taking a walk with me.' Addressing Loris, he went on, 'It isn't raining, and it shouldn't be too bad underfoot if we walk up to and along Stonywood Ridge.'

She needed a walk, but the last thing she wanted was Jonathan Drummond's company.

About to politely refuse, she thought better of it. His continuing presence at Monkswood was only going to invite more trouble, but if she could get him to where they wouldn't be overheard and warn him he might see sense and decide to leave as soon as possible.

'A walk sounds like a good idea,' she said with what cordiality she could muster. 'I could do with a breath of fresh air and some exercise.'

Looking somewhat surprised by her daughter's prompt acceptance, Isobel said, 'In that case I'll go and get ready for church. See you at lunchtime. With a bit of luck Mark will be here by then.'

An unholy gleam in his eye, Jonathan murmured, 'That sounds like fun.'

Ignoring his remark, Loris jumped to her feet. Just in case her father returned, the sooner they were out of the house the better she'd like it. 'Well, if you want to go for that walk...'

'Indeed I do.' Following her from the now empty breakfast-room, he added, 'Though as evening shoes aren't exactly suitable for cross-country hikes, I may need to borrow a pair of brogues.'

'I take it you know which is Simon's room?' she asked curtly, leading the way upstairs.

'Yes. Isobel, as she insisted I call her, took me along there earlier.'

Watching his companion's soft mouth tighten, he smiled grimly. 'I'm quite aware that you would sooner I'd just sneaked off like some criminal, or even vanished in a puff of smoke, rather than meet your mother.' As Loris's colour rose, he added, 'But when I was on my way downstairs, I ran into her...'

It seemed to be the morning for unfortunate meetings, Loris thought with wry humour.

'I was forced to explain my presence, and why I was still wearing evening dress. She was very gracious.'

'Yes, she would be,' Loris said drily, remembering his impeccable evening clothes.

Picking up her meaning instantly, he asked ironically, 'So you think it would have been better if I'd claimed kinship with Sir Hugh Drummond?'

'No, I don't. And if you're expecting me to apologise for her snobbery...'

'I'm not. You can hardly be held responsijble for her faults. Though she may well be responsible for yours.'

Loris flinched. 'If you think I wanted you to go because I was ashamed of you—'

'Didn't you?'

Golden eyes flashing, she denied, 'No, I most certainly did not. I *was* ashamed. But it was of myself.'

He gave her a keen, curious glance. 'I don't—'

They had reached the door of her room and, before he could complete whatever it was he was going to say, she turned the knob and asked quickly, 'Perhaps we can get ready and talk later?'

'By all means.' Without further ado, he disappeared in the direction of Simon's room.

As soon as Loris had replaced her thin waistcoat with a cream wool jumper, and changed into walking shoes and an anorak, she hurried back.

He was waiting in the corridor, similarly attired.

They left the house without speaking and, following the old red brick wall that bounded the Monkswood Estate, took the path that ran between it and the woods.

It was cold with a blustery wind but, though the clouds looked threatening, the impending rain had held off. They were both bare-headed, and collars turned up around their ears, they walked briskly, avoiding a litter of small branches and storm debris.

When they reached clearer, rising ground, she slowed a little and, walking side by side, they fell comfortably into step. He seemed appreciably taller this morning, and she realised it was because she was wearing flat heels.

She was wondering how to broach the subject of his leaving when he broke the silence to say, 'After your initial rather *cool* reception, I'm curious to know why you agreed to come walking with me.' Mockingly he added, 'I don't suppose it was because you wanted my company?'

'You don't suppose right,' she informed him shortly. 'I wanted to ask you to go.'

'Tell me something. Is it just *me* you can't bear the sight of? Or do you prefer all your one-night stands to quietly disappear the following morning?'

'How dare you?' she choked, almost too furious to speak. 'I don't go in for one-night stands. Last night was the first and only time I've ever...'

'Cheated on your fiancé?' he suggested, as she paused to search for the right words.

'Allowed myself to be seduced.'

'Without wishing to sound ungallant, may I point out that you *invited* it.'

'I did no such thing,' she flared.

'You came back to my room on the pretext of bringing me a razor—'

'That *wasn't* a pretext.' Seeing he was far from convinced, she insisted, '*Truly* it wasn't.'

He frowned. 'Why don't you admit that the whole thing was just another game of tit-for-tat?'

'Tit-for-tat?' she echoed blankly.

'Your fiancé had gone off with another woman, so you invited me to stay the night, to have his room, so that I was *handy*, so to speak.'

Remembering the little scene on the dance floor, she stopped walking abruptly and turned to him, a look of horror on her face. 'You don't honestly think that? Think I was just *using* you to retaliate?'

'What else can I think?'

Suddenly it seemed very important to convince him that she'd had no such intention. 'You're wrong. Quite wrong,' she cried passionately. 'I may have a lot of faults, but I'm not that kind of woman. A kiss on a dance floor, when everyone else was kissing, would have been one thing, but I would never have dreamt of going to those lengths...'

'Well, if it wasn't a spot of retaliation, and you don't go

in for one-night stands, why did you come back to my room?'

'I've told you.'

'You mean it really *was* just to bring me a razor?'

'Yes.'

'Then all I can say is you're remarkably naïve.'

'Stupid would be a better word,' she corrected him bitterly.

He took both her hands in his and said gently, 'I'm sorry.'

'For thinking so badly of me? Or for seducing me?'

'Both. I'm not in the habit of seducing other men's fiancées, except...'

'Except when they invite it?'

Shaking his head, he said, 'I'm sorry, I completely misread the signs. I thought you wanted me to make love to you as much as I wanted to. It seemed a—' He broke off abruptly, then went on, 'I should have realised I was mistaken when you ran like a frightened rabbit this morning. Believe me, I didn't mean it to be like this, and I blame myself very much.' He released her hands. 'If you'd like to go back to the house now, I'll leave as soon as I've changed.'

It was what she had wanted to hear, yet, fundamentally honest, she found she couldn't let him go thinking he was entirely to blame.

Lifting her chin, her face as red as a poppy, she said, 'It's quite true that the razor wasn't a pretext; it's also true that I've never before indulged in casual sex—'

He raised an eyebrow at the *casual*. 'I thought it was rather more than that.'

'How could it be? Two virtual strangers...'

'Did the fact that we were virtual strangers matter? Wasn't how we made each other feel much more important?'

When, not knowing quite what to say, she remained silent, he pursued, 'I thought you enjoyed it as much as I did. Was I wrong again?'

No, he wasn't wrong. It had been wonderful, but she wasn't about to tell him so.

Ignoring the question, she went on doggedly, 'The point I'm making is that you weren't wholly to blame. I'm as responsible for what happened as you are. I *did* want you to make love to me.'

With betraying candour, she added, 'It's so *unlike* me. That's why I couldn't face you this morning. I felt dreadfully ashamed. I thought you'd think I was *easy*. In the event, you thought even worse of me.'

'For which I'm sincerely sorry.'

'I'm sorry too. Sorry for involving you in something that could have very unpleasant consequences.'

He gazed down at her enchanting face. Her golden eyes were serious beneath a black, wind-ruffled fringe, her small nose was red with cold and her generous mouth looked pinched.

Suppressing a powerful desire to kiss some colour into those pale lips, he said abruptly, 'Let's walk on. It's getting cold standing here.'

Because her mind was on other things, Loris had scarcely noticed the cold until then. But as he spoke she became aware that her feet were numb and her whole body was chilled and on the verge of shivering. Trying to stop her teeth chattering, she objected, 'But I thought we were going back.'

'It's a fair way back, and you look half-frozen. What if we walk as far as the Lamb and Flag—it'll only take a couple of minutes—and have a pot of hot coffee?'

She was torn. The prospect of some hot coffee was a very welcome one, but at the same time she wanted him safely out of the way before Mark arrived and her father discovered what had happened.

As she hesitated, Jonathan took her hand. 'Come on, it's starting to rain.' Fingers twined in hers, he began to hurry her up the lane that led to the pub.

The Lamb and Flag, a picturesque black and white half-timbered building with overhanging eaves and a decided list to starboard, was an old coaching inn, left mercifully unmodernised.

Inside, the white walls were of rough plaster, and the low ceiling was oak-beamed. In the inglenook fireplace at the far end of the room a huge log fire blazed and crackled. The floor was made of grey stone slabs, polished smooth by time and the passage of many feet.

At the moment, however, the place was empty, apart from the buxom landlady behind the bar who was replacing glasses.

'Nasty cold morning,' she greeted them cheerfully.

'It is,' Jonathan agreed.

As though to add point to their words, a flurry of sleet was thrown against the leaded windows.

'What will you have?' She gave them a big, hospitable smile.

'Can you manage a large pot of coffee?'

'I can indeed. If you want to take a seat by the fire, I'll fetch it over to you.'

Having helped Loris off with her anorak, Jonathan removed his own and hung them both on one of the large wooden pegs just inside the door.

She saw that he'd replaced his jacket with a dark-green sweater that made him look even fairer, and even more attractive.

Feeling the unwelcome pull of that attraction, she carefully avoided his eyes as they crossed to the fire. When they were comfortably ensconced in front of it, Loris took off her shoes and stretched her icy feet gratefully to the warmth. Some life was returning to them by the time the landlady brought over the coffee and two heated pottery mugs.

Addressing them both, she said, 'Though we're not expecting many customers on a morning like this, there'll be some food ready in about half an hour, if you want to eat.' Then, to Jonathan, 'It's one of your favourites today. Chicken and pasta bake.'

'It sounds as if you're a regular,' Loris remarked as the landlady disappeared kitchenwards.

'I've popped in a few times since I've been back,' he said casually.

'I thought you lived in town?'

'Yes, I do, during the week. But since I returned to England I've been in this area most weekends, visiting old haunts.'

Loris reached to pour the coffee, which was good and hot and accompanied by thick, country cream and brown sugar.

She didn't usually take either, but, with no weight problem to worry about, she treated herself to a spoonful of sugar and a generous helping of cream, while Jonathan drank his black.

Both their cups had been drained and replenished, and Loris was trying to think of the best way to tell him what he would have to know, when he pre-empted her by remarking, 'You mentioned something about unpleasant consequences...'

'Yes.' She sighed. 'When Mark finds out what's happened, he's bound to be livid.'

'I wouldn't have thought he had any justification for being livid,' Jonathan remarked levelly. 'After all, he was, in a manner of speaking, the first to stray from the fold.'

'He's not likely to take that into account. In any case,

two wrongs don't make a right—' even as she spoke, Loris was unhappily aware how very prim and self-righteous she sounded '—and in a way, I drove him to it.'

Jonathan's fair, well-marked brows rose. '*You* drove him to it? Surely you don't mean by being late for the party?'

'Well, partly… Though there was a lot more to it than that.'

'A growing incompatibility?' he hazarded.

'Certainly not.' Seeing he was waiting for an explanation, her colour rising, she added, 'It's something I'd rather not talk about.'

'But because you feel guilty, to salve your conscience, you intend to confess all?'

'No. The truth is, I don't have much option. You see, when I was leaving your room this morning I ran into my father in the corridor. I was carrying my clothes. Last night's party dress…'

'Ah! A dead giveaway.' Humorously, he added, 'So why didn't he come bursting in with a shotgun?'

'Because it was Mark's room, and he didn't realise that Mark hadn't come down as planned.'

'I see… And of course he was used to you sleeping with your fiancé?'

As she began to shake her head he said, 'No, that doesn't make sense. If your parents know you two sleep together, why were you given separate rooms? Surely it wasn't just for the look of the thing?'

'They don't know.'

'Then you were quite used to corridor creeping?'

'No,' she said sharply.

He lifted a quizzical brow. 'You mean if you were under your parents' roof you went all Victorian?'

She failed to answer, and he queried thoughtfully, 'When your father saw you leaving, as he thought, Longton's bed, was he unhappy about it?'

'The contrary, I think, after what had happened at the party. You see, Mark and he have always got along very well, and he's looking forward to having him for a son-in-law…'

'That's understandable. They're similar types.'

'No, not really…' But even as she started to deny it she knew he was right; they *were* similar types. Her mother had already spotted it.

Though she had done her utmost, Loris had never really got along with her father. Now, made uncomfortable by the sudden realisation of how alike he and her fiancé were, she bit her lip.

'So, while he had no objection to you sleeping with Longton, there'll almost certainly be the devil to pay when he discovers that it *wasn't* Longton you'd spent the night with.'

'Exactly,' she said. Adding with renewed urgency, 'That's why I want you to leave before Mark gets here and he *does* find out.'

'I'm not much for running. Unless you've decided to run with me?'

'No, I haven't. What would be the use? I'll have to face them all some time, so I may as well get it over with. But the sooner *you* go the better…'

She reached for her shoes in preparation for leaving.

A hand on her arm, he stopped her. 'There's no hurry. As it's already gone twelve…'

Gone twelve! She hadn't realised how late it was.

'…and I can vouch for the cooking, I suggest we grab a spot of lunch before we start back.'

As she began to shake her head, he asked coaxingly, 'Wouldn't you sooner lunch here, just the two of us in front of a good fire, rather than at Monkswood?'

The true answer was yes. Almost anything would be preferable to lunching at home. But there simply wasn't time.

'You didn't have any breakfast,' he went on, 'so you must be getting hungry.'

'No... No, I'm not.'

'Well, I am.'

Her agitation obvious, she insisted, 'But we haven't *time* to stay for lunch. Surely you can get something to eat on the way back to London?'

'I've decided not to go back just yet.'

'But you *must*...'

Mark was possessive, and tended to be jealous for no good reason. On one occasion he'd threatened to knock a waiter down merely for 'ogling' her.

Now there *was* a good reason she shuddered to think what might happen. If he lost his temper and it came to a fight Jonathan was a few inches shorter, slimly built and a good three stone lighter.

'Mark can be very intimidating when he loses his temper,' she added.

'Dear me,' Jonathan said mildly. 'I really can't think of anything worse than being intimidated by a six-feet-four-inch rugby forward.'

She gritted her teeth. 'I wish you'd be serious.'

'You think I'm not?'

'This is no laughing matter. He'll be absolutely furious.'

'Won't he be furious with you too?'

'Yes,' she admitted. 'But he wouldn't hit a woman—'

She broke off as the landlady emerged to say, 'If you want to eat, it's just ready. Shall I bring it through?'

Loris was about to politely refuse when Jonathan answered easily, 'That would be great, Mrs Lawson.'

As Mrs Lawson bustled away, Loris begged desperately. '*Please,* Jonathan...'

'It's nice of you to be so concerned about me.'

'It's not *nice*, it's *necessary.* You've never seen Mark

when he's in a rage. While he wouldn't dream of hitting a woman, he'll have no compunction about beating up a man.'

'And you faint at the sight of blood?'

Concerned for his safety, and angry with him for treating the whole thing so lightly, she felt her eyes fill with tears of frustration. 'Don't you see? If you get hurt I'll feel to blame.'

Taking her hand, he raised it to his lips and said gently, 'There's no need to worry. While I'm far from being Superman, I'm not exactly a seven-stone weakling. I can take care of myself.'

Suddenly, without rhyme or reason, she felt it likely that he could.

As though reading her mind, he smiled at her and suggested, 'So why don't you forget about it and enjoy your lunch?'

'I'm not sure I can,' she admitted, blinking away the tears.

'Afraid *I'll* beat *him* up?' he asked quizzically.

Smiling in spite of herself, she shook her head. Then said in a heartfelt voice, 'It's all such a *mess*.'

'Some good may come of it.'

'*No* good will come of it,' she corrected. 'Have you stopped to think that with both my father and Mark gunning for you, your job might well be on the line?'

'I must admit I hadn't.'

'That was why I was hoping you'd go before anyone had seen you or knew who you were. Now it's too late…' With a sudden flare of hope, she added, 'Unless I could persuade Mother to forget all about you.'

'I should imagine it's a bit late to try,' Jonathan said matter-of-factly. 'Both your mother and father will almost certainly be back home by now. And, unless he's encountered any major problems, Longton should be there too… Ah, here's lunch.'

CHAPTER FOUR

THOUGH convinced she couldn't eat a thing, at Jonathan's insistence Loris tried the chicken and pasta bake and found it very tasty.

'Keep eating,' he urged. 'Things may be in a mess, but starving yourself isn't going to help matters.'

Knowing he was right, she obeyed, and found she was hungry after all.

'Mmm, delicious,' she murmured as she finished the last bite. 'It's equally as nice as they make at Il Lupo.'

'Where and what is Il Lupo?'

'A little basement restaurant quite close to Piccadilly. If I'm eating in town and I'm anywhere near Shear Lane I usually have lunch there. The food's good and remarkably cheap.'

'With a rich father I wouldn't have thought *cheap* was a necessary factor.'

'What has having a rich father got to do with it? I've been independent since I left school.'

'Surely he helped you get through college?'

'No. I took weekend and evening jobs to do that.'

'Why should a wealthy man leave his only daughter to fend for herself?'

'Perhaps he thought it would be character-building. Or Mother might be right when she calls him an old skinflint.'

Afraid of Jonathan pursuing the matter, she was relieved when Mrs Lawson appeared with wedges of golden-crusted apple pie and stilton, and piled more logs onto the fire before going to serve a couple of men at the bar.

The two men had drunk their pints and left before she returned with a freshly made pot of coffee.

'An excellent meal,' Jonathan congratulated her. 'It's a pity more people weren't here to enjoy it.'

'Things are always quiet at this time of the year, but now there's only Arthur and me to run the place it suits me fine. Just ring the bell on the bar if you want any more coffee.'

As Loris started to pour the steaming liquid Jonathan's eyes fixed on the magnificent half-hoop of diamonds she wore, and he asked casually, 'How long have you been engaged?'

'Three months.'

'Any wedding plans?'

'Nothing's settled yet...' Mark had wanted an early-spring wedding, but, feeling panicky at the thought of being rushed, Loris had pleaded for a summer wedding. 'Though we've talked about getting married at the end of June.'

'You said Longton will be furious with you... Do you think he'll want to end the engagement?'

With quiet confidence, she answered, 'No, I'm sure he won't.'

'What about you? Do *you* want to end it?'

'I don't think so.'

She wanted a husband, a home and a family while she was still young, and Mark had been the first man to attract her since Nigel.

'In spite of how he treated you last night?'

'I've told you, it was very largely my own fault.'

'So, apart from being late, what did you do to upset him enough to make him want to take another woman to bed?'

She half shook her head, wishing he'd let the subject drop.

But, refusing to, he persisted, 'After seeing them together on the dance floor, you don't seriously believe he took Miss Gresham home because she was ill?'

'No, I don't.'

'And you're not angry about it?'

'Of course I'm angry. But, as I keep saying, I was partly to blame.'

'Tell me how?'

Seeing he had no intention of giving up, she said wearily, 'When I went over to Mark to apologise for being so late he started talking about how beautiful Pamela Gresham was and how she fancied him. He was hoping to make me jealous...'

'Any particular reason?' Jonathan queried.

'He wanted me to agree to sleep with him that night, but because we were going to be at Monkswood I refused. I didn't like the idea of sleeping with him under my parents' roof.'

Realising how ridiculous that must sound in the circumstances, she blushed hotly before going on, 'He tried to persuade me, but I still didn't feel comfortable about it. He wasn't in a mood to take no for an answer, and suggested that we went back to his flat before going down to Paddleham. I was about to agree, when he got impatient and said something like, "I'm warning you. This time, I don't intend to take no for an answer—"'

Suddenly realising how revealing those words were, she stopped in dismay.

Noting the *this time*, and adding it to what he already knew, Jonathan asked carefully, 'So what did you say?'

'I lost my temper and told him he'd have to. He said, "Damn it, if you won't come back to my flat with me, I know someone who will."'

'He meant Miss Gresham, of course?'

Loris nodded. 'He boasted, "She'd come like a shot, and I might just ask her." I said, "Why don't you?" and walked away.'

'Good for you!' Jonathan applauded.

'But, don't you see, if I *hadn't*, if I'd agreed to go back to his flat, none of this would have happened and we wouldn't be in this mess.'

'Did you *want* to go back to his flat?'

'Not really,' she admitted, looking down. 'After what had happened I wasn't in the right mood. But I thought it was time I...'

Narrowed eyes on her face, he probed, 'Time you *what*? Went to bed with him?'

He watched the sweep of dark lashes flicker against her high cheekbones before she said, 'Yes.'

'But you hadn't previously.' It was a statement rather than a question.

The fact that she had never slept with Mark was something she would have preferred Jonathan not to know. It raised too many questions. Yet she couldn't bring herself to lie about it.

When she failed to deny it, he pursued, 'Do you love him?'

'I do.' Then, almost as if she was trying to convince herself, 'Of course I do.'

'So why haven't you slept with him? It's almost the norm these days to go to bed with one's fiancé.'

Wanting to tell him to mind his own business, she found herself saying weakly, 'For several reasons. It's a long story.'

'I've got all day.'

At her instinctive rejection of that, he said, 'Now it's this late there's no point in rushing back, so tell me why you haven't slept with Longton. He must have kept pressing you to?'

Knowing that Jonathan wasn't about to drop the subject until she told him what he wanted to know, she gave in to the pressure. 'Yes, he did. But I...'

'Kept putting him off?'

'Yes.'

'I'm curious to know why. He's a good-looking, macho man, if you like that type—and you obviously do or you wouldn't be engaged to him—and you're a warm, passionate woman.'

'But I'm not really.'

'You were last night.' Watching her cheeks grow warm, and thinking how beautiful she was, he probed, 'What gave you the idea you weren't?'

Looking anywhere but at him, she admitted, 'I'd had a previous relationship that didn't work out. It left me feeling disillusioned and…inadequate.'

Without really knowing why, she found herself telling him about Nigel.

She had never even told Mark about Nigel. Perhaps because they seldom really *talked*. As well as watching a lot of sport on TV, Mark liked parties and entertaining, getting out and about. And on the few occasions they did have time for a conversation he tended to take it over. He was a talker rather than a listener.

Studying her expressive face, Jonathan asked, 'How old were you then?'

'Eighteen.'

His jaw tightened, as though he felt either anger or pain. 'And you say you were engaged? Did your father and mother approve?'

'Yes, they were all for it. Nigel's parents were family friends.'

'And doubtless rich?'

'Yes.'

'Was that why you agreed to marry him?'

'No, it wasn't. If you must know, I thought I was in love with him.'

'So what happened? Why did you finally break up?'

She told him why, flatly, dispassionately, adding, 'Somehow, being treated like that destroyed my confidence in myself as a woman...'

'But surely it was different next time?'

'There was no next time.'

'You mean you've steered clear of men all these years because that selfish young swine not only cheated on you but made you half believe you were frigid?'

'Not entirely.' She strove to be fair. 'No one had attracted me enough to make me *want* to try again, until I met Mark.'

'But you've just admitted that you've kept even *him* at arm's length.'

'Yes.' Looking into the flames, she sighed. 'I didn't really *intend* to. Somehow it just happened...'

The same as last night had just happened. But in the opposite way.

His eyes on her half-averted face, he remarked softly, 'Knowing you're anything but frigid, it strikes me as odd that you weren't willing to sleep with someone you've told me you love.'

Something about the way he spoke made her look at him. He was smiling a little, as though well satisfied.

Realising with a shock of surprise how she had bared her soul, as well as her body, to a man who was scarcely more than a stranger, she felt her throat go dry.

Swallowing hard, she waited for him to ask the obvious question. A question she had yet to find an answer to. *So why me?*

But with a sensitivity she could only be heartily thankful for, he smoothly changed the subject. 'You mentioned you were an interior designer... What does your work involve? Selecting furniture? Fabrics? Colour schemes?'

'Quite often the lot. And every project is a new challenge. That's what makes it so fascinating...'

All at once there was a feeling of ease, a rapport between them.

'It would have been fun to design for my own place,' she added wistfully, 'but all I could find to rent was a furnished flat. Though I suppose from a purely practical point of view that's given me more time for my clients.'

'How do you choose your clients?'

'I don't. They choose me. I follow up every enquiry, and make suggestions and preliminary sketches, but unfortunately I don't always get the job.'

'Can't you charge for wasted time?'

'Not until I'm better known. At the moment I have to offer the first consultation free, and as the rent they charge for my flat is exorbitant, when I fail to get a job I have to tighten my belt.'

'With a wealthy fiancé?'

'I wouldn't dream of asking Mark to help.'

Letting that go, he suggested, 'Some places must be harder to design for than others?'

'Some *clients* are harder to design for than others... They ask advice, but they already have a preconceived idea in their minds of what they actually want. Sometimes it takes some winkling out, and even when I've succeeded it isn't always easy to translate it into a workable scheme. But there's nothing I would rather do, and when something works, and you *know* it's right, there's a tremendous amount of job satisfaction...'

Temporarily forgetting all the troubles the weekend had brought, she became animated as, responding to his interest, she talked with fluency and enthusiasm about her love of colour and design, and her pleasure in her work.

'It sounds like a passion that will last a lifetime,' he observed.

Some of the sparkle died out of her face. 'Mark wants

me to stop working after we're married,' she said flatly. 'He said a rich man's wife has no need to work.'

'*Financial* need, no. But there are other considerations just as important.'

'Mark doesn't seem to think so.'

'So what will you do with yourself?'

'Apart from sit and count my money all day? I don't really know.'

It was a sore point, and, turning away, she began to pull on her shoes. 'It's time we were getting back.'

'Perhaps you're right.'

Strolling over to the bar, he rang the large brass bell that waited there and, when Mrs Lawson appeared, paid her for the meal, adding a generous tip.

'Will we see you next weekend?' she asked.

'I'm not sure. It all depends.'

'Well, all I can say is I hope it's better weather next time.'

When Loris had added her thanks to Jonathan's, they pulled on their anoraks and made their way outside into the greyness.

A mixture of rain and snow was being driven before a bleak, easterly wind, and after the comfortable warmth of the fire it felt bitter.

Heads down, and walking as quickly as possible, they set off back. Neither was wearing gloves, and Jonathan walked with his hands thrust deep into his pockets.

Loris did the same, but the pockets in her anorak, which was fashionable rather than practical, were too shallow to afford much protection.

Glancing sideways at her, Jonathan asked, 'All right?'

'Yes.'

He reached to take hold of her hand and, finding it was like ice, returned both his hand and hers to the warmth of his pocket.

There was something *caring* about the gesture that brought an odd little lump to her throat.

The rain grew heavier, and soon they were both soaked to the skin. In spite of all the problems that loomed ahead, when the house came into view it was a welcome sight, its lighted windows suggesting warmth and comfort.

Hoping against hope that they wouldn't meet anyone, Loris chose to go in by the rear door, and to use the back staircase.

They were lucky, and made it upstairs without seeing a soul. At her bedroom door, she turned to glance at the man by her side.

His neat ears were red and his thick lashes were beaded with moisture; his hair was plastered against his skull and rivulets of water ran down his face. But, despite his saturated state, he had an air of ease, of calm self-assurance.

'No one's seen us come back,' she said with relief, 'so if you get changed as quickly as possible—'

'I was looking forward to a hot, leisurely shower,' he said plaintively.

'But don't you see? There's still a chance...'

'To do what?'

'To *leave*, of course.' Urgently, she added, 'Go out the way we came in, and when you've got your car turn left and take the back drive—'

'And leave you to face the music alone?'

'It's what I *want* you to do. Facing them won't be pleasant, but no one will do *me* any harm.' She put a hand on his arm and shook him. 'Go, while there's still a chance. Staying will only add to the problems.'

'That's a matter of opinion.'

'It's a matter of *fact*,' she hissed at him. 'Your presence is bound to inflame Mark... Oh, *please*, Jonathan, go.'

'We're in this together, and the only way I'll go is if you go with me.'

Though she was tempted, she shook her head. 'What would be the good of that?'

'Exactly. There's no point in either of us running away. The best thing by far would be to have a showdown and get it over with.'

He sounded almost as if he was enjoying the prospect.

Opening the door to her room, he gently pushed her inside. 'Now, why don't you go and get out of those wet things before you catch a chill?'

Accepting that she wasn't going to budge him, she went through to the bathroom and stripped off.

Standing under the steaming water, she waited until her frozen body was thawed out before reaching for the shampoo.

As well as the comfort the hot water brought, she felt an inner glow of warmth. Though common sense insisted that it would have been better if Jonathan had gone, she felt a sneaking relief that he had refused to leave her to face things alone.

When she had towelled herself thoroughly, and rubbed her hair, she put on a fleecy robe and went to find some dry clothes.

Dressed in a grey skirt and a fine woollen blouse the colour of wet lilac, she brushed her hair and made-up lightly. Then, mentally girding her loins, she went out, closing the door behind her.

Jonathan was strolling down the corridor towards her. His hair had dried to what she now recognised as its normal corn-colour, and was smoothly brushed. He was wearing well-cut trousers and a black polo-necked sweater that made him look both attractive and oddly dangerous.

Wondering what had made a word like *dangerous* spring to mind, she realised it was something to do with his quiet, but absolute, confidence.

Hands loose by his sides, a glint in his eyes, he was

whistling something half under his breath. It was, she recognised after a moment, the theme from *High Noon*.

'That sense of humour will get you into trouble one day,' she said crossly.

He grinned, white teeth gleaming. 'Ah, so you like old movies?'

Responding to his charm, she admitted, 'Better than some of the modern ones.'

'Remember *The Ghost and Mrs Muir*…?'

'Oh, yes… And *The Babysitter*…'

Discussing their favourite black and white films, they made their way downstairs.

They were crossing the spacious hall when the library door opened and Mark came out. His tense expression changed to one of mingled annoyance and relief when he saw Loris.

'Where on earth have you been? Your mother said you'd gone out for a walk mid-morning.'

'Yes, that's right.' She was surprised by how steady her voice sounded.

'You've been out so long I was beginning to think you'd gone back to town instead.'

'We stopped for coffee,' Jonathan said smoothly, 'and when it came on to rain I persuaded Loris to stay at the pub for lunch.'

Mark's heavy head swung round, and he glared at the younger man. 'What the hell are you up to, Drummond?'

At that moment Mrs Delacost came down the stairs and crossed the hall, holding a package in her hand.

Glancing curiously at the little group, she addressed Loris, 'I wonder if you happen to know where Sir Peter is? I've some pictures taken in Monte I promised to show him.'

'I'm afraid I don't—'

'I've just this minute been speaking to him.' Mark produced a charming smile. 'He rang to apologise for leaving his guests so long, but unfortunately he's been delayed by a slight accident.'

'Oh, dear! He wasn't hurt, I hope?'

'No, I'm happy to say. He and his bailiff were returning from checking on storm damage to the estate when a plank bridge they were driving over collapsed and the Land Rover ended up in the stream.

'Luckily the water was only a few feet deep, so neither man was in any real danger. At the moment they're trying to drag the Land Rover out with a tractor.'

'Oh, dear, I'm so sorry. So terribly sorry. Poor, poor Sir Peter! What a perfectly *dreadful* thing to happen, and just when—'

Mark cut short the commiserations. 'As our hostess is lying down with a migraine, I wonder if you'd be kind enough to tell the other guests what's happened and convey Sir Peter's sincere apologies?'

'Oh, certainly.' Apparently well pleased at being given such an important task, she hurried towards the sitting-room.

Seeing Mark was about to return to the attack, Loris suggested urgently, 'If there's no one in the library, let's go in there. We don't really want to stand about in the hall.'

The library was a big, handsome room, with a billiard table at one end and a low leather suite grouped around a glowing log fire. Twin standard lamps were burning and it was comfortably warm.

As soon as the door had closed behind them, and swinging to face the younger man, Mark said brusquely, 'I asked you what the hell you're up to.'

'Up to?' Jonathan drawled. 'I'm afraid I don't quite understand.'

'Don't come the innocent with me. First you push your nose in and ask Loris to dance, and then you go out of your way to drive her down here.'

'Well, if you remember, *you* were otherwise engaged.'

'What the devil do you know about it?'

Loris noticed that though Mark loomed over the other man somehow he failed to diminish him in the slightest. Size, she realised, wasn't important. Jonathan exuded a kind of quiet strength, a feeling of authority, that made him any man's equal.

Now he answered blandly, 'I happened to notice you leaving the hotel with another woman.'

'That's none of your damn business.'

'I decided to make it my business when I saw your fiancée standing abandoned in the rain.'

'So you turned into Sir Galahad?' Mark sneered.

'If I remember rightly, Galahad was a knight of immaculate purity, so I'm afraid the comparison is hardly fitting in view of—'

Terrified of what he was going to say next, Loris rushed into speech. 'Jonathan offered to drive me home when there were no taxis immediately available.'

'A likely story.'

Coldly, Loris remarked, 'I understood you drove *Pamela* home for the same reason?'

Looking momentarily disconcerted, Mark decided to ignore that and press on. 'But instead of taking you home Drummond drove you all the way down to Monkswood, no doubt hoping to get a foot in the door.'

'I couldn't go home because I'd lent my flat to Judy and her husband for the weekend, so I *asked* Jonathan to bring me here.'

'Well, it seems he made the most of the opportunity.'

'Driving conditions were so bad I begged him to stay the night.'

Mark grunted his displeasure. 'Well, it's now late afternoon, so what's he still doing here?'

Hating the way they were talking about Jonathan as

though he wasn't there, she said, 'Mother invited him to stay for the rest of the weekend.'

'If he wasn't *planning* on staying, how come he had clothes with him?'

'He didn't—'

'Isobel was kind enough to lend me some of her stepson's,' Jonathan finished evenly.

Loris felt sure he'd deliberately used her mother's name to rattle the older man.

If so, he'd succeeded.

Red in the face, Mark bit out, 'You're a damn sight too presumptuous. Who the hell gave you permission to call her Isobel?'

'She did.'

'No doubt because she thought you were *somebody*. How many lies did you tell her?'

'None.' A gleam in his eye, Jonathan admitted, 'Though I may have misled her a little.'

'I bet you did. Well, get it into your head that you don't belong here. You're not in our class, and never will be.'

'I think I can stand it.'

'Damn and blast your arrogance! Take it from me, Drummond, you've outstayed your welcome. You can leave as soon as you like.'

'I'll be happy to leave when *my hostess* tells me I'm no longer welcome.'

His brown eyes blazing with temper, Mark said, 'I've had more than enough of your insolence. You can get out of here now! This minute!'

Standing his ground, refusing to be intimidated, Jonathan murmured, 'Strange... I must have missed something somewhere. You see, I hadn't realised this was *your* house.'

Baring his teeth, Mark cried furiously, 'You think you're mighty clever, but if you don't leave of your own accord I'll have you thrown out.'

'Then you don't think you're big enough to do it personally?'

'Plenty big enough, and believe me it'll give me the greatest pleasure.'

'Don't!' Loris cried as Mark advanced threateningly on the younger man. 'This *isn't* your house and you've no right to throw anyone out of it.'

'*Try* to throw anyone out of it,' Jonathan goaded.

'You're asking for it,' Mark snarled.

'Leave it, Mark,' Loris said sharply. 'You know as well as I do that my father won't want any trouble when there's a house party going on.'

'So you feel you need to protect your Sir Galahad?' Mark sneered. 'Well, I bet he'll be only too happy to hide behind a woman's skirts... Won't you, Drummond?'

'Not at all. I'm quite capable of fighting my own battles.'

'Then why aren't you squaring up to me now?'

'Firstly because you're six inches taller and several stone heavier than I am. Secondly because I'm in someone else's home. And, thirdly, because I don't want to have to hurt you.'

Infuriated beyond endurance, Mark made a lunge at his tormentor.

Jonathan sidestepped and, using his opponent's weight and impetus to his own advantage, executed a textbook judo throw.

Mark's heavy body thudded onto the carpet and, half-winded, he lay for a second or two before struggling unsteadily to his feet. Shaking his head as if to clear it, he muttered, 'Why, you...!'

As he drew back his fist Loris cried, 'Stop it, the pair of you! How can you behave like this when at any moment one of the guests might walk in?'

Still groggy, Mark staggered a little, and, seizing his arm, she steered him to the nearest chair and pushed him into it.

Then, her knees feeling like jelly, she sat down abruptly in the chair opposite and glared angrily at Jonathan who, looking cool as a cucumber, was lounging against the mantel.

He raised his hands in mock surrender. 'I'm sorry.'

'So you should be. You're equally to blame.'

'You mean I should have let him throw me out?'

'I don't mean anything of the kind. But you know quite well you deliberately provoked him.'

'And you would have preferred me to have kowtowed?'

'No, I wouldn't. But I would have preferred you to have been a little more…' She hesitated, trying to find the right word.

'Conciliatory?' he suggested.

'*Reasonable.*'

'Do you really believe that my being "a little more reasonable" would have made any difference?'

Sighing inwardly, she silently admitted that she didn't. Mark had been out for blood from the word go. If Jonathan hadn't stood up to him he would only have taken it as a sign of weakness. Now at least, Mark being Mark, he would respect his adversary…

But it seemed she didn't know him after all.

'Damn you, Drummond,' Mark muttered. 'You may think you've won, but you're nothing short of a fool if you imagine I'm going to let someone like you get the better of me. *I'm* running BLC, and you're just a jumped-up office boy…'

'Oh, I'm a little more than that,' Jonathan said mildly.

'Well, whatever you are, you won't be with the firm much longer.'

'If that's a threat—'

Mark showed his teeth in a smile that was more like a

snarl. 'It is indeed. Make no mistake about it. You're for the chop.'

Loris's stomach tied itself in knots. Mark had reacted just as she'd first feared... And before he'd even discovered the worst.

But, appearing far from concerned, Jonathan was advising him coolly, 'As *Cosby's* own BLC, I doubt if you'll be able to get rid of me without their say-so.'

'I'll get their agreement, no matter what it takes.'

'Personal likes and dislikes don't figure in the equation. You'll have to put forward a good reason for dismissing me.'

'Don't worry, I'll find one. And if I can't find one I'll invent one.'

'I noticed you were pretty good at inventing things when Isobel gave us your version of why you drove Pamela Gresham home.'

Seeing Mark was about to explode, Loris took a deep breath and seized the initiative. She leaned forward and asked shortly, 'Do you still want to marry me?'

Startled, he said, 'What?'

Focusing all her attention, blotting out the man who was standing quietly in the background and forcing Mark to do the same, she repeated, 'I asked if you still want to marry me?'

'Of course I still want to marry you. You know I'm mad about you.'

'In view of what's happened I thought you might have changed your mind.'

'If you mean Pamela, before you start accusing me of anything, I told your mother—'

'She might believe that absurd story about taking the woman home because she was ill, but in view of what you said earlier I certainly don't.'

He ran a restless hand over his dark crinkly hair. 'Now

look here, Loris, I only said what I did to make you jealous. You must know I had no intention of going through with it.'

Ignoring his bluster, Loris demanded, 'Did you take her back to your flat?'

'No. Like I said, I took her to her place.'

'And you stayed.'

'No, no I didn't...' He couldn't look her in the eye.

'Come off it,' she said bluntly.

'Well, just for a coffee.'

'Don't take me for a fool, Mark.'

His face sullen, he said, 'All right, so I did stay. But it's your fault. You drove me to it. A man has needs.'

Guiltily, Loris had to acknowledge this as the truth. It had been partly her fault that Mark had gone off with Pamela, but she needed to make sure it never happened again.

'What about a woman?'

Looking nonplussed, he began, 'But you—'

'I'm talking in wider terms. If *men* have needs, wouldn't you agree that *women* do too?'

'Yes, I suppose so,' he said grudgingly.

'Only *suppose*?'

'Very well, they do. But it's different for a man.'

'In what way?'

'A man can satisfy those needs and it doesn't have to mean anything.'

'But not a woman?'

'With women it isn't just physical. They have to have emotional ties.'

'Is Pamela in love with you?'

'What? No, of course she isn't.'

'She merely fancied you?'

'Look, Loris—'

'So it *can* be purely physical?'

'All right, so it can.'

'And if a man can make love to a woman without it "meaning anything", and expect to be forgiven, then you must admit that the reverse is true?'

'Okay, I admit it.' Then, warily, 'Though I don't understand what you're getting at.'

'I'm trying to put paid to the old double standard that some men still cling to.'

'Men tend to be possessive about their women. It's natural.'

'But is it *just*? These days we have equality, so shouldn't it work both ways? You slept with Pamela and you expect me to forgive you, to go on as if nothing had changed...'

'Well, it hasn't—'

Cutting through his words, she demanded, 'But would you forgive me if I told you I'd slept with Jonathan last night?'

Knowing her too well to be alarmed, he asked with mock seriousness, 'Did you?'

'Yes,' she said baldly.

CHAPTER FIVE

JUST for an instant he looked shaken, then, obviously deciding it was merely an attempt to pay him back, he changed his expression to one of amused indulgence.

'I'm quite serious, Mark.'

Though his slight smile disappeared, she knew he didn't believe her.

He couldn't credit that she'd held him off for so long and then chosen to go to bed with a man she'd only just met. A man he'd contemptuously called a wimp and whom he still regarded as his social inferior.

But, pretending to take it seriously, he asked, 'So because you thought I was sleeping with someone else, you made up your mind to do the same?'

'I didn't make up my mind to do anything. It just happened. He was using your room...I took him one of Simon's razors...'

'Then I suppose he made a pass at you and you just couldn't resist his manly charms?'

Ignoring the sarcasm, she agreed quietly, 'Something like that.'

'Very well,' Mark said magnanimously, 'I forgive you. It's over and forgotten. We'll never mention it again.'

He totally refused to see the truth, she realised, because it was wounding to his pride, his self-esteem, to even *consider* that she might seriously have preferred another man to him.

'And you still want to marry me?'

'Yes, I still want to marry you. But I think it would make sense to bring the date forward. It's not as if we're planning on a big wedding, so instead of waiting until June let's get married as soon as possible.'

After a moment's thought, she said, 'I'll agree to that on two conditions.'

'What are they?'

'First, I'd like to keep on working…' Seeing his face darken, she specified, 'At least up until the time we *were* going to be married.'

'All right,' he agreed reluctantly. 'What's the second condition?'

This was the most important one, and Loris paused to choose her words with care. 'I want you to promise me that, no matter what, you won't take any further action against Jonathan.'

As though just remembering the other man's presence, Mark scowled in his direction.

'You seem mighty keen to protect him.'

'Please, Mark.'

'Very well, but I want *your* promise that you won't see him again, or have anything else to do with him.'

'I'll promise, in exchange for your assurance that you won't have anything else to do with Pamela—or any other woman for that matter.'

He nodded, and had the grace to flush slightly. 'I give you my word that I won't.' He smiled tentatively at her and Loris smiled back, convinced he meant it.

Then, turning to the younger man, who was still leaning against the mantel, his face inscrutable, Mark said curtly, 'And in the future you'd better keep your nose clean and stay well out of my way. In fact it would be no bad thing if you asked to be transferred back to the States…'

When his adversary said nothing, Mark added, his ego fully restored, 'Now, suppose you get out of here?'

Coolly, Jonathan informed him, 'I'll go when Loris asks me to.'

Just as he finished speaking the library door opened and Peter Bergman walked in. He was wearing smart country tweeds, and his iron-grey hair was smoothly brushed and still damp from the shower.

'What a day! The weather's absolutely foul, and I've been out since just after breakfast.' Then, to Mark, 'It's a pity you weren't with me. Reynolds isn't the most useful man in a crisis, and I could have done with your help.'

'I'm sorry I wasn't here in time.'

Peter frowned. 'But I thought... You didn't come down last night?'

'No, I was held up. I only got down here a couple of hours ago.'

His cold-blue eyes fixed on his daughter, Peter demanded, 'Then how did you get here?'

Before she could answer, Jonathan said levelly, 'I drove Loris down.'

As though becoming aware of the other man for the first time, Peter said, 'I know your face. You're with Cosby's aren't you? PA to William Grant?'

'That's right.'

'I'm afraid I can't recall your name.'

'Drummond. Jonathan Drummond.'

In answer to her father's unspoken *What the devil is he still doing here?* Loris explained, 'The conditions were so bad that I asked Jonathan to stay the night.'

'Which room did you put him in?'

It could have been a casual enquiry, but Loris knew only too well that it wasn't. Having gained assurance from her earlier stand, however, she replied steadily, 'Mark's.'

His face darkening with anger, Peter turned to glower at Jonathan.

Bearing in mind that there were now two people who had it in for him, and fearing the promise she'd extracted from Mark might not be enough to keep him out of trouble, she added hurriedly, 'Mother did ask Jonathan to stay for the rest of the weekend, but unfortunately he can't.'

She got to her feet and, turning to Jonathan, said formally, 'Thank you for bringing me down. Now, I know you want to be on your way before it gets too dark—' a grey, murky dusk was already pressing against the windowpanes '—so have a good journey back.'

'You weren't thinking of coming with me?'

'No.' Swallowing, she held out her hand.

Taking it in his, he asked carefully, 'Quite sure you've made the right decision?'

Knowing he was asking about a great deal more than just going with him, she met his brilliant eyes without flinching and said, 'Quite sure.'

'Then please give your mother my thanks and my apologies for leaving without seeing her.'

Becoming aware that he was still holding her hand, she withdrew it abruptly. 'Goodbye.'

'*Au revoir.*'

Glancing from one man to the other, he sketched an ironic salute, and a moment later the latch clicked quietly behind him.

Staring at the closed door, knowing she would never see him again, she felt a sudden surge of regret, a feeling of loss and loneliness that was almost like a physical pain.

But she couldn't let herself feel like this about a virtual stranger, a man she knew scarcely anything about.

She had opted to stay with Mark, to live the future she had chosen, and so long as her father didn't wreck things she would consider herself lucky.

Taking a deep breath, she turned to face her father.

He was standing with his back to the fire, looking like an enraged turkeycock. His jowls quivering, he said, 'It strikes me that for a man in his position Drummond's a damn sight too sure of himself...'

Loris glanced uneasily at Mark, waiting for him to add *his* condemnation. She was surprised when he said nothing, until she realised that he would hardly want to lose face by mentioning his own humiliation.

'I don't know what the devil Isobel was thinking of, asking someone like him to stay.'

When no one made any comment, Peter demanded of his daughter, 'How long have you known him?'

'I met him for the first time last night.'

It wasn't at all the answer he'd been expecting, and he failed to hide his surprise.

'At the party?'

'Yes.'

'Did you know he was just an employee?'

'Yes, Mark told me.'

Well aware of how her father's mind worked, Loris guessed he was already starting to doubt the conclusion he'd reached earlier and, for Jonathan's sake, she was pleased.

'How did you get to know him?'

'He asked me to dance.'

'Damn cheek. Why did you accept?'

'Why shouldn't I have accepted? Mark was dancing with Pamela Gresham.'

Peter had noticed Mark and his partner closely entwined. He harrumphed. 'Then what? Did Drummond pester you?'

'Certainly not. When the dance ended he said goodnight and walked away.'

Aware that the mention of the blonde had made her fiancé uncomfortable, and remembering how he'd tried to bully Jonathan, Loris added with a touch of malice, 'I wouldn't have seen him again if Mark hadn't had to do his good deed for the evening...'

'Good deed? What good deed?'

Trying just a shade too hard to sound convincing, Mark told the same tale he'd told Isobel.

'It was Alan Gresham's daughter...she suddenly felt faint... There wasn't a taxi available at that minute, so I offered to drive her home. Unfortunately I couldn't find Loris to tell her.'

'It was after they'd gone,' Loris went on to explain, 'and Jonathan saw me standing in the rain, that he came up and offered me a lift.'

Knowing his future son-in-law, Peter—who was no fool and could read between the lines—decided to let the subject drop. He and Mark, with the same attitude to women, shared a man-to-man relationship.

Knowing Loris, he was satisfied he'd been wrong. She wasn't the kind to play games with a man she'd only just met.

He threw a couple of logs on the fire and, turning to Mark, began to talk business. 'When things have settled down and are running smoothly, I've decided to come into the office less. Once or twice a week should be enough.'

'You mean you'll be working from home, or letting go of the reins?'

'Gradually letting go of the reins. I'll be sixty-one soon, and I'd like to give more time to running the estate...'

Watching the two men, Loris could only be thankful that, in spite of making a complete fool of herself and deserving to pay for it, she seemed to have got off lightly and she and Mark were back on good terms.

Now all that remained was to forget about Jonathan and his brief intrusion into her life, and put the whole thing behind her.

She only hoped that he would have the sense to go back to the States. Though Mark had given his word not to hound him, the two men were so antipathetic to each other that if they came into contact they were bound to clash.

And next time Jonathan would undoubtedly come off worst.

She wouldn't think of Jonathan any more.

But having decided that, and in spite of all her efforts, for the rest of the afternoon and throughout dinner she found herself unable to think of anything but him.

Later, when she reluctantly agreed to fill in at bridge, her mind wasn't on the game, and she made so many mistakes that she was thankful Mark, rather than one of the other guests, was her partner.

When the rubber ended, and the men drifted towards the billiard table, instead of joining the ladies for a chat in the living-room she picked a book from the shelves at random and sat by the library fire.

Though well written, it failed to grip her and after a while the click of the billiard balls became soporific and, her head nodding in the warmth, her eyelids gradually drooped.

Half-asleep and half-awake, her wayward thoughts returned to Jonathan.

She could see his face as clearly as if he was standing there. His well-shaped head and clear-cut features, the way his thickly lashed green eyes crinkled at the corners when he smiled his charming, slightly lopsided smile, his chiselled lips and the firm chin with its intriguing cleft...

But it wasn't only how he *looked* that pleased and beguiled her, it was the man himself. His quiet strength and assurance, his awareness, his sense of humour and warmth.

She recalled the night spent in his arms, how his generosity and his obvious pleasure in her had carried her to the heights, how easily the passion and sweetness of his lovemaking had elicited an answering passion.

By removing a deep-rooted fear and restoring her faith in herself as a woman he had given her a precious gift, and she would be grateful to him for the rest of her days.

It was very largely that fear that had made her reluctant to commit herself to an earlier wedding date. But now she could go ahead and marry Mark without worrying that she might fail him as a wife, so some good had come out of her lapse...

'You look ready for bed.' Mark's voice broke into her thoughts.

Looking up, she saw that the game of billiards had ended and the men were clustered round the small bar, helping themselves to a nightcap.

'I am,' she said, and got to her feet.

'I'll walk you up.'

'Aren't you having a nightcap with the others?' she asked, knowing he usually had a whisky and soda.

'I'm not bothered.'

As they climbed the stairs he remarked, 'You've been very quiet all evening.' Then, a shade uneasily, 'Are you all right?'

It was unusual for Mark to ask such a question, and, touched, she answered, 'Fine. Just tired.'

At the door of her room, he asked, 'Can I come in? Or was that remark about being tired simply to warn me off?'

'No, it wasn't. It happens to be true.'

'So can I come in or not?'

Intending to say yes, she found herself saying, 'I'd rather you didn't.'

'Damn it, Loris, we're getting married as soon as it can be arranged. Anyone would think you didn't *want* me to make love to you...'

How could she let one man make love to her while her head was full of thoughts of another?

'Tonight I really hoped you'd say yes.'

'I'm sorry Mark, I *can't*.'

Picking up her desperation, and looking slightly embarrassed, he said, 'Oh… Oh, I see. Then perhaps I will have that nightcap after all.'

He kissed her with a marked lack of passion, and retreated down the stairs.

Rather than feeling guilty because she'd innocently misled him into thinking it was the wrong time of the month for her, all she could feel was relief as she prepared for bed.

But she couldn't go on like this, she lectured herself crossly. She really *must* put Jonathan right out of her head before thoughts of him compromised her future with Mark.

Over the next few days Loris discovered that was easier said than done. Though on her return to town she had made a strenuous effort not to think about Jonathan, whenever she relaxed her guard he simply walked in and took over.

He even came between her and her work. When, gazing at a wall with rapt attention, she should have been visualising colour schemes, all she could see in her mind's eye was his face.

Worse still was the treacherous way that her mind and body conspired together. Memories of the night they had spent together would sneak past her defences and filter into her consciousness, and her newly awakened body would react by growing heated and languorous and longing for his.

On Thursday, she paid a morning visit to a client with a mews cottage not far from Piccadilly. Vexed by her inability to concentrate, she decided to have lunch before going on to her mid-afternoon appointment at Bayswater.

After several days of lowering skies and periodic heavy downpours, it was raining steadily again as Loris hurried along Shear Lane. Furling her umbrella, she dived down the basement steps and into Il Lupo.

'*Buon giorno.*' She was greeted by the rotund and smiling white-aproned owner, who hung up her mac and disposed of her umbrella before showing her to a small table in an alcove.

In common with the others it had a red-checked tablecloth, a lighted candle stuck in a wine bottle, and a plastic-covered menu in the red, white and green of the Italian flag.

She was gazing unseeingly at the menu, recalling the delicious chicken and pasta bake she had shared with Jonathan, when, as though her thoughts had conjured him up, a familiar voice said, 'Well, hello! I decided to have lunch here in the hope of seeing you.'

Wearing a smart grey business suit and a matching shirt and tie, he was standing smiling down at her.

Her heart gave a strange lurch and her breathing quickened. Despite his wet hair he looked well turned out, and even more handsome than she remembered.

As she gazed up at him, her golden eyes registering shock, he asked, 'May I join you?'

Apparently taking her silence for assent, he sat down opposite.

'No,' she begged belatedly, 'please don't. I promised Mark I wouldn't see you again.'

'Well, I made no such promise,' he said, a glint in his eye, 'so you can put the blame on me.'

Seeing all too clearly what kind of mood he was in, Loris considered getting up and leaving.

But, finding herself strangely unwilling to walk away, she said weakly, 'If Mark finds out he'll be very angry... I wish you'd go.'

'Go? I've only just come. I haven't had any lunch yet.'

'Then why don't you sit somewhere else? There's plenty of space.'

'If he found out that we were both in the same restaurant,

do you seriously think my sitting at the next table would make him any less angry?'

Knowing he was right, she admitted, 'No. That's why I'd like you to go. It's not safe.'

Dropping his voice to a gravelly, Humphrey Bogart rasp, Jonathan leaned towards her and, almost without moving his lips, asked, 'Is he having you followed, doll?'

Biting back a smile, she said, 'Of course he isn't having me followed.'

'Then how will he know? Or do you feel compelled to tell him?'

'No, I don't feel *compelled* to tell him, but I don't want anything else on my conscience.'

He shook his head gloomily. 'Heavy enough, is it?'

'If you must know, it is!'

'Oh, well, in that case it might make more sense to tell him. Confession's good for the soul.'

'If you'd only go,' she begged, 'there'd be nothing to tell him.'

'It could already be too late,' Jonathan said dramatically. 'The office is only a few blocks away. He might be homing in on Il Lupo right now, intent on having lunch.'

'You must be joking! Mark lunches at the Ritz. He wouldn't be seen dead in a place like this.'

'Well, if he's not likely to walk in at any moment why are you so jumpy?'

When she said nothing, looking at the open menu, he asked blandly, 'I take it you haven't ordered yet?'

Throwing in the towel, she admitted, 'No.'

'Then may I suggest the *farsumagru*? I noticed it on the ''Today's Specials'' board. If it's as good as I used to have in Sardinia, I think you'll like it.'

'What is it exactly?'

'A kind of stuffed meat roll, with eggs and cheese and herbs.'

Loris nodded her agreement, and when a young black-haired waiter appeared at his elbow Jonathan ordered *farsumagru* for them both, and a carafe of red wine.

Thinking it would be safer to steer clear of personal topics, and noting his mention of Sardinia, Loris remarked, 'The other night you said you'd done some travelling?'

'Yes. Before I settled in the States I spent a while taking a look at some of the world's more out-of-the-way places.'

'Such as?'

He named a few, and until their meal arrived kept her well entertained with stories and anecdotes about the people he'd met and the sometimes strange things that had happened.

The *farsumagru* was every bit as good as he'd suggested it might be, and for a while they ate in silence. Then, taking a sip of her wine, Loris asked, 'Are you a born traveller? Do you still get itchy feet?'

'I enjoy an occasional trip, but on the whole I'm more of a home bird than a traveller.' Ironically, he added, 'As conscience is said to make cowards of us, so unrequited love can make travellers of us. I guess it's the need to try and escape the pain.'

'Unrequited?' She found herself echoing the word. It was strange to think of any woman he had loved not loving him back. But though he'd spoken lightly, as if he were joking, for some reason she felt sure he wasn't.

He shrugged his shoulders. 'I wasn't good enough for her... However, that was a long time ago.'

But there must have been plenty of women since then—recalling his experienced and skilful lovemaking, she went hot all over, and a little shiver ran through her—or maybe just one special woman?

Only too aware that she should let the subject drop, she still found herself asking, 'So are you married now?'

'No.'

'And no plans to?'

'Oh, yes, I have plans...'

Though she knew she was being dog-in-a-manger, his answer gave her no pleasure.

Watching her face, he added, 'I'm having to work on them. Regrettably, the woman of my dreams—the woman I'm hoping to marry—is involved with someone else at the moment.'

She waited to see if he would elaborate further.

He didn't. Instead, he asked, 'Is your wedding still on?'

'Of course it's still on.'

'I was hoping you'd changed your mind. Longton isn't the man for you. He doesn't know you. And he's far too selfish to even understand let alone *fulfil*, your needs—'

Because what he was saying disturbed her, she broke in sharply, 'What makes you so sure? Mark and I have known each other for months. It's *you* who doesn't know me.'

His gaze steady, he objected, 'I should say that in one sense I know you a great deal better than he does.'

Her eyes fell, and despite all her efforts she felt herself starting to blush.

Watching the tide of colour rise in her cheeks, Jonathan added, 'Unless, your doubts about being frigid now removed, you've spent the last two or three nights in his bed. Have you, Loris?'

She hadn't intended to answer, but as though he'd willed the truth out of her she found herself saying, 'No, I haven't.'

His faint sigh of relief was audible.

'But don't get the wrong idea,' she added firmly, 'I *am* going to marry him. It's all arranged.'

There was a short pause. Then, as though accepting the inevitable, he asked, 'So when is the wedding to take place?'

'A week tomorrow.' Realising how flat her voice sounded, she smiled brilliantly.

Frowning, he said, 'As soon as that? Is it to be a church wedding?'

She shook her head. 'Register office. Mother's bitterly disappointed, but, having been divorced, Mark wants to keep the whole thing very quiet, no fuss.'

Jonathan raised a well-marked brow. 'No honeymoon either?'

'No. At least not until the summer.'

'What are you doing about your job?'

'Working until a couple of days before the wedding.'

'Then what?'

'I'll be carrying on at least until June, as Mark and I agreed.'

'I thought he might have managed to talk you out of it?'

'He's tried,' she admitted. 'But after we're married he wants to live in the house his parents left him—a house that's fully staffed. I can't begin to imagine how I'd fill my time. Perhaps it won't be so bad when we start a family,' she added hopefully.

'Then you want children?'

'Yes.'

'Does Longton?'

'Of course.'

'What makes you so sure?'

'When I told him I'd like children, he said he would too.'

'That surprises me.'

'Why should it surprise you?'

His green eyes holding no warmth, his voice brittle as ice, Jonathan observed, 'Well, he doesn't show much interest in the one he's got.'

'What?' she asked blankly.

Jonathan repeated his observation.

'I don't know what you mean. He and his first wife didn't have any children.'

'He and his *wife* might not have had any, but his ex-fiancée certainly does—'

Her jaw dropped. 'His *ex-fiancée*?'

'The one you supplanted.'

With certainty, she said, 'I didn't supplant anyone. The whole idea's ridiculous! Mark had no ties when I met him.'

'How do you know?'

'He said so.'

'And you believed him?'

'Why shouldn't I have believed him? He had nothing to hide. He told me about his divorce—'

'That was common knowledge, so he was forced to. But did he tell you *why* his wife divorced him?'

'They were incompatible. They found it impossible to live together.'

'I understood that the thing she found impossible to live with was his penchant for other women.'

'I'm quite aware that Mark likes women, but that's so with a lot of men, and it doesn't mean he'll do anything about it when we're married. I'm also aware that women find *him* attractive.'

'And you're prepared to live with that?'

Challenged, she said, 'Maybe I wouldn't want a man that no other women would bother to look twice at.'

'I gather his first wife didn't feel that way. Fortunately, or *unfortunately*, however you care to look at it, and possibly because she *was* his wife, she was by no means as reconciled to his numerous affairs as the woman who came after her.'

'I don't believe he had "numerous affairs" while he was married, and he told me he hadn't had a relationship until he met me since he and his wife separated.'

'How long did you say you'd been engaged?' Jonathan asked abruptly. 'Three months, was it?'

'Yes.'

'Then while he was putting a ring on *your* finger, your predecessor—whom he'd earlier promised to marry—was in a private nursing home awaiting the birth of their baby.'

Aghast, Loris whispered. 'No, you *must* be mistaken! When we've talked about children Mark's never breathed a word about having any. And there hasn't been so much as a whisper...'

'He's managed to keep it very quiet. In fact I doubt if anyone, including your father, has the faintest inkling.'

Loris lifted her chin and looked him in the eye. 'You've only been over from the States a few weeks, so how did *you* get to know all this?'

'For reasons which I'd prefer not to go into I don't want to disclose my source. However, I can assure you that it's absolutely true.'

Flatly she said, 'I'm sorry, but I don't believe a word of it. Mark has his faults—he's arrogant, quick-tempered, and he can be insensitive at times—but he isn't the kind to behave as callously as you're trying to make out.'

'I'm not "trying to make out" anything. I'm simply giving you the facts as I know them.'

'Well, I'm sure you've been misinformed. And as you don't want to tell me where you got hold of these *facts*, I'll continue to regard the whole thing as a complete fabrication.'

'Use your common sense, Loris. Why should anyone make up a story like that?'

'I can't imagine,' she said shortly. 'Unless it's someone with a grudge against Mark, someone who's just out to stir up trouble.'

Recalling how much animosity there was between the two men, and wondering how pure Jonathan's own motives were, she asked, 'Why did you make it your business to tell me?'

'I thought you should know about this other woman. She knows about you... Oh, no, Longton didn't tell her. She read about your engagement in the papers. I must say I'm rather surprised he agreed to have it put in.'

'Well, he did. Anyway, if this ''other woman'' knows about me, why hasn't she kicked up a fuss?'

'I understand that he supports her quite generously, but on the understanding that she keeps her mouth shut and stays in the background. For the sake of their child, and because, in spite of everything, she still loves him and lives in hopes of getting him back on a *permanent* basis, she's prepared to put up with it.'

'Are you saying he still sees her?'

'Oh, yes, he visits her a couple of times a week.'

'I don't believe it. Why should any woman allow herself to be treated so shabbily?'

'Because, though he had other women while they were together, he swore they meant nothing to him, that it was *her* he loved, and she's fool enough to believe him...'

Disconcerted, Loris wondered. Suppose the story was true? But if it *was*, and he'd had any feelings for the woman who was the mother of his child, surely he would have married her rather than propose to someone else?

Slowly, she said, 'Just for the sake of argument, if he had a cosy little set-up, where this woman was willing to ignore his affairs, why should he have asked me to marry him?'

'My guess—and this *is* just a guess—is that he saw you, *wanted* you, and, because of *who you are*, and because you weren't easy like the rest, he decided he'd have to marry you to get what he wanted. Also, being married to Sir Peter Bergman's daughter will give him a certain standing, an added prestige, as well as keeping the business in the family.'

Jonathan's reasoning was plausible and, shaken despite herself, Loris avoided those clear green eyes that saw too much.

Looking at her downbent face, he asked gently, 'You honestly believe he loves you?'

'He said he did.'

'I'd be surprised if he can even spell the word,' Jonathan said caustically. He added, 'His mistress may try to delude herself that he still loves her—though I don't know how she can after the way he's treated her—but that kind of man is incapable of loving anyone but himself.'

He sounded so bitter, so *concerned*, that Loris found herself wondering whether this woman might possibly be the one Jonathan wanted to marry. Though if it was true that she'd been having a long-term affair with Mark, it did seem unlikely.

Taking a deep breath, she asked, 'What about the child? You say Mark has a child?'

'Yes, he has a baby daughter. A daughter that he almost totally ignores.'

Loris was shocked. Even if he had no feelings for the mother, how could any man ignore his own child?

As though reading her thoughts, Jonathan advised quietly, 'Before you decide to go ahead with the wedding, it might be as well to ask yourself what kind of husband and father a man like him is going to make... Unless you're afraid of the answer?'

His question had the smooth abrasiveness of pumice-stone, and suddenly she knew without a shadow of doubt that, for whatever reason, he didn't want her to marry Mark.

Her earlier suspicion that he was simply out to make trouble returned in a rush. She took a deep breath. 'You said you'd decided to lunch here in the hope of seeing me…'

His eyes on her face, he waited silently.

'Why? Was it just so you could tell me this story about Mark having a mistress and a child?'

'You sound accusing. Would you rather have gone ahead with the wedding without knowing?'

She shook her head. 'No, I suppose not.'

If it *was* the truth she did want to know… Though she was sure it *wasn't*, she reminded herself hastily.

But, whether it was true or not, she guessed that he'd told her purposely, in order to blacken Mark's character and throw a spanner in the works.

She was oddly disappointed. Somehow it seemed unworthy of him.

Hoping he would refute the suggestion, she asked, 'I take it this is your way of trying to get back at Mark?'

'You could say that,' Jonathan admitted. 'Though probably not for the reason you imagine.'

Angry and disillusioned now—she hadn't put him down as petty or vindictive—she gave him a look of cold hostility. 'For whatever reason, I think it's despicable to try to poison my mind against him.'

Pushing back her chair, she jumped to her feet and made for the door. Grabbing her mac *en route*, she struggled into it and, fumbling with her umbrella, almost ran up the basement steps.

Rain was still pouring from a sky nearly as dark as night. The pavement shone wet and gleaming in the lights; the gutters ran with water.

She had gone only a short distance when it occurred to her that she had rushed off without paying the bill. Her steps faltered and she half turned.

Then, changing her mind, unwilling to face Jonathan

again, she hurried on. Let *him* pay. He'd had his money's worth—discrediting Mark, upsetting her, and in the process destroying what had been her growing respect for him.

Strangely enough, the latter mattered most of all.

CHAPTER SIX

LORIS had reached the far end of Shear Lane and was waiting to cross the road when Jonathan suddenly appeared by her side. He was bare-headed, the collar of his stone-coloured mac turned up against the rain.

The lights changed. Calmly taking charge of her umbrella, his other hand beneath her elbow, he crossed with her.

Picking up the conversation as though there had been no interruption, he said, 'I wasn't trying to poison your mind, merely open your eyes. As I told you the night we met, Longton isn't a very nice character.'

'And as I told you, that's a matter of opinion. At least he doesn't go sneaking behind people's backs...and he's honest enough to admit when he's in the wrong.'

'Would you call hiding the fact that he has a mistress and a child honest?'

Jerking her elbow free, she retorted curtly, 'As it happens, I don't believe a word of it.'

'Then when you see him tonight try asking him.'

But when his afternoon meeting ended Mark was flying to the Continent on business. He wouldn't be back until tomorrow night. Suddenly she knew that was much too long to wait.

Impatient to get at the truth, to hear Mark refute the allegation once and for all, she said, 'We're quite close to the offices, and he should be back from lunch any time, so why not ask him now?'

'Why not, indeed? And don't forget to watch his face while you're asking him.'

But, already starting to anticipate one difficulty, she pointed out, 'The problem is, he's bound to want to know where I heard such a story.'

'Feel free to tell him.'

Although she was upset and angry with Jonathan, she couldn't do that. It would be as good as signing his death warrant.

'No, I...I don't want to tell him. It would only cause a great deal of trouble.'

'You mean he'd find some way to dismiss me? Don't worry about that.'

'I don't want you to lose your job through me.'

'That's heartening,' he said ironically. 'Judging by the inimical look you gave me earlier, anyone would have thought a firing squad was too good for me.'

'Well, what else can you expect? You slander the man I...' about to say *love* she changed it to, 'I'm going to marry—'

Stopping in his tracks, Jonathan turned towards her. Still holding the orange umbrella sprinkled with white daisies over her head, he took her chin between the finger and thumb of his free hand and made her look at him.

His hair dark and dripping, rain running down his face, he said quietly, 'You're wrong on at least one of those counts, and I hope on both. Slander is a *false* statement, and everything I told you was true. Though I dislike and disapprove of men like Longton, it gave me no pleasure to have to do what I just did. But it was necessary to put you in the picture before it was too late.'

More shaken than she cared to admit, she jeered, 'So you regard it as your mission in life to stop me marrying Mark? Well, if I need a knight in shining armour, I'll let you know.'

Jerking free, she carried on walking. 'Otherwise I'd like

it if you'd mind your own business and stay out of my life.'

Keeping pace with her, he said solemnly, 'I'm not sure I can do that.'

With an odd kind of flutter, she demanded, 'Why not?'

He sighed. 'Well, it would be such a waste.'

She glanced sideways at him. 'You mean if I marry Mark?'

'Not exactly.'

'Then what *do* you mean?'

'Well, apart from the fact that you owe me a lunch, I've just bought a new tin of metal polish.'

It was indicative of her state of mind that it took her a second or two to catch on. He meant he was already her knight in shining armour!

Gritting her teeth and staring straight ahead, she walked even faster.

In less than a minute they had reached the elegant old building that housed the BLC offices, and were mounting the steps with a straggle of staff just returning from lunch.

Though most people were stopping just clear of the doors to wipe their feet, the marble floor of the large lobby was wet from dripping macs and umbrellas. Jonathan shook and furled Loris's umbrella, and presented it to her gravely.

Dropping it into one of the troughs provided for visitors, she thanked him, her voice cold.

Mark's suite of offices was on the top floor, next door to her father's, and she was halfway to the lifts when, a hand on her arm, Jonathan stopped her. 'Aren't you forgetting something?'

'Of course,' she said acidly, 'I'm so sorry.' She fumbled in her shoulder-bag for her purse. 'I still owe you for lunch.'

He stopped her. 'That wasn't quite what I had in mind.' Green eyes looked steadily into amber. 'A civil goodbye would have been nice...' Glancing across the lobby, he added, 'But now circumstances favour something a little more demonstrative.'

Before she could begin to guess his intention he cupped both her elbows and, drawing her towards him, covered her mouth with his.

Taken by surprise, she made no attempt to struggle, merely stood there, acquiescent, while he kissed her lightly but proprietorially, making her heart start to race and the world tilt on its axis.

As he released her and stepped back, leaving her face wet from the contact with his, she looked up dazedly to see Mark standing stock-still just inside the entrance, glaring in their direction.

His expression made it plain that he'd seen the little incident, and she knew without a shadow of a doubt that he'd been *meant* to.

Before she could begin to regain her equilibrium, a man she recognised as William Grant, one of Cosby's top executives, walked past.

Noticing Jonathan, he paused. 'If you could spare a moment, Mr Drummond? There's something I need to ask you about before the afternoon meeting.'

'Of course. Would you like to come up to my office?' Smiling at Loris, Jonathan added pleasantly, '*Au revoir*, Miss Bergman.'

Still feeling stunned, knocked off balance, she watched the two men carry on towards the lifts.

A moment later, his face black as a thundercloud, Mark was looming over her. Seizing hold of her wrist, he demanded in a furious undertone, 'Damn it, Loris, are you *trying* to provoke me?'

'Of course not. I—'

'You promised you wouldn't see Drummond again. Next thing I know you're kissing him, not only in public, but right under my very nose. What the hell do you think you're playing at?'

'Mark, let go of my wrist!'

His grip tightened even more. 'Well, answer my question.'

'Let her go.' Jonathan's voice, though quiet, cracked like a whip.

Startled, Mark exclaimed, 'Why, you—!'

'Do as I say, unless you want to end up flat on your back with everyone looking on.'

Letting go of Loris's wrist, Mark turned on his adversary, his big hands clenched into fists of rage. 'Don't be a fool, man,' Jonathan said in the same quiet, even tone. 'There's no point in making a scene.'

'What's the matter? Scared?' Mark taunted.

'Not at all.' His voice matter-of-fact, Jonathan added, 'But I don't want to be involved in a fracas unless I'm forced. I've never cared for violence. However, if you lay another finger on Loris I'll be tempted to forget my scruples and break your neck. Is that clear? Oh, and in answer to your question, she wasn't "playing at" anything. Loris didn't kiss *me*. *I* kissed *her*. She had no choice in the matter, and is totally blameless. So if you want to take it out on anyone, it will have to be me.'

That wasn't strictly true, Loris was forced to admit. She could have pulled away, she could have smacked his face, but she'd done neither. Like someone under a spell, she had just stood there and let him kiss her. Enjoyed it even. She hastily snapped off the disloyal thought.

'Now, if you'll excuse me,' Jonathan went on, 'William Grant is waiting for me.' Over his shoulder he added, 'But don't forget what I said.'

His lips drawn back over strong white teeth, Mark snarled, 'Of all the arrogant, overweening young upstarts—'

'Please, Mark,' Loris interrupted with a touch of desperation, 'let's go up to your office. We can't talk standing here in the lobby.'

Without a word, but obviously still seething, he turned and headed across to the lifts.

Thankful they were leaving, Loris followed him.

She breathed a sigh of relief to find that there was no sign of Jonathan and William Grant amongst the little knot of people waiting. The last thing she wanted was for them all to be forced to ride up together.

When she and Mark got out of the lift on the top floor, they walked a yard or two along a wide corridor before turning the corner to his suite of offices.

As he led the way through the outer office, Mark gave his grey-haired secretary curt instructions that they weren't to be disturbed.

Obviously well used to him, she enquired calmly, 'You haven't forgotten you have a meeting in your office at two-thirty?'

'No, I haven't forgotten,' he snapped, before leading the way into the inner sanctum.

Mark's huge office was luxuriously carpeted and furnished, with an imposing desk and a built-in bar. Displayed in a glass case were several cups and trophies, and a series of first-class sporting prints adorned the walls.

By this time reaction had set in. Feeling distinctly shaky, Loris dropped her bag, pulled off her mac, and took a seat in one of the big leather armchairs. Mark—perhaps because it gave him back his feeling of authority—chose to sit behind his desk.

On his desk top, along with all the latest technology, was a picture of Loris.

She was oddly touched to see it there.

Before she could decide just how to begin, he said brusquely, his heavy face set and angry, 'You'd better start by telling me why you broke your promise not to see Drummond again.'

Sounding cooler than she actually was, she said, 'I didn't break my promise. Well, not on purpose…'

'Then what were you two doing together?'

'I'd decided to have lunch before going on to my next appointment. I was looking at the menu when he suddenly appeared and sat down at my table.'

'Out of the whole of London, he just happened to choose the same restaurant? What a remarkable coincidence!' Mark said incredulously.

'It wasn't exactly a coincidence,' she admitted. 'While he was at Monkswood I mentioned that when I was in town I often lunched at Il Lupo, as it was good and cheap… And of course it's quite close to here.'

'So he went there purposely, hoping to see you?'

Instinctively trying to save Jonathan's skin, she lied, 'I can't say whether he went purposely or not. Maybe it just happened…'

'So when you'd shared a nice cosy lunch, you couldn't bear to leave him?'

'No… I left the restaurant first. I was waiting to cross Shear Lane when he caught up with me, and we walked the rest of the way here together.'

'Why did you come *here* rather than going on to your next appointment?'

'I wanted to see you. I need to talk to you.'

'And whatever it is couldn't have waited until tomorrow night?'

'No, it couldn't,' she said flatly. 'It's important.'

Unconvinced, he brushed her assurance aside, and went back to his interrogation. 'So what the devil was Drummond doing mauling you about?'

Though his kiss had rocked her, she remembered the

lightness of it, the finesse, and she objected, 'I'd hardly call it "mauling me about"...'

Mark's scowl told her she was making things worse.

In an effort to be more conciliatory, she explained, 'I was leaving him, intending to come up to your office, when he stopped me. He said I'd walked away without even saying goodbye. That's when he...he kissed me.'

'He wasn't afraid I'd see him?'

'Quite the opposite,' she said drily. Then wanted to kick herself.

Mark cottoned on immediately. 'You mean he'd seen me come in, and he did it on purpose to annoy me?'

'I'm afraid so.'

'Well, believe me, he'll live to regret it... After the way he tried to make a fool of me in front of quite a number of the staff—'

'I thought he was trying to stop you making a fool of yourself.' Realising she'd been less than diplomatic, Loris wished she'd guarded her unruly tongue.

'Of course you would have to stick up for that swine,' Mark said harshly.

'I'm not sticking up for him. But remember you promised that, no matter what, you wouldn't take any action against him. That was why I agreed to bring the wedding forward.'

His face tense, he demanded, 'You're not backing out now, just because of Drummond?'

Knowing there was little else she could do until Mark had calmed down, and reminding herself that Jonathan had asked for everything he'd got, she said, 'No, I'm not backing out. But I would like you to keep your side of the bargain.'

Noting more than a hint of relief mingling with the anger in his brown eyes, she added, 'Please, Mark, can't we let the matter drop and get onto what I came for?'

He moved his heavy shoulders in an irritable gesture. 'Very well. You said it was important, so I suppose it's something to do with the arrangements for the wedding?'

'Not exactly.' She swallowed. 'You told me that after you and your wife split up you didn't have a relationship until I came along.'

When he said nothing, she added, 'Is that true?'

His expression closed, he said, 'Yes, it is.'

'You didn't get engaged to anyone else?'

'Engaged? Certainly not.'

'But you lived with someone?'

'Look, what are you getting at?'

'I heard there was another woman in your life—'

'*You* are, and have been, the only woman I've had a relationship with since my marriage broke up.' Then, quickly, 'If you're thinking of Pamela, I'd never even set eyes on her before the party. She was just a one-night stand, and you know quite well why. You're not still holding that against me?'

'No, this has nothing to do with Pamela.'

Sounding impatient now, he asked, 'Then what has it to do with?'

'I heard that after your wife left you lived with someone else, and that she had a baby by you.'

'*What?*' He jumped to his feet. 'Where in hell's name did you hear a preposterous story like that?'

'Where I heard it isn't important. Is it true?'

'Of course it isn't true!' Mark looked so upset she believed him straight away. She told herself she felt relieved and her face softened. 'I'm sorry, Mark.'

He shook his head and replied, 'I don't blame you for thinking the worst of me—especially after Pamela. But I've learnt my lesson. I may have been a bit too easily led when it came to the opposite sex in the past, but when we're married I swear I won't so much as *look* at another woman.

You're all I've ever wanted, and with you in my bed, and a family of my own, I'll be the happiest man in the world.'

Before she could reply, he came around the desk and kissed her. When he pulled back and smiled at her, Loris told herself that his speech was all that she could have wanted, and that she was doing the right thing in marrying him. But she couldn't help feeling slightly uneasy at the memory of Jonathan's earnest face as he'd told her of Mark's supposed mistress and child. He'd almost convinced her!

Breaking into her thoughts, Mark asked, 'Where did you hear about this, anyway? I'd very much like to know.'

Shaking her head, she said, 'It doesn't matter.'

'It matters to me. Damn it, Loris, *who* told you? Whoever dug it up was clearly just trying to make trouble.'

Watching his big frame stiffen, she knew he had guessed the truth.

'*Drummond!* Who else? It was him, wasn't it? I ought to have realised at once... Well, this time he'll find he's definitely overstepped the mark. I'll show him who's boss. I'll get him sacked if it's the last thing I do!'

Loris bit her lip. Though she didn't believe Jonathan's story, she thought he did. The person who'd fed him the lies could well have been one of the business enemies Mark had made in the past, trying to discredit him with Cosby's. Yes, that was the most likely explanation—so it wasn't really Jonathan's fault.

Only too aware that it was touch and go, and she'd have to tread carefully, she said, without undue emphasis, 'Don't you think you might be jumping to conclusions? Allowing yourself to be prejudiced?'

'You mean it *wasn't* Drummond?'

'Is it likely he'd know a thing like that when he's only been over from the States a short time?'

'Well, if it wasn't him, who the devil was it?'

'As I've already said, it doesn't matter.'

Seeing he looked far from happy at being put off, she smiled at him. 'And I know the truth, so, rather than keep talking about it, I'd much sooner forget the whole thing.'

Anxious to get away before he pressed her any further, she reminded him, 'Haven't you a meeting scheduled for two-thirty?'

'Yes.' He glanced at his watch. 'They'll be here any minute.'

'Then I'd better go.'

He took her in his arms again and smiled down at her, his face transformed by charm. It was easy to see why so many women fell for him.

She felt a stirring of the old excitement, the kind of attraction that had first drawn her to him, and when he kissed her she kissed him back with an enthusiasm she hadn't displayed recently.

'That's much more like it,' he said with satisfaction, and kissed her again, enjoying the warmth of her response.

In just over a week they would be married, she thought with a little glow, and once they were man and wife, the tension that of late had soured their relationship should soon disappear. They would be at ease with one another, free to enjoy their future together...

Mark drew back with a sigh, and, glancing at the couch, said ruefully, 'It's a great pity about that meeting, but I'm afraid it's far too late to cancel it.'

Flustered, blushing a little at the thought of making love in his office, she pulled on her mac, gathered up her bag, and headed for the door.

Her hand was on the doorknob, when he said, 'If the flight's on time, I'll be round at your place about six-thirty tomorrow evening.'

'Fine.' She turned to smile at him and blow him a kiss before closing the door behind her.

She was still smiling when she reached the end of the corridor and turned towards the lifts.

The smile died from her lips when she saw Jonathan, his eyes on her face, leaning nonchalantly against the wall opposite. He had dried off, she noticed, and his hair, once more smoothly brushed, had returned to its normal fairness.

Oddly disconcerted by his presence, she asked crossly, 'Have you nothing better to do than lie in wait for me?'

His eyebrows shot up. 'You think I was lying in wait for you?'

'Yes. Otherwise what would you be doing lurking in the corridor?'

'Would you believe it if I told you I'm *en route* to join a meeting in Longton's office?'

Made suspicious by the way the question was phrased, she demanded, 'Are you?'

'I'm supposed to be.' Shamelessly, he added, 'Though I must admit that my real object *was* to lie in wait for you and find out how things had gone.'

Pressing the call button for the lift, she said haughtily, 'Well, as I've no intention of telling you, perhaps you'd better get on your way rather than waste the firm's time.'

A gleam in his green eyes, he mocked, 'You're starting to sound just like the boss's daughter.'

'I *am* the boss's daughter,' she reminded him tartly as the lift sighed to a halt and the doors slid open.

It was empty, and without a backward glance she stepped inside.

Jonathan followed close on her heels.

'I thought you were supposed to be going to the meeting,' she said sharply, as he reached to touch one of the buttons.

'There are more important things in life than attending meetings.'

Drily, she observed, 'I just hope Mr Grant agrees with you.'

'I'm sure he will. He's a good man, and on most things we're in complete accord. He'll back me all the way.'

'For your sake, I hope so.'

'Does that mean Longton's gunning for me?'

'It means you can't afford to take any *more* risks.' As she finished speaking the lift sighed to a stop and the doors slid open.

Eager to escape, Loris was halfway out when she realised that they were on the second floor, rather than in the foyer.

Before she could dig her toes in Jonathan had thrown a firm arm around her waist, swept her across the corridor, through a door opposite, and into a small, functional office, the antithesis of Mark's.

'What are you doing?' she cried, pulling free. 'I haven't got time to play silly games.'

'It wasn't silly games I had in mind. More a serious talk.'

'I've an appointment in Bayswater at three-thirty,' she said coldly.

'That will give us ample time. I'll call you a taxi when we've finished.'

As she started to protest, he added smoothly, 'I'll even pay for it.'

He was standing between her and the door, and though his stance was casual she felt convinced he had no intention of letting her leave until he'd learnt what he wanted to know.

'Won't you sit down?' he suggested politely.

Her common sense insisted that he wasn't likely to man-handle her, and she toyed briefly with the idea of telling him to go to hell and simply walking out.

But, as though his will was stronger than hers, she found herself weakly taking a seat in one of the plastic-covered swivel chairs.

He came and sat on the corner of the desk, and, crossing his arms, asked, 'So how did it go?'

'How did what go?'

Ignoring her attempt to stonewall, he said, 'When you rounded that corner you were smiling.'

'There's no law against it.'

'You hardly looked like a woman who's just learnt her fiancé isn't to be trusted.'

'Perhaps that's because I hadn't learnt any such thing.'

'So you didn't ask him?'

'Yes, I did.'

'And he denied the whole thing?'

'I don't see that what went on between Mark and me is any of your business.'

'For reasons that I won't go into at the moment, I'm making it my business.'

When she sat stubbornly silent, he sighed. 'Oh, well, if *you* won't tell me what happened, I'll have to ask Longton.'

'Do you really think he'd tell you?' she demanded incredulously.

'He might see sense. But if I have no alternative I'm prepared to beat it out of him.'

That quietly spoken threat should have seemed ridiculous, but she had no doubt—not only that Jonathan *meant* what he said, but that he could *do* it.

She shuddered, before asking caustically, 'Wouldn't it be easier to beat it out of me?'

'I've never struck a woman in my life, and I've no intention of starting now. Though there are other more enjoyable ways...' All at once he was standing over her, his eyes on her mouth.

Panic-stricken at the thought of him kissing her, she cried, 'Don't! Don't you dare touch me... All right, I'll *tell* you...'

'Dear me,' he murmured mildly. 'If I'd realised what an effective approach that was I'd have used it earlier.'

'And I thought Mark was good at intimidation,' she said bitterly.

Jonathan's smile was grim. 'He might be good at intimidation, but, remembering how happy you looked when you left him, I strongly suspect he's better at lying.'

'I happen to believe him,' she said stoutly.

'If you'd care to tell me what he said, I'll be able to judge for myself.'

Reluctantly, she said, 'He denied it completely.'

'And you believe that load of clap-trap?' Jonathan asked incredulously. 'Use your brains, Loris. He's lied to you before and he's lying to you now.'

Back on the see-saw of doubt, and hating it, she jumped to her feet, forcing him to step back a pace.

'You're wasting your time,' she said coldly. 'And I'd much prefer it if in future you stopped trying to interfere in my life and kept your nose out of Mark's affairs. In fact it would be better all round if you went back to the States. Now, if you don't mind, I want to leave.'

'Would you like me to call you a taxi?'

'No, thank you.' Picking up her bag, she headed for the door.

CHAPTER SEVEN

JONATHAN easily got there first, and for a moment she thought he was going to prevent her leaving, but instead he reached to open the door for her.

'*Au revoir*, Miss Bergman.'

'*Goodbye*, Mr Drummond.'

'Oh, just one more thing…'

Like a fool, she paused and turned.

The door was promptly closed.

A split-second later her bag thudded to the floor, her arms were pinned to her sides, and his mouth was on hers.

This time she struggled hard, but he held her easily, effortlessly. When she attempted to kick his shins her feet were neatly hooked from beneath her, leaving her completely off balance.

At first his kiss was punitive, conveying only too clearly the anger he felt. But after a moment or two it gentled and turned into a series of soft, plucking baby-kisses, kisses that coaxed and beguiled and made her want to open her mouth to him.

Her lips pressed tightly together, she was trying to resist the temptation when, with a suddenness that caught her by surprise, he nipped her bottom lip between his teeth.

It was just hard enough to make her gasp, and he took instant advantage, deepening the kiss until the world reeled and heat surged through her body.

She was lost, mindless, when he lifted his head, and, setting her on her feet, bent to retrieve her bag and hand it to her.

An instant later there was a tap at the door, and it opened to admit one of the girls belonging to the junior staff.

Perhaps sensitive to atmosphere, she glanced curiously from one to the other. 'Sorry to disturb you, Mr Drummond, but Mr Grant asked me to remind you about the meeting.'

'Thank you, Caley. Please will you tell him I'll be along directly?'

As, looking as though she'd like to linger, the girl turned to go, Jonathan said to Loris, 'Well, I'll say *au revoir*, Miss Bergman. Many thanks for your time and help... Allow me to see you out.'

His obsequious manner was contradicted by the devilish gleam in his eyes.

Gritting her teeth, she stalked past him without a word and, too agitated to wait for the lift, took the stairs down to the foyer.

It was still raining hard, and, retrieving her umbrella, she set off through the downpour. At the corner she spotted a cruising taxi and flagged it down. It would be the last straw if she was late for her appointment.

It was after five when Loris got back to her flat. She felt unsettled and dispirited. Her appointment had proved to be disappointing, as it had soon become apparent that, rather than being serious about a commission, all the owner of the penthouse wanted was free advice. Which meant that the time she had put aside the following day to do preliminary sketches was now time wasted.

And, as if that wasn't bad enough, she had been unable to get Jonathan Drummond out of her head. Over and over again some mental video had replayed the afternoon's events.

The way he had forced her to confront Mark... The way he had defended her in the foyer... The way he had kissed her… The way he had succeeded in putting fresh doubts in her mind…

Not for the first time, she found herself wondering what he hoped to gain by throwing a spanner in the works.

It was clear that he disliked Mark and wanted to prevent her from marrying him. But *why*? There had to be more to it than mere dislike. Despite all that had passed between them, it couldn't be because he had any romantic interest in her. He'd admitted to having wedding plans of his own.

Thoroughly disgruntled, wishing she'd never set eyes on Jonathan Drummond, she went through to the kitchen to make herself a cup of tea. While she drank it, she listened to the messages on her answering machine.

The first one added to her gloom by cancelling an appointment she had made for the next day, and that was followed by several that were merely run-of-the-mill. Only the last one was of real interest. The caller was a Mrs Marchant who, having seen and admired some of Loris's work, wanted her to look over a small manor house near Fenny Oak.

After a brief description of the twelve-roomed property, the friendly-sounding voice went on, 'We've just recently bought Fenny Manor. It's only partially furnished, and the whole place has been badly neglected, so it all needs refurbishing. To be honest I've neither the time nor the talent for such a project, so we'd like to know as soon as possible whether you'd be interested? If you could fit in a visit tomorrow, or even better tonight, we'd be very grateful.

'By the way, money's no object, and if you did decide to accept the commission, you'd be given a completely free hand. Perhaps you'd let us know?'

She had left a telephone number.

It sounded exactly the kind of big, exciting project Loris had always hoped for, and being busy tonight would take her mind off other things.

Her spirits rising, she tapped in the digits, and after a couple of rings the same pleasant voice answered, 'Hello?'

'This is Loris Bergman.'

'Oh, Miss Bergman, it's very kind of you to call back so quickly. I'm only too aware of how short the notice is, so I dared hardly let myself hope you'd be free tomorrow.'

'As a matter of fact I can get over tonight,' Loris said.

'Oh, that's absolutely wonderful! But we're a little way out of London. I don't suppose you've ever heard of Fenny Oak? It's a small hamlet not very far from the village of Paddleham.'

'As a matter of fact I know the area. It's only a few miles from where my parents live.'

'Excellent. Do you happen to know Watersmeet? Well, Fenny Manor stands on the strip of higher ground between the River Fenny and the River Mere. It's the only house on the island, so you can't go wrong. At the bottom of Watersmeet Lane, which is signposted as a private road, there's an old stone bridge over the Fenny... You do have a car, by the way?'

'No, I don't. With most of my work being in London, and taking into account the traffic jams and the difficulties of parking, it's easier to use taxis.'

'Well, if you come by taxi we'll be more than happy to meet your expenses. Oh, and before I forget, the recent floods have weakened the bridge to the point where it may be unsafe for vehicles, so you'll need to ask the taxi to wait on the far side and walk over. But it's only a hundred yards or so to the house. If you can tell us roughly what time you expect to arrive, I'll watch out for you.'

Wondering when they had their evening meal, Loris asked, 'What time would suit you best? Seven-thirty? Or later perhaps?'

'Make it seven-thirty if you can, and if you've no other

plans why not have dinner with us? Get the feel of the place…'

'Thank you, that would be nice.'

It was a pitch-black night and the rain was still falling steadily as, just before seven-thirty, Loris's taxi drove through the picturesque hamlet of Fenny Oak and turned down Watersmeet Lane.

Their lights made a bright tunnel between bare hedges and waterlogged fields, and gleamed on the surface water that covered the roadway to a depth of several inches.

Prewarned on booking that it might entail waiting for a couple of hours or more, the driver, a chatty, middle-aged man who owned his own cab, had said with cheery unconcern, 'Don't worry, love, I'm used to it. It's all part of the job. A packet of sandwiches and a newspaper help to pass the time. And if I wasn't sitting waiting I'd be battling with the London evening traffic. So what's the odds?'

Now, as the road dipped, and the level of the water rose correspondingly, he said judiciously, 'Let's hope it doesn't get any deeper, or we might have a job getting back.'

They approached the end of the lane to find that it opened out onto a wide, cobblestoned area lit by two old-fashioned streetlamps.

A stone bridge crossed the river at this point and a little way beyond, set on higher ground, Loris could see the bulk of a house, its lighted windows a welcoming sight.

The River Fenny, little more than a gentle stream in the summer, was now swollen and fast-flowing. Its brown muddy water, swirling along branches and other storm debris, battered at the bridge supports and, filling the arch, surged against the old stonework.

Coming to a halt on rising ground that formed the approach to the bridge, the driver suggested, 'If you jump out here, you shouldn't get your feet wet.'

'Thanks. Sure you'll be OK? It won't be very warm, just sitting.'

'I'll be fine. If I do get chilly I can always run the engine a bit.'

Loris tightened the belt of her mac, pulled on her sou'wester-type rain hat, and stepped out into the downpour. Slamming the cab door behind her, she hurried across the bridge.

The force of the water seemed to shake its very foundations, and in the light from the lamps she could see where some of the mortar between the stones that formed the roadway was starting to crumble away. It was quite scary, and she was glad to get to the other side.

The drive, running between sloping green lawns, was paved and well-lit, and as she climbed the steps to the terrace a door opened, spilling golden light onto the flagstones.

A slim, attractive woman, about her own height, with grey eyes and fair curly hair, was waiting in the doorway. She appeared to be in her late twenties or early thirties.

'Hello, Miss Bergman, I'm Jane Marchant.' She smiled with real warmth, and, drawing Loris into a large panelled hall with a beautiful old staircase running up the centre, exclaimed, 'What absolutely dreadful weather! Let me take your wet things.'

Hanging Loris's raingear and her shoulder bag on the hall stand, she added cheerfully, 'Dinner's almost ready, but before you sit down to eat suppose I just quickly show you over the house? That way you can get some first impressions.'

Though the signs of neglect were only too obvious, Fenny Manor was both charming and spacious, a house of character, with thick walls and mullioned windows.

By the time the brief tour was completed and they had ended up in a big, homely kitchen, with oak settles and a flagged floor, Loris knew it was just the kind of place she'd love to work in.

Standing in front of the glowing stove, surveying the white plaster walls and black-beamed ceiling, she said as much.

'I'm pleased you like it.' Jane Marchant smiled her relief. 'It would have been a pity if you'd hated the sight of it, after being brave enough to turn out on such a miserable night.'

Returning her smile, Loris said, 'Door to door hardly counts as being brave. It's the taxi driver having to wait in the cold I feel sorry for.'

'Well, there's no need for the poor man to sit outside in the cab. I'll pull on my coat and go and ask him to come in.'

Hurrying to the door, she paused to say, 'By the way, that archway leads to the dining-room, if you'd like to go through...'

The dining-room was the only room Loris hadn't yet seen, but, deciding to wait for her hostess to return, she stayed where she was, wondering idly if there was a Mr Marchant.

There had seemed to be no one else at home, but Jane Marchant had said have dinner with *us* and, in the only bedroom that was furnished, Loris had noticed a man's hairbrush and a neatly-coiled tie.

What she hadn't noticed, and it only now struck her as strange, was any real sign of *feminine* occupation. Jane Marchant must be one of those tidy women who put everything away...

Bringing her mind back to practicalities, she turned her attention to the kitchen. The stove was standing in what had once been a huge fireplace—judging by the rough outline on the plaster—and set in the wall close by were two small oak doors to what, she guessed, was an old salt cupboard.

If the fireplace could be opened up again...

There had been no sound, but, suddenly convinced that someone was watching her, she swung round.

Standing silently in the archway, casually dressed in corduroy trousers and a black polo-necked sweater, was Jonathan Drummond.

As, hardly believing her eyes, she gaped at him, he said easily, 'I was wondering what was keeping you.'

'What on earth are *you* doing here?' she croaked.

'I live here. Or at least I will when everything has been sorted out.'

Advancing on her, he put a light hand at her waist, and urged, 'Do come through. Otherwise the meal will be past its best.'

Stunned and speechless, she allowed herself to be shepherded into a candle-lit dining room and seated at a long refectory table.

Watching her host—presuming he *was* her host—start to open a bottle of white wine, Loris realised with a strange sinking feeling that Jane Marchant must be the woman he wanted to marry.

She had introduced herself as *Mrs* Marchant, and when talking about his plans Jonathan had said the woman he was hoping to marry was involved with someone else at the moment.

And when she'd asked what he was doing here, he'd answered, 'I live here. Or at least I will when *everything has been sorted out...*'

So were they just waiting for Jane Marchant's divorce to come through before they officially moved in together? She had said, *'We've only recently bought Fenny Manor...'*

It was clear that on his salary Jonathan could never have

afforded to buy a place like this, so if they *were* partners *she* must be the one with money.

But after all his taunts about marrying for money, unless he was the world's biggest hypocrite, she couldn't imagine him getting married for *that* reason. He must love Jane Marchant...

Though if he did, and was so close to marrying the woman of his dreams, why had he taken *her* to bed?

The answer had to be that he was a red-blooded man who had seen the opportunity and seized it.

Much as Mark had with Pamela.

A one-night stand, with no feelings on either side.

Yet there had been something tender and caring about Jonathan's lovemaking. Something that had seemed to make the whole thing special.

Or was it simply her own response that had made her think so? Perhaps all *he'd* done was pretend he was making love to the woman he loved...

It shouldn't matter. But somehow it did.

As though following her thoughts, he asked, 'So what do you think of Jane?'

Loris swallowed. 'I like her very much.' Then, driven by the need to know for sure, she asked huskily, 'I suppose you *love* her?'

'Yes,' he answered simply.

Staring down at the white damask tablecloth, she wondered why, when she loved Mark and was about to marry him, the knowledge that Jonathan loved another woman was so bitter.

But *did* she love Mark? Wasn't it more that, she having decided she wanted a husband and a family, he'd been the only man to attract her? *Until Jonathan...*

No, she mustn't think like that. It was much too late. After wearing Mark's ring for three months, and with all their wedding plans made, there was no way she could change her mind now.

In any case, the whole thing was probably nothing more than pre-wedding nerves. Once they were married, she would know she'd done the right thing.

She was consoling herself with that thought when a little demon of doubt reared its ugly head to ask, but what if, when it was too late, she knew she'd done the *wrong* thing…?

'I hope you like Spanish food?' Jonathan's voice made her look up with a start.

Endeavouring to pull herself together, she answered, 'Yes, I do.'

Having filled first her glass and then his own with Chablis, he lifted the lid from a skillet keeping warm on a hotplate.

Watching as he began to serve the steaming rice dish, she became aware for the first time that the table was set for only two people. Puzzled, she asked, 'Isn't Mrs Marchant eating with us?'

The candle flame picking up a little glint in his eye, he answered, 'Jane doesn't like Paella.'

With a sudden realisation of how long her hostess had been gone, and remembering the state of the bridge, Loris asked urgently, 'Do you think she's all right?'

'I'm sure she is.' He appeared calm, unconcerned.

Shaking her head, Loris said, 'You don't understand— she went out to speak to the taxi driver. Surely she should have been back by now?'

'She won't be coming back.'

'What do you mean, she won't be coming back?'

'I mean she's going home.'

'Going home?' Loris echoed blankly. 'Doesn't she live here?'

'No, she lives over at Harefield.'

'Oh, but—'

'Please make a start on your meal before it gets cold,' he broke in firmly, 'and after we've eaten I'll be happy to tell you anything you want to know.'

Seeing by his face that she was going to get nowhere until she'd complied, Loris picked up her fork.

When their plates were empty, and she'd refused a piece of *torta*, he poured coffee for them both and suggested, 'Why don't we drink our coffee in front of the living-room fire?'

He pulled back her chair and ushered her into the adjoining room, which had oak-panelled walls and an arched door through to the hall.

It looked cosy and intimate, with a single standard lamp casting a pool of light and a log fire blazing cheerfully in a wide stone hearth.

In front of the fireplace was a thick, white sheepskin rug, and in a semicircle around it a comfortable-looking three-piece suite and an oval coffee table.

When Jane Marchant had briefly shown it to her Loris had thought it a most attractive room, and a second look served to confirm that conclusion.

'Let me take your jacket; it's warm in here.' Before she could demur, Jonathan had slipped her bilberry-coloured jacket from her shoulders and hung it over a chair.

Taking a deep breath, she began, 'Now perhaps you'll tell me—'

'Why don't you make yourself comfortable first?' he broke in smoothly, indicating the couch with a long, well-shaped hand.

Biting her lip, she reminded herself that, for the moment at least, he was calling the tune. Determined to keep as much space as possible between them, however, she avoided the couch and took a seat in the nearest armchair.

Smiling at her choice, he sat down on one of the wide arms of the chair and cocked an eyebrow at her expectantly.

All her awareness focused on the man by her side, Loris took a nervous gulp of her coffee. Then, trying to hide how disturbing it was to have him so close, she said as calmly as possible, 'Would you mind telling me why Mrs Marchant thought it necessary to mislead me?'

'I asked her to,' he admitted unrepentantly. 'I told her exactly what I wanted her to say... Though as it happens she had seen and admired some of your work, so that bit at least was true.'

'It must be the only bit that was.'

He sighed. 'She disliked having to mislead you, and only did it to please me.'

'I fail to see why it was necessary,' Loris said stiffly.

'Would you have come if *I'd* asked you to? Of course you wouldn't. The way things are at the moment you'd have run a mile first.'

'If you were so sure of that, I don't know what you hoped to gain by bringing me here under false pretences.'

His eyes on her face, he asked, 'Do you like the house?'

'Yes,' she admitted.

'Wouldn't you like to work on it?'

Of course she would—if he had no connection with it. As it was... 'No, I wouldn't,' she said flatly.

He raised a fair brow. 'Why not?'

'*Why not?* You must be joking! Mark and I are getting married in a week.'

'You told me you intended to keep working at least until June.'

'I do. But not for you. So I'm afraid you've wasted your time, and mine.' Feeling suffocated by his nearness, she struggled to her feet.

'Going somewhere?'

'Home,' she said succinctly.

'How are you planning to get there?'

'Just in case you've forgotten, I have a taxi waiting for me.'

Above the black polo-neck his hair looked bleached of colour, and his heavy-lidded eyes gleamed green as a cat's. 'I think not.'

Loris glanced at him sharply, then in response to his quiet air of certainty she hurried over to the window and, parting the curtains, peered out.

The living-room was at the front of the house, overlooking the river and the cobbled area where the taxi had drawn up to wait.

Through the pouring rain she could see the taxi was no longer there.

Turning on him, she demanded angrily, 'What did you do? Pay him off and tell him to go?'

'Not exactly.' He rose to face her. 'I suggested to Jane that she told him there was no need to wait, as you'd decided to stay the night, and then used the cab to get home herself.'

Her heart starting to thud against her ribs, Loris said, 'She must be very trusting if she was prepared to go off and leave another woman here...'

'She trusts me implicitly,' he assured her, straight-faced.

'I fail to see why she should, when she knows perfectly well that I had no intention of staying the night.'

'*Had?* Does that mean you've changed your mind?'

Gritting her teeth, she said, 'No, it *doesn't* mean I've changed my mind. So perhaps you'll be good enough to call me another taxi.'

'I'm afraid I left my mobile at the office, and the phone here isn't connected yet,' he said smoothly.

'You're lying. I rang Fenny Manor late this afternoon and spoke to Mrs Marchant.'

'I can assure you she was at Harefield then. I was with

her when she left the message, and also when you phoned back later.'

Thoroughly agitated now, Loris said, 'Well, as you're responsible for me being stranded here, I must ask you to drive me at least as far as the nearest phone box.'

'I'm afraid I have no transport, and even if I had it wouldn't be safe to drive over the bridge.'

'If you have no transport, how did you both get back from Harefield?'

'We came by taxi. After going through some deepish water on my way from London my car was playing up so, rather than chance getting stuck, I left it at Jane's to be looked at.'

He seemed to have an answer for everything, though she was convinced it was all just a clever fabrication.

Wondering what kind of game he was playing, what his intentions were, she fought down a feeling bordering on panic and announced firmly, 'Then I'll walk to the village and phone from there.'

'The way the water's still rising you'd have a job to make it on foot... And, apart from that, it must be getting a bit risky to cross the bridge.'

Shuddering at the memory, she nevertheless said, 'Well, I'll have to chance it. Anything's better than being trapped here.'

He smiled crookedly. 'Death before dishonour? How very melodramatic.'

'It's nothing to joke about,' she told him vexedly. 'Mrs Marchant may trust you now, but what would she say if she knew what happened on Saturday night?'

'I'm sure she wouldn't mind. Jane's extremely broad-minded.'

'Well, *Mark* isn't, and if he discovered I'd spent the night here alone with you—'

'Oh, we won't be alone. Elizabeth is here.'

'Elizabeth? Who's Elizabeth?'

Stooping to throw another log on the fire, he answered, 'Our resident ghost. A friendly one, so they tell me. Though I haven't encountered her personally.'

'*Will* you be serious for once? As I've absolutely no intention of working for you, and we're both about to get married…'

He gave her a quick sidelong glance from between thick gold-tipped lashes. His expression held a hint of amusement.

'You *are* aren't you?' she demanded.

'Hopefully.'

'Then what's the *point* of all this?'

Looking serious now, he said, 'I thought while we were both still single it would be nice to spend another night together.'

'*Nice!*' she choked. 'You must be out of your mind!'

'I'm aware that in the morning you had some second thoughts, but on the whole you seemed to enjoy it enough to be willing to repeat the experience.'

'You know what?' she said shakily. 'When you're on the point of marrying someone else, that's the most immoral suggestion I ever heard!'

He looked pained.

'I don't know how you had the nerve to criticise Mark,' she went on, two bright spots of angry colour appearing in her cheeks. 'Compared to you, he's practically a saint!'

Jonathan smiled derisively. 'He's very far from being a saint. Believe me, any criticism I made of Longton was quite justified. He's a womaniser and a bully. Look at the way he treated you.'

Taking her right hand, where the cuff of her cream silk blouse failed to hide a slight red mark, he gently touched his lips to the inside of her wrist.

It was the sort of thing Mark would never have dreamt

of doing, and, oddly shaken by the tenderness of the gesture, she jerked her wrist free.

'That was as much *your* fault as Mark's. If you hadn't gone out of your way to make trouble—'

'Now, is that a nice thing to say?' he complained.

'It may not be nice, but it's a fact. And one of these days, if you go on like this, you're going to end up in serious bother. Each time you've come up against Mark you've deliberately provoked him, and if I'd admitted it was *you* who told me the story about the mistress and the baby—'

'You didn't?'

'No, I didn't. In fact I convinced him it wasn't you. Otherwise you'd have had no job left by now.'

Finding it a relief to let off steam, she continued to berate him. 'You just don't seem to care; you were even late for the meeting, and in your position...'

Her voice tailed off as something struck her. 'You said you were at Harefield with Mrs Marchant when she left the message on my answering machine...?'

'That's right.' An unholy gleam in his eye told her he was following her train of thought.

'The message was timed at three-fifty. You should have still been at the office—so why weren't you?'

'I'll give you one guess.'

She half shook her head, unwilling to believe it.

When he said nothing, merely waited, she stammered, 'Y-you don't mean Mark...?'

'Fired me?'

'Did he?'

'He tried. As soon as I walked into the meeting he cursed me roundly and told me to get out.'

Concerned, despite herself, she asked, 'Couldn't William Grant help?'

'I didn't want him to. It suited me to go.'

Of course… Wasn't he planning to marry someone with money?

Wearily, she asked, 'So this plan to lure me down here and force me to stay the night, was it done simply for revenge?'

'What do you think?'

'I think you're utterly despicable.'

'That's a pity, because I think you're quite enchanting.'

Turning her back on him, she headed for the door.

For the second time that day he was there before her, his back to the panels.

'Please get out of my way,' she said curtly. 'I want to go.'

When he made no move, she insisted, 'I mean it. I'm not joking.'

'Neither am I, when I tell you I have no intention of letting you leave here at least until morning… And possibly not then.'

Her heart starting to throw itself against her ribs, she protested, 'You can't keep me here.'

'I rather think I can,' he corrected mildly.

'*Please*, Jonathan,' she begged.

'I intend to,' he assured her with a little smile. 'In fact I can promise you *delight*…'

'No!' Heat running through her, she whispered, 'I don't want to make love with you, and if you try to force me I'll never forgive you. Never!'

'I've no intention of trying to force you.'

Her relief was short-lived as he added, 'I'll find ways of pleasuring you that will make you more than willing to come to bed with me…'

Every nerve in her body tightened and, to her horror, she felt the stirrings of desire. Scared to death now, not so much of him as of her own reactions, she moistened her dry lips.

'You're starting to want me already, without me even touching you,' he taunted.

'No!'

'Don't lie to me, Loris, I can see it in your face, in the way your body is already responding to the mere thought.'

She had never in her wildest dreams imagined herself in this kind of predicament. For more than three months she had *tried* to respond to Mark's caresses, his passionate kisses, and not been as moved as this, so how could Jonathan affect her so strongly with just a look and a few words?

Aware that her nipples were growing firm, and terrified that he'd see the evidence of her arousal though the thin silk of her blouse, she crossed her arms over her chest.

The betraying gesture made him laugh softly.

Turning away abruptly, she went to stand by the fire. If she couldn't prevent herself weakening, she must find some way to hide it.

When Jonathan said he wouldn't try to force her, she believed him. If she could only say *no* and mean it, he wouldn't touch her.

But, as though he held the key to her newly awakened sexuality, her body was only too responsive, so it was all down to will-power.

CHAPTER EIGHT

WELL, she had never been short of that, Loris told herself hardily, then jumped a mile as Jonathan came to stand close behind her.

Moving aside the swathe of long dark hair, he touched his lips to the soft skin of her nape, making her shiver.

'Don't,' she said raggedly. 'I don't want you to touch me.'

'My sweet little liar...' He nibbled at the sensitive juncture where the neck and shoulder met. 'You *do* want me to touch you.'

He slid his hands over her ribcage and let them rest so that his thumbs just brushed the undersides of her breasts. She could feel their warmth through the fine crêpe de Chine of her blouse.

Standing irresolute, she wondered frantically what would be her best means of defence. Would it be to turn and fight, or try to ignore what he was doing to her?

Deciding on passive resistance, she feigned indifference while his mouth travelled slowly up the side of her neck, biting and teasing, sending little *frissons* of excitement running through her.

She was so busy trying to resist the delicious torment of his tongue-tip exploring the warm hollow behind her ear that she was scarcely aware of his fingers deftly undoing the buttons of her blouse.

Not until his hands were cupping breasts protected only by a dainty scrap of satin and lace did she fully appreciate her danger.

And then it was almost too late.

His thumbs were rubbing lightly across her nipples, arousing a suffocating excitement when, his lips brushing her ear, he whispered, 'I know quite well you're not indifferent. I can feel your heart pounding, and your breath coming faster.'

'That's revulsion,' she said thickly.

He laughed. 'I've always liked a woman to have a touch of fighting spirit.'

'If you don't take your hands off me this minute, I'll show you more than a *touch* of fighting spirit.'

'Be careful,' he warned, 'there's nothing that inflames a man's passion more than a struggle.'

Guessing he'd only said that to make her stand submissively, she pulled herself free and swung round, her hand raised to slap his face.

She gave a little gasp as his fingers closed around her wrist.

His grip loosened immediately. 'Forgive me, I forgot about the bruise.'

Then, holding her hand lightly, he offered his cheek. 'Feel free to go ahead and slap me if it will make you feel any better.'

The mocking smile that accompanied his offer was like a match to a powder keg.

Smiling back with saccharine sweetness, she said, 'I'm sure it will,' and, swinging her left hand, gave him a slap across the face that cracked like a pistol shot and jerked his head sideways.

For an instant they both froze. Then as he lifted his hand she flinched away, wishing desperately that she'd controlled the flare of temper.

Seeing that involuntary movement, he said quickly, reassuringly, 'It's all right.' Then, gingerly feeling his cheek, 'I'm only assessing the damage.'

Shaken to the core, because she was anything but a violent person, she said, 'I'm sorry. I shouldn't have done that.'

'I asked for it,' he admitted ruefully. 'It just came as something of a surprise...'

Perhaps he'd presumed she wouldn't have the nerve, Loris thought as she pulled her blouse together and began to fasten the buttons with unsteady fingers.

As though he'd walked into her mind and read her thoughts, with wry self-mockery he explained, 'If you'd used your right hand I would have felt the muscles tense and seen it coming. I just hadn't allowed for the fact that you might be ambidextrous.'

His attitude was amused, in no way menacing, and she started to breathe more freely. Though her body still clamoured for his touch, the moment of danger seemed to have passed.

She had won.

Tucking her blouse back into her skirt, she said as lightly as possible, 'Well, now you know I'm not a woman to be trifled with, perhaps you'll allow me to get my coat and leave.'

Smiling grimly, he said, 'My dear Loris, you've only won a preliminary skirmish, not the war.'

Before she could react to the threat in his voice, she found herself lying flat on her back on the sheepskin rug.

He had gone down with her, his arms breaking her fall. Even so, for a second or two she was shocked into stillness. Then she began to struggle furiously.

Gently, he pinned her arms above her head with one hand and used the weight of his body to hold her there.

She continued to writhe and struggle futilely, until, realising that he'd spoken the truth when he'd said, 'There's nothing that inflames a man's passion more than a struggle' she abruptly froze.

With a crooked smile, he said, 'Yes,' and watched as she

blushed hotly. 'But if, in the next five minutes, I can't make you admit you want me, then I promise I won't touch you.'

His free hand cupping her chin, so she couldn't turn her face away, he bent his head and kissed her lightly.

She kept her teeth clenched, and after a second or two his lips began to wander over her cheeks, her temples, her closed eyelids, bestowing soft, butterfly kisses.

When they returned to resume their teasing, she was forced to redouble her efforts to keep her mouth closed against him.

If his kisses had been hard and grinding she would have found it easier to fight, but these coaxing, beguiling little caresses that promised such delight made her *want* to open her mouth to him.

She shuddered as his tongue-tip traced the outline of her lips and slipped between them to tease the sensitive inner skin, but somehow she held on.

Slowly and carefully, for the second time that night, he undid the buttons of her blouse, and opening it, nuzzled his face against the swell of her breasts.

'Don't, please don't…' The words ended in a gasp, as through the thin scrap of ivory satin she felt the damp warmth of his breath.

A moment later he had released the front fastening of her bra and pushed aside the cups, giving him free access to her beautifully shaped breasts and dusky pink nipples.

As he teased them with mouth and fingers, causing needle-sharp sensations, she moaned a little, the exquisite pleasure almost too much to bear.

While his mouth continued its torment, his hand moved down to slip off her shoes, before returning to travel up over her nylon-clad calf and knee to find the band of bare skin above the lacy top of her stocking. It paused there for an instant before moving further to discover the dainty satin briefs.

As she held her breath, his fingertips followed the high-cut leg of her briefs up to her hip and back again. There they paused to softly stroke the silky skin of her inner thigh.

Her whole body was on fire now, alive with wanting. Nothing else existed but this man and what he was doing to her. There was no past, no future, only the here and now, and an overwhelming need.

But, instead of going on to fulfil that need, the hand was withdrawn.

Suddenly she found she was free, and Jonathan was standing looking down at her. As she lifted a dazed face he took both her hands and helped her to her feet.

Her eyes wide and unfocused, she staggered a little. Standing aloof, he caught her shoulders and steadied her.

'Jonathan, I…' Swaying towards him, she put her arms around his neck and pressed her body against his in a wordless plea.

Refusing to hold her, he insisted, 'I'd like to hear you say it.'

Thickly, she said, 'I want you to make love to me.'

'Well, first we'll have this off.' He removed the engagement ring she was wearing and tossed it carelessly onto the wide mantelshelf.

Then, refusing to hurry, making her wait, he began to undress her. When her skirt, blouse, half-slip and bra were in a pile on the floor, and she was standing in her stockings and briefs, he slipped his hands inside her briefs to cup her buttocks, before bending his head to tease her eager nipples with his tongue once more.

'Please…' she whispered, in an agony of suspense.

Straightening, he slipped off his shoes and socks, pulled his sweater over his head and tossed it aside, before taking her hands and guiding them to the belt on his trousers.

She had never undressed a man before and, eagerness making her clumsy, she had a struggle to undo the buckle.

When it was finally unfastened, she fumbled with shaking fingers to unclip the waist.

Taking pity on her, he did the rest for her, stepping out of the trousers and sliding his dark silk shorts over lean hips.

With shoulders much broader than she'd first imagined, his body was graceful and symmetrical. He carried not an ounce of spare flesh and had the toned fitness of an athlete, the muscles rippling beneath skin that was smooth and tanned and healthy.

As she stared at him, her throat dry, he ordered softly, 'Let me look at you.'

Obediently she pushed the briefs down and stepped out of them, then, one hand on his shoulder to steady herself, stripped off first one stocking and then the other.

When she was completely naked she stood and let him look his fill, feeling no embarrassment, only a sense of gladness that what he saw so obviously pleased him.

'You're *beautiful*,' he murmured, almost reverently.

'So are you,' she said huskily.

Taking her hands, he drew her to him, naked flesh to naked flesh, her head on his shoulder.

All urgency gone, for a moment she closed her eyes, content to just let him hold her. The warmth and the clean male smell of him were precious and *familiar*. It was like coming home after a long time in the wilderness.

Putting a hand beneath her chin, he turned her face up to his and kissed her softly.

It was the barest brushing of lips, but it felt like a commitment, and she knew without a doubt that she loved this man. Had loved him since the moment she'd first set eyes on him.

It was *right, inevitable, ordained*, even, that they should be lovers.

Drawing back a little, she smiled at him and touched his

cheek wonderingly. Then, with a single fingertip, she traced first the cleft in his chin, and then his mouth—a mouth that, with its combination of cool asceticism and warm sensuality, always sent little quivers of excitement running through her.

He took her hand and kissed the finger, then, putting the tip in his mouth, sucked it.

Her stomach clenched, and abruptly the urgency was back.

Reading that urgency, he reached to switch off the standard lamp, then, in the firelight's glow, drew her to him and kissed her again, this time with passion and an urgency of his own.

Opening her mouth to him, she put her arms around his neck, and when he gently eased her down onto the thick sheepskin rug she pulled him down with her.

Loris surfaced slowly, her whole being steeped in happiness and a deep contentment. Her mood was languorous, her body relaxed and well satisfied, sleek as a cat's.

For a while she lay, still half-asleep, savouring this feeling of bliss, remembering the previous night and Jonathan's lovemaking. How he had ravished her—in the best meaning of the word—the heights he had carried her to, the way his promise of delight had been more than fulfilled.

She recalled the feel of the thick sheepskin rug beneath her, the warmth of the fire on her bare flesh, the way the leaping flames had gilded his face and hair and turned the body poised above her into a golden-limbed Apollo.

Afterwards they had lain contented in each other's arms until the fire had dwindled into glowing ashes and the air had grown cool.

Unwilling to destroy that perfect aftermath, Loris would have stayed there until morning if, feeling her slight shiver,

Jonathan hadn't gathered her up in his arms and carried her upstairs.

There, desire stirring once more, lighting up the darkness, they had made love until, sated, they had fallen asleep, her head on his chest, her body half supported by his.

Now she became aware that she was alone in the big bed, and watery sunlight was casting the shadows of the leaded windowpanes onto the white walls.

It was a new day.

With that realisation her brain kicked into action, and within seconds the icy wind of reality had shrivelled her happiness and blown it all away like so many dead leaves.

She might love Jonathan—and despite his faults she *did* love him, with all her heart and soul—but he wasn't hers to love. He belonged to another woman. He *loved* another woman.

Last night's determined seduction had meant nothing except that he'd *wanted* her. On his part it had been a purely physical thing, just a stolen night of passion that he should never have suggested. It had been utterly wrong of him.

She, in her turn, had been stupidly weak and wicked to agree to it. She had behaved very badly, not only as far as Mark was concerned, but Jane Marchant too.

What in heaven's name had she been thinking of?

In truth she hadn't been thinking at all. Only *feeling*. And now it was too late. The damage was done.

At least in *her* case.

Jonathan might be able to go on as if nothing had happened, but she couldn't. Last night had irrevocably altered things. How could she go ahead and marry Mark knowing full well she didn't love him?

The answer was, she couldn't.

But with all the wedding plans made how could she bring herself to tell him that she'd changed her mind? That it was all over? He was bound to take it badly, and she'd never wanted to hurt him.

Feeling bitterly ashamed, and guilty at the way she'd treated him, she stifled a groan. She'd always thought of herself as having reasonable morals, but now her actions had lowered her in her own eyes.

She had behaved like a wanton.

All at once, as though leaving Fenny Manor would enable her to leave some of the guilt behind her, she couldn't wait to get away.

There was still no sign of Jonathan, and the house felt quiet and somehow empty. A glance at her watch showed it was after twelve.

As she swung her feet to the floor she noticed two things: her clothes and shoes had been gathered up and placed neatly on a chair, and on the bedside table there was a cup of cold coffee with a folded piece of paper propped against it.

Opening the note with hands that were suddenly unsteady, she read it.

> As time is getting on and we've a busy day ahead, I've decided to fetch the car. I wanted very much to kiss you before I left, but it seemed a shame to chance waking you. Love, J.

Love, J...

Her breath caught in her throat, and just for an instant a wild hope made her heart soar.

Then common sense brought her down to earth with a bump. It was no doubt just a casual, meaningless end to a note or letter, rather than a declaration of his feelings.

Of course he didn't love her. He'd already said he loved Jane Marchant.

As far as *he* was concerned last night had been simply an enjoyable episode, a last fling without any *involvement.*

If he knew how she felt he'd no doubt be uncomfortable, embarrassed by the unforeseen and unwanted complication.

It seemed she'd made a fool of herself all the way round. If he discovered the true state of affairs, what little was left of her self-respect would be trampled into the mud.

The only way she could keep any pride at all was to let him believe that last night had been no more to her than it had been to him.

If she *could.*

He'd written, '*we've* a busy day ahead', but if she spent the day with him she might be unable to hide how she felt... Which meant she must go now, at once, before he returned. Her secret would only be safe if she never had to see him again.

She had no idea how he would get to Harefield, or how long it would take him, but, judging by the cold coffee, he'd already been gone for some time.

He might be back at any minute.

Struggling out of bed, she made her way across to the *en suite* bathroom, where the scent of shower gel still hung in the air and drops of water clung to the frosted glass of the shower stall.

On a shelf, as though waiting for her, there was a Cellophane-wrapped toothbrush and a new tube of toothpaste.

She brushed her teeth and showered as quickly as possible, then, grimacing at having to wear yesterday's clothes, she ran a borrowed comb through her hair before hastening down the stairs.

She had pulled on her mac, thrust her rain hat into one of the pockets and gathered up her bag, when she remembered the ring.

It was on the mantelshelf where Jonathan had tossed it.

Dropping it into her bag, she hurried to the door once more, and as she pulled the door open exclaimed, 'Oh!'

An elderly woman, her face mirroring Loris's surprise, was standing on the doorstep, a key in her hand.

'Sorry, did I startle you?' she asked.

'I didn't know anyone else lived here,' Loris said, feeling foolish.

'I don't actually live here,' the woman explained. 'I just come in on a daily basis to take care of things. It's only five minutes' walk from my cottage, so it's nice and handy.'

Seeing her chance, Loris said, 'Well, if you're local, perhaps you can help me? I need to call a taxi, so can you tell me where the nearest phone box is?'

'Oh, if it's a taxi you're wanting, Jeff Middleton's your man. He owns the smallholding right at the end of the lane, but he runs a one-man taxi service on the side.'

'Thanks.' Throwing her a grateful smile, Loris hurried down the steps to the drive. It was still damp underfoot, but the sky was clear for the first time in days and overnight the level of the river had dropped.

In the daylight the bridge looked a great deal stronger and safer than it had done the previous night, and she crossed it without fear.

With its bare hedges and lack of trees there was no cover on the lane, and, her heart in her mouth in case Jonathan's car should appear, she started up it. Though the verges were muddy and waterlogged, the roadway itself was now clear of water and, alternately running and walking, she made good time.

She had just reached the end and identified the smallholding when she heard the sound of an approaching car.

Darting into the gravelled entrance, she hid behind a somewhat ramshackle hen-house while she watched Jonathan's white saloon drive past and turn down the lane.

'Is it eggs you're wanting?'

The voice made her jump. She turned to see a youngish, fresh-faced man wearing a thick navy sweater over a pair of scruffy trousers.

'No…no, thank you. I need to get into London, and I was hoping to hire a taxi.'

'When for?'

'Well, now.'

'Be with you in a minute. Just need to fasten up the goats. You can get in if you want.' He jerked a thumb at a beaten-up Cortina that stood in the drive.

She climbed in and slammed the door, thanking her lucky stars that she'd just made it in time.

Anxious as she was to get moving, it seemed an age before the man returned and, wiping his hands on a piece of oily rag, got behind the wheel.

'Second call out so far today,' he remarked as he turned the key in the ignition and the engine roared into life. 'Took the new owner of Fenny Manor over to Harefield this morning.'

With a grinding of gears and jerk or two they were off, their tyres crunching on the gravel. They were just about to pull out of the drive when, from nowhere it seemed, the white saloon appeared and drew up in front of them, blocking the exit.

Jonathan jumped out and came strolling over as Jeff Middleton rolled his window down.

'Hello again, Mr Drummond.'

'Afternoon, Jeff. I see you have my guest with you.'

'Just driving the young lady into London.'

'I'm going there myself, so I'll be happy to take her…'

'No, thanks, I'd rather go with Mr Middleton.'

Ignoring Loris's protest, Jonathan produced a small roll of notes which smoothly changed hands. 'Might as well save you a job.'

'Can't say I haven't got plenty to do,' Jeff agreed and, stuffing the notes into his pocket, climbed out of the car.

Jonathan came round to open Loris's door and, ignoring the angry look she gave him, helped her out.

His hand lightly holding her elbow, he escorted her over to his car and settled her in before slipping behind the wheel.

As always his touch set her pulses racing and made her breathless, and she had to struggle to hide how *conscious* she was of him.

They drove for a while without speaking, then he broke the silence to ask, 'So what made you decide to run away?'

'I wasn't running away, simply leaving. What did you expect me to do? Take up permanent residence?'

'Would that be such a bad thing?'

'I've never really fancied a *ménage à trois*,' she said coldly.

'If the thought of Elizabeth bothers you, I could always call in an exorcist.'

'It isn't the thought of *Elizabeth* that bothers me...'

'Well, I wasn't thinking of asking Longton to live with us.'

'Oh, you're quite *impossible*,' she snapped.

'If you keep on saying that I may well develop a complex,' he said plaintively.

'What I *could* do with you developing is the ability to stay out of my life,' she told him tartly, while her treacherous heart rejoiced just to be with him.

'Is that what you really want, now you won't be marrying Longton?'

She took a deep, steadying breath, and asked, 'What makes you think I won't be marrying him?'

Though she knew that her question had shaken him, Jonathan's voice was even as he observed, 'You're not wearing his ring.'

Feeling in her bag, she retrieved the ring and slipped it back on.

'You don't still intend to go through with the wedding?'

'Of course,' she lied.

His jaw tightened. 'I thought last night might have meant something to you? Might have made you change your mind?'

She tried to say something light, dismissive, but all at once tears pricked behind her eyes and she found herself unable to speak. Instead she shook her head.

'Very well, discounting last night,' he said almost roughly, 'Longton still isn't the man for you. You've just told me you don't fancy a *ménage à trois*, but that's what you're letting yourself in for. Though he wants you enough to marry you, he isn't prepared to give up his mistress—'

'That's not true. He swore he didn't have one and I believe him.'

There was a short silence, then, apparently realising he was getting nowhere, Jonathan changed tack. 'Where is Longton today?'

'He's away on business.'

'So you weren't planning to see him?'

'Not until tonight. If his plane isn't late he'll be at my flat for about six-thirty.'

Jonathan said no more, and they drove for the next few miles in silence. They were coming up to a pleasant-looking country pub and, pulling into the car park, he stopped the engine and suggested, 'You must be more than ready for a drink and something to eat?'

Her mind had been far too busy to let her think of food, but all of a sudden she felt thirsty. 'A cup of coffee wouldn't go amiss,' she agreed.

They made their way inside and, sitting by the window, ordered ham sandwiches and a pot of coffee.

Head bent, busy once more with her thoughts, Loris ate and drank abstractedly.

Studying her preoccupied face—the dark silky brows and lashes, the pure bone structure, the neat nose and lovely, passionate mouth—Jonathan thought she was the most exquisite thing he'd ever seen.

All at once becoming aware of his scrutiny, she glanced up.

'Penny for them?' he offered.

Without meaning to, she found herself admitting, 'I was thinking about Mrs Marchant.'

'Oh?'

'How long have you known her?'

'Quite a long time.'

'Then you knew her while you were still living in the States?'

'Yes. Jane and her husband came over to stay with me from time to time.'

Jonathan's remark made her wonder if he was responsible for the break-up of the other woman's marriage. If he was, it seemed to make things so much worse.

Her conscience bothering her, Loris asked, 'Wouldn't she be terribly upset if she found out about last night?'

'I very much doubt it. As I told you, she's extremely tolerant.' Seeing his companion frown, he observed, 'You don't look too happy?'

'I just can't understand any woman being that tolerant. Are you certain—?' She stopped speaking abruptly.

'Certain about *what*?' he asked.

'That she really loves you?'

'Oh, yes, I think she does.'

He sounded so laid back, so sure of himself, that for a moment Loris was silent, wondering about his values, how he regarded marriage.

She had thought, from some of the things he'd said, that

he had good old-fashioned principles. But suddenly she wasn't so certain. Suddenly she had doubts about what kind of man he really was.

Needing to know, she asked, 'What sort of marriage do you envisage?'

He raised a fair brow. 'In what way?'

'I mean do you intend to have one of those modern marriages where each partner goes their own way?'

'Good Lord, no! As far as I'm concerned that isn't a real marriage. I want total commitment on both sides, a loving and stable home in which to bring up our children.'

'So after you're married there'll be no more nights like last night?'

The devilish smile she had come to like so much danced in his eyes. 'I certainly hope so...'

Seeing the doubt on her face, he added, 'But I'd like the woman involved to be my wife.'

In one way it was the answer she had hoped for. It meant that she hadn't been wrong about him. But at the same time it was like a knife turning in her heart.

As she sat still and silent, trying to absorb the pain, he said casually, with a glance at his watch, 'I guess we'd better be moving.'

They had been late eating and it was mid-afternoon by the time they left the pub. In sharp contrast to the last time they had shared a pub meal the sky was a clear baby-blue and the day, though cold, was bright.

Their route into London was clogged by traffic, and while Jonathan concentrated on his driving Loris fell into a brown study.

By the time she surfaced they had reached the outskirts of town and were turning off the main road and into Bladen Place.

'This isn't where I live,' she said.

'No, I know it isn't.' He slid from behind the wheel and

came round to open her door. 'But I've stopped here to show you something.'

Bladen Place was a quiet cul-de-sac. Its two-storey houses, though not luxurious, looked well-built and well-maintained, with neatly kept front gardens.

As Loris got out, she noticed that at number 23, the house Jonathan had parked in front of, the bedroom curtains were still drawn.

Unlatching the gate, he led the way up the path and, taking a Yale key from his pocket, quietly opened the door.

The hallway was small, but very nicely furnished. Red-carpeted stairs led up to a long landing, with two closed doors.

As he drew her inside, she glanced at him, made uneasy by his manner. 'What—?'

He put a finger to her lips and said softly, seriously, 'For everyone's sake I was hoping to avoid this, but as I can't think of any other way to convince you... Go up the stairs and open the right-hand door.'

Seized by a sudden apprehension, she found herself pleading, 'Won't you come with me?'

Shaking his head, he said decidedly, 'My presence would only make things worse.'

As, not liking the situation at all, she hung back, he gave her a little push and whispered sternly, 'Go on, where's your fighting spirit?'

With the greatest reluctance, she began to climb the stairs. When she reached the landing, she glanced back.

The hall was empty and the front door was closed.

Her feet noiseless on the thick carpet, she approached the right-hand door. Gritting her teeth, she turned the knob and pushed the door open.

With a feeling of *déjà vu*, she saw two people in the big double bed. Propped up on pillows, they were lying in each other's arms. Mark's eyes were closed in sleep, but the woman was staring straight back at Loris.

The little scene brought back such bitter memories of Nigel and his paramour that Loris felt gall rise in her throat, and thought for a moment she was going to be sick.

But it was immediately obvious that this woman was no brazen slut. She was young, little more than a girl, dark-haired and dark-eyed, with a kind of fragile dignity and a pretty, gentle face.

Though she sat quite still, cradling Mark's dark head against her breast, her expression revealed a tumult of feeling. She looked uncomfortable and apprehensive, yet oddly determined...

The only thing she didn't look, Loris realised, was surprised. She had been *expecting* the door to open, *waiting* for it.

As though the tension had communicated itself to the sleeper, he stirred and grunted.

Pulling herself together, Loris quietly closed the door and, hurrying down the stairs, let herself out. As the latch clicked gently behind her, she heard a baby start to cry.

By the time she reached the pavement Jonathan had turned the car round and was waiting by the kerb. Desperate to leave that painful little scene behind her, she jumped in and fastened her seat belt.

Responding to that unspoken urgency Jonathan let out the clutch, and in a moment they were pulling out of the cul-de-sac and joining the main traffic stream.

With a glance at her white face, he queried, 'Sure you're all right?'

Unable to tell him that it was being reminded of Nigel that had upset her far more than seeing Mark in another woman's arms, she answered obliquely, 'I will be when I know the full facts.'

Jonathan looked doubtful. 'Are you sure you want to talk about it just yet?'

'Why not?' she asked bitterly. 'Seeing my fiancé in bed with another woman is starting to lose its sting. In fact it's getting to be a habit.'

'I'm sorry it was necessary to put you through that.' His regret sounded genuine. 'If you hadn't still been determined to marry Longton I would have spared you that shock.'

It *had* been a shock, but nowhere near the shock it might have been if she had continued to believe she was in love with Mark.

Taking a deep breath, she asked, 'How did you manage to engineer it?'

'It wasn't a set-up,' Jonathan denied quietly.

'It must have been. I could see from the girl's face that she was expecting me, and you had a key to the door.'

'Yes, she gave me a key, and, yes, she was expecting you about that time. But she didn't lure Longton there especially, if that's what you're thinking. Apparently he enjoys what he calls "a spot of afternoon delight", and makes a habit of going to his love-nest two or three times a week. For one thing, it's easier to cover his tracks in the daytime. All he needs to do is say he's out on business, and who's to know he's spent most of the time in bed with his mistress? Take today, for instance. You thought he was away on business. Well, he was. He simply caught an earlier flight back to give him a few hours free.'

'I still don't understand how you know all this. How you became involved. Why you went to all this trouble. Why it *matters* to you. It has to be something more than mere disapproval, or even enmity...'

'It matters to me because the girl who was with him is Linda Marchant, Jane's sister-in-law, and Jane cares about her.'

CHAPTER NINE

THAT simple fact explained everything—why Jonathan had seduced her after the St Valentine's party, why he'd kissed her in BLC's foyer, why he'd lured her down to Fenny Manor...

In short, it explained why he'd been so determined to prevent her marrying Mark. It was for the sake of the woman he loved.

It even explained why Jane Marchant had been so willing to help him...

Loris felt as though a giant fist had closed around her heart and was squeezing the life out of it.

'What did you think of Linda?' Jonathan's tense question broke into her thoughts.

'Does it matter what I thought of her?' she asked wearily.

'Yes. It matters to me.'

Sighing, she answered truthfully, 'I thought she looked young and sweet, and surprisingly innocent.'

Jonathan's expression relaxed a little. 'She's far from being a tart. She was just seventeen and a naïve schoolgirl when he first seduced her. She's only nineteen now, and a really nice person. It's a great pity she's so crazy about that lying—' He broke off abruptly.

After a moment he continued more mildly, 'Believe me, both she and Jane were sincerely sorry to do this to you. They only agreed to my plan because Linda was desperate to keep the father of her child and Jane wanted to help. I hope you'll be able to forgive all three of us.'

'I suppose I should be thanking you for saving me.' Picking up the irony in the words, he frowned.

When she said nothing further, he asked carefully, 'Have you decided what you're going to do?'

Unhesitatingly, she answered, 'I shall give Mark back his ring.' And without too many qualms.

There was no mistaking Jonathan's relief.

'When I left you to go upstairs on your own I wondered if he'd succeed in talking his way out of it... But you weren't in the house for more than a minute, so I presume he either didn't try to make excuses or you didn't stay to listen to them?'

'He didn't even see me. He was asleep.'

'That might save a great deal of trouble. Linda was worried to death about having to try and explain how you came to know enough to be there at just the right time, and also how you got in... Unless you intend to tell him everything when you give him back his ring?'

'No, I don't. I shall merely tell him that I *know* he lied to me. Then as far as I'm concerned the whole thing's over and done with. I just hope she manages to find some happiness with him. I know now I never could have.' In spite of all her efforts, her voice sounded forlorn.

Jonathan reached over and gave her hand a quick squeeze. 'You'll find your share of happiness, I promise.'

It seemed unlikely, to say the least, when the man she had fallen in love with had merely used her to help the woman *he* loved.

She took a deep, shuddering breath and began, 'Tell me something...'

When she paused, trying to think how best to phrase it, he gave her a sidelong glance and asked encouragingly, 'What would you like to know?'

'I was wondering if your coming over to England with Cosby's was just a coincidence, or did you *choose* to come?'

'It wasn't a coincidence.'

'So you came over purposely to stop me from marrying Mark?'

'You could say that.'

A little edge to her voice, she said, 'Well, your mission's succeeded.' Then, with concern, 'But in the process you've lost your job... Unless Cosby's would let you work for them in the States?'

'I'm sure they would. But, having just acquired Fenny Manor, I don't happen to want to go back to the States. In any case, I'm hoping to be married quite soon.'

'Of course.'

And, as Jane Marchant obviously had money, he was under no immediate pressure. Though she couldn't believe he was the sort of man who would be content to let a woman keep him for any length of time...

Slanting her a glance, he remarked, 'You don't sound too happy about it.'

'Why shouldn't I be?' she said desperately. 'But I was just thinking that when you've got a wife to support it might be as well to have an income. What if I can persuade Mark to give you back your London job?'

His voice suddenly cold as ice, Jonathan queried, 'And how would you do that?'

'Not the way *you're* thinking.'

'I'm glad about that. I should hate to have to break his neck after all. So how?'

'A spot of blackmail.'

Looking amused now, he said, 'I hadn't figured you as a blackmailer. But do go on, you intrigue me.'

'Well, I could save his pride by telling my father and all his posh friends that we've decided we just aren't compatible... Or I could threaten to tell them exactly *why* I'd decided to end the engagement.'

Jonathan laughed. 'Simple, but I dare say very effective.'

Reaching for her hand, he raised it to his lips and kissed

the palm. 'Thank you, my love, I'm grateful. However, it's not necessary. I've no intention of working for Longton.'

Shaken by the endearment, Loris bit her lip. If only she *was* his love...

Perhaps, subconsciously, she'd wanted that since the moment they'd met. It had been so short a time, a matter of days, yet his effect on her life had been powerful.

But so much of it had been for the good.

If she'd married Mark she would have ended up as bitter and disillusioned as her mother. Jonathan, albeit for his own ends, had saved her from that, and she should be grateful.

Rather than have a husband like Mark, it was better not to marry at all. Though it was sad when, for the first time, she felt a whole woman and longed for the warmth of a loving relationship.

But not just *any* relationship.

She knew now that Jonathan was all she'd ever wanted, a man she could have been happy with, and she envied Jane Marchant with a wrenching envy that felt as if it was tearing her apart.

But envy wasn't a pleasant emotion, she reminded herself, and Jane Marchant—after having one failed marriage—was entitled to a second chance of happiness, to a husband who loved her, and a family.

The very things she herself wanted.

But unless, some time in the future, another man came along that she could love—and in the light of what had happened so far that seemed extremely unlikely—her career would have to take the place of a husband and family.

For once, the thought of her career failed to cheer her.

The Friday-night traffic proved to be unduly heavy, and, roadworks causing a bottleneck on the route Jonathan had chosen, they found themselves crawling along in a stop-start queue for several miles.

Refusing to get stressed, he put on some relaxing music

and whistled quietly to it, while Loris, tired from the previous night's lack of sleep and a veritable turmoil of emotions, leaned her head against the padded headrest and closed her eyes.

She was just rousing when Jonathan's voice said cheerfully, 'Here we are at last.'

Refreshed, she opened her eyes to find they had reached the block of flats where she lived and were turning into the underground car park.

Wondering how he'd known exactly where to bring her, she informed him, 'I'm afraid you're not allowed down here. It's for residents only.'

Taking not the slightest bit of notice, he drove down the long steep ramp until he reached the barrier.

In her smuggest 'you should have listened to me' voice, she said, 'I'm afraid you'll have to back up now.'

Green eyes glinting, he asked, 'Oh, why's that?'

'Because you have to have a resident's swipe card to raise the barrier.'

'You mean like this?' Producing a blue and white plastic card from his pocket, he swiped it through, and obediently the barrier rose.

A moment later he was pulling into one of the numbered parking bays. Catching sight of her expression, he asked innocently, 'Isn't this allowed either?'

'Not unless you're a resident, and this happens to be your bay.'

'I am, and it is.'

'What?' she said, failing to understand.

'I said I *am* a resident, and this *is* my parking bay.'

'But this is where *I* live,' she objected stupidly. He put on a thunderstruck expression. 'Gosh! Does that mean we're actually neighbours?'

'I do wish you'd be serious,' she said, not for the first time.

'While we're living in the same building I'll be the soul of gravity,' he assured her, and, jumping out, came round to open her door.

As they crossed to the lifts she tried to make sense of it. 'How do you come to be living here?'

'Simple. One of the service flats became vacant and I took a short lease on it.'

Strange things *did* happen, but with all the accommodation available in London surely this was too much of a coincidence? However, seeing by the gleam in his eye that he was quite prepared to go on teasing her, she decided to let the matter drop, merely asking, 'Which floor do you live on?'

'The same as you.'

'In a minute you'll be telling me you have the next-door flat.'

'I'm afraid not,' he said regretfully. 'We're at opposite ends of the building.'

When the lift stopped at the seventh floor he followed her out and turned to walk with her.

'I thought you lived at the opposite end?'

'So I do,' he agreed, unperturbed.

On reaching her door, he waited while she fished in her bag for the key, then opened the door for her.

'Thank you.' As steadily as possible, she added, 'I suppose, unless we meet by chance, this is goodbye.' She held out her hand.

'How very formal,' he mocked gently. Ignoring the proffered hand, he tilted her chin and kissed her lips.

A lover's kiss, it was bestowed with a possessive ardour that knocked her off balance and made her feel giddy. It seemed to offer a commitment and ask for a response.

When finally he raised his head, she lifted heavy lids and gazed up at him. Her golden eyes looked dazed, the pupils large and black.

Putting an arm around her waist, he urged her inside and closed the door behind them, before following her through the tiny hall and into the living-room.

Trying hard to regain her equilibrium, she queried thickly, 'If you intended to come in, why did you kiss me goodbye?'

'Oh, I didn't kiss you *goodbye*. I just took the opportunity to kiss you.' Glancing at her from beneath long gold-tipped lashes, he confided, 'I enjoy kissing you.'

Feeling she ought to scold him, but unable to, she stayed silent.

Looking around the living-room, with its beige and cream colour scheme, he remarked casually, 'All these flats are alike. Quite pleasant, but impersonal and far from exciting.'

Vexed that, while she was still shaken to the core, he could sound so unmoved and prosaic, she asked tartly, 'Did you follow me in for the sole purpose of criticising the decor?'

'Certainly not. There are much more important things to be done…' Then, with a hint of satisfaction, 'You told me Longton was coming at six-thirty, so if he didn't get held up he should be arriving any minute…'

A sudden suspicion made her ask, 'You weren't thinking of being here when Mark comes?'

'Of course.'

Fearing trouble, she cried sharply, 'No, I want you to go now! I don't want you to be here.'

'I'll keep out of it and let you handle things, if that's what you want, but I've no intention of leaving you alone.'

Knowing he was thinking of the slight bruise on her wrist, she said, 'No, really, there's absolutely no need to stay.'

His face serious, he asked, 'Just suppose Longton lost

his head and decided to use a little force to get what he's always wanted?'

Shocked, she whispered, 'No, he wouldn't.'

'Can you be certain of that?'

Could she?

Seeing the doubt on her face, he said grimly, 'Well, I've absolutely no intention of chancing it.'

The peal of the doorbell cut through his words.

'Stay here,' she hissed at him and, closing the door between the living-room and the hall, went to answer it.

Wearing a dark, well-tailored business suit, Mark was waiting. Looking a little surprised when she didn't immediately invite him in, he bent to kiss her.

She turned her head sharply away, so that his lips just brushed her cheek.

He frowned. 'Something wrong?'

'Yes.' Pulling off her engagement ring, she handed it to him.

Surprised into taking it, he stood staring down at the sparkling half-hoop of diamonds, before demanding angrily, 'What's going on? Why have you given me back my ring?'

'Our engagement's over,' she told him flatly.

'Don't be a fool. We're getting married in a week's time.'

'We're not getting married at all. You can tell everyone that we realised just in time that we aren't compatible.'

'Aren't compatible? Of course we're compatible! I don't know what's brought this on…' Then, a shade guiltily, 'Unless it's my sacking Drummond…? Look, let's go in and talk about it…'

Her heart in her mouth, she stood her ground. 'There's nothing to talk about. Unless you'd like to tell me where you spent the afternoon?' Watching some of the colour leave his face, she said, 'No, I didn't think you would.'

'Don't be idiotic, Loris,' he blustered, 'you know perfectly well I've been away on business.'

'You might have been on business this morning, but this afternoon you were visiting your mistress.'

'Whoever told you that was lying—'

'It isn't a lie, and you know it.'

'Believe me—'

'It's no use, Mark I *know*.'

'I don't see how you can *know* something that isn't true—'

'But it *is* true. You were at 23 Bladen Place, which is a quiet little cul-de-sac off Bladen Road. While you were there, the bedroom curtains were closed—'

His heavy face turning brick-red, he burst out, 'How the hell could you know a thing like that, unless you were having me followed?'

When she failed to deny it, he seized her hand. 'All right, so I admit I was there. But you're the only woman who means anything to me. It was just sex, and once we're married—'

Freeing her hand, she said wearily, 'I've heard that before from you and I just don't believe it. You'd better go, Mark.'

'If only you'd be prepared to forgive and forget, and marry me, I promise—'

'No more promises.' Her own conscience far from clear, she went on, 'I'm prepared to forgive and forget, but I'm not prepared to marry you.'

'Look, I'm sorry I lied to you—'

'It's not just that. I've realised I made a bad mistake. I don't love you, and there's no way I can marry a man I don't love.'

Seeing by his face that he was apparently genuinely upset, she added, 'I'm sorry, Mark, I never meant to hurt you. But it really *is* all over between us.'

Hearing the finality in her voice, he thrust the ring into his pocket and turned to walk towards the lifts.

Thankful that it was over, Loris closed the door and, trembling in every limb, went back to the living-room and sank into a chair.

Turning away from the window, where he'd been standing looking over the lights of Chelsea towards the river, Jonathan asked quietly, 'Was it very traumatic?'

'It wouldn't have been as bad if I hadn't felt so conscience-stricken.'

'Compared to Longton, you've very little to feel conscience-stricken about.'

'I don't know how you can take things so lightly,' she said with some asperity. 'You know quite well that we're both as bad as Mark.'

'Though I agree that neither of us are *entirely* blameless, I really don't think we belong in that category,' he objected mildly. 'However, as it's getting on for seven, we must leave that discussion until some other time.'

Taking her hands, he drew her to her feet. 'You've got about half an hour to get dolled up and—'

'Why do I need to get dolled up?' she broke in. 'I'm not going anywhere.'

'We're going out to dinner.'

'Oh, no. I—'

'Do you want to sit in and mope?'

'No, of course not…'

'So it's dinner at La Ronde and then we'll be spending the night at—'

'Are you crazy?' she cried. 'I've no intention of spending another night with you!'

He sighed. 'That's a shame… And just when I was starting to think you're getting to like the idea of being seduced.'

'As you've already achieved what you set out to do,

there's no further need to seduce me,' she pointed out with betraying bitterness.

'I wasn't intending to,' he assured her easily. 'At least not tonight. Tonight will be the height of propriety. We shall have different rooms and be well-chaperoned. But as we haven't got a lot of time, I'll explain the whole thing later... Now, go and get ready, there's a good girl. Oh, and don't forget to pack your night things, a change of undies, and your prettiest suit or dress, just in case.'

'But I—'

'No more arguments now. All the arrangements are made.' Opening the bedroom door, he gave her a gentle push. 'Off you go.'

Feeling as dazed and buffeted as if she'd been gathered up and swept along by some whirlwind, she pulled the door to behind her and began to sort through her drawers and wardrobe.

Having packed her overnight bag, and laid out the clothes she intended to wear, she went into the bathroom and, stripping off, stepped under the shower, her thoughts in a turmoil.

His self-imposed task accomplished, she had expected Jonathan to walk quietly away. That he should have further plans had come as a complete surprise, and she wondered uneasily what he was up to.

But, in spite of all her misgivings, her heart was beating faster with excitement and her spirits had risen with a bound at the prospect of spending the evening in his company.

Dried and perfumed, her flawless skin and dark brows and lashes needing no make-up, she coiled her hair into a gleaming knot on top of her head before putting on a calf-length silk evening dress.

A simply-cut sheath that she'd seen in Harrods and

bought in a rare moment of extravagance, it was a mix of tawny colours that echoed the gold of her eyes.

With it was a plain bronze jacket that somehow added to the exotic effect. Dull gold shoes and a matching bag finished off the ensemble.

Ready, she hesitated, her misgivings as to whether what she was doing was *sane* returning in force. Wouldn't spending more time with him only make the inevitable parting worse?

Perhaps, both for Jane Marchant's sake, and her own, she should dig in her heels and refuse to be coerced?

But soon he would be going out of her life for ever, and this last chance to spend a few more bittersweet hours in his company was far too precious to waste.

Picking up her small case, she opened the door to the living-room. Profiled against the dark window, Jonathan was standing quite still, staring blindly at the carpet, obviously deep in thought.

He must have been back to his own flat, she realised, because he was freshly shaved and had changed into impeccable evening dress.

For a moment she watched him unobserved, drinking in the sight of him, his lithe figure, his handsome profile, his hair, darkened and still a little damp from the shower.

As though her silent scrutiny had disturbed his concentration, he glanced her way.

There was a look on his face that she had never seen before. A look of doubt, of uncertainty, as if he had suddenly lost confidence in himself and whatever it was he'd been planning.

Almost instantly that look was gone, replaced by his usual quiet assurance.

His eyes swept slowly over her from head to toe. 'Wow!' he said softly. 'You look absolutely stunning…'

Absurdly pleased by his approval, she felt herself blushing.

Watching the colour rise in her cheeks, he remarked, 'And no lipstick. Even better!'

'You don't like lipstick?'

'I prefer you without. It means I can kiss you.'

Before she could object, he was suiting the action to the words.

When he released her, she said weakly, 'You shouldn't kiss me. It's not fair to Mrs Marchant.'

'Will it stop you worrying if I tell you that Jane won't mind in the slightest?'

'No,' Loris said unhappily, 'she *ought* to mind. Pretending not to mind puts her in the same class as Linda. Is that what you want?'

'Heaven forbid!' Jonathan exclaimed piously, and, taking her case, hurried her to the door. 'If we don't get a move on we're going to be late.'

The evening traffic was heavy, as usual, and it was a few minutes before eight when they reached Mayfair and drew up outside the restaurant.

La Ronde was both modern and imposing, a single-storey circular building, with an overhanging roof and lots of slanting smoked-glass windows.

Having helped her out, Jonathan handed over his ignition keys to one of several attendants in evening dress who were parking the cars.

Loris saw he was accorded the same deference as the man who had preceded them driving a Rolls-Royce.

The whole place had an air of opulence that oozed money, and Loris wondered nervously if her companion realised what he was letting himself in for.

A hand at her waist, he escorted her up the steps and into the foyer where they were immediately greeted by a grey-haired man in immaculate evening dress.

'Good evening, Mr Drummond. The rest of your party have already arrived and are waiting in the bar.'

Looking entirely at ease, as if he belonged in these sumptuous surroundings, Jonathan said casually, 'Thanks, we'll go through.'

Wondering who 'the rest of the party' could be, Loris allowed herself to be ushered into the bar, where a few well-dressed people were seated, either on bar stools or at small glass-topped tables.

A hand beneath her elbow, Jonathan steered her towards one of the tables where a young couple were sitting chatting.

The woman who was seated with her back to them had fair curly hair, while the nice-looking man sitting opposite her was dark.

At their approach, the nice-looking man rose to his feet and gave them a friendly smile. At the same instant his companion turned her head.

The woman with him was Jane Marchant.

Loris caught her breath.

Knowing there was no way she could face an evening in Jane Marchant's company, she would have turned and run, but, as though reading her mind, Jonathan put his arm around her and, ignoring her beseeching glance, urged her forward.

Short of creating a scene, there was little she could do, and a moment later he was making the introductions.

'My sister Jane, you already know...'

Sister! Jane Marchant was Jonathan's sister! Loris tried hard not to blush as she recalled the conclusions she'd jumped to.

'Hello, again.' Jane Marchant, looking pretty in powder-blue, gave Loris a somewhat uncertain smile.

'And this is David Marchant, Jane's husband. David, I'd like you to meet Loris Bergman...'

Feeling as though she was in a dream, Loris said, 'How do you do?' and held out her hand, liking this tall, spare man on sight.

His fingers closed over hers in a firm grip. 'It's nice to meet you. I gather that my wife and brother-in-law have rather turned your life upside down.'

'You weren't supposed to say that!' Jane scolded.

Unabashed, he asked Loris, 'All the same, it's true, isn't it?'

'Quite true,' she agreed, and they smiled at each other like conspirators.

Watching the pair of them, her relief obvious, Jane said, 'I have to admit I owe you an abject apology, Miss Bergman.'

'Please, won't you call me Loris? And there's no need for any apologies. I just hope that things work out for your sister-in-law.'

'Thank you. That's very generous of you.'

Jonathan took Loris's hand and gave it a squeeze, just as the *maître d'* appeared to show them to their table.

The restaurant was spectacular: its tables, set with crystal glasses and fresh flowers, were by the windows, widely spaced, and arranged like the spokes of a wheel.

'Isn't this lovely?' Jane exclaimed. Then, turning to Loris, she added sincerely, 'I'm so pleased you decided to come. I did wonder if Jonathan would be able to persuade you.'

'At one point I thought even my abundant charm might not be enough to do the trick,' he said ironically.

'Charm, my foot,' Loris retorted, 'he simply bulldozed me.'

They all laughed, and, the ice well and truly broken, took their seats.

The evening proved to be a great success. Both Jane and her husband were warm and outgoing, and while they ate an excellent meal, and drank a glass of vintage champagne, the conversation flowed easily.

By tacit consent they kept the topics light and impersonal, and with Jane's gentle wit complementing Jonathan's dry sense of humour they laughed a lot.

But while Loris listened and smiled and contributed a word here and there, part of her mind was mulling over what she'd learnt.

During the drive to Paddleham that first night Jonathan had mentioned a married sister, and now Jane and he were together she could see the faint likeness she'd missed earlier.

If only she hadn't jumped to entirely the wrong conclusion it would have saved her a great deal of anguish...

Or if Jonathan had told her the simple truth.

It must have been quite plain that she believed Jane to be the woman he was hoping to marry and, though he'd been careful not to tell her any lies, he'd allowed—no, *encouraged*—her to go on believing it.

But why? He must have had a reason.

Sighing inwardly, Loris resolutely pushed away the unsolved puzzle and made an effort to join more fully in the conversation.

As soon as the dessert plates had been cleared away, Jane gathered up her evening bag and, smiling, said to Jonathan, 'I think it's high time we were on our way. Give you and Loris a chance to talk.'

Both men rose with her, and David pulled out her chair.

Surprised by the suddenness, Loris asked, 'Aren't you staying for coffee?'

Patting her still-flat stomach, Jane announced cheerfully, 'Since I've been pregnant I've gone off both coffee and tea...'

Putting an arm around her, David said, 'And, apart from that, as prospective parents we need our quota of sleep.'

'Thank you both for a lovely evening,' Jane added. Then, a shade hesitantly, 'Hope to see you in the morning. Bye, now.'

David smiled at Loris and clapped Jonathan on the shoulder before turning to follow his wife.

'Alone at last!' Jonathan said dramatically. Reaching across the table, he took Loris's hand, and, lifting it to his lips, dropped a kiss into the palm.

The romantic little gesture rocked her.

His eyes on her face, he said, 'I hope the evening hasn't been too much of a strain?'

'Not at all.' Her voice wasn't quite steady. 'I liked both your *sister* and her husband.'

'I'm pleased.'

'Why didn't you tell me she was your sister?'

'If you remember, I did.'

'I mean *before* this evening...'

A waiter brought coffee and the conversation stopped until he'd served them both and moved away.

Taking a deep breath, Loris went back to the attack. 'You must have realised that I thought she was the woman you wanted to marry?'

'Yes, I did,' he admitted.

'Then why did you let me go on thinking it?'

'I'll tell you later. In the meantime, you tell me what made you jump to that conclusion?'

'You'd mentioned previously that you had plans to marry, but that the woman in question was "involved with someone else". So when Jane introduced herself as Mrs Marchant, and you said you loved her and she loved you, it seemed logical that she was the one...'

When he said nothing, she added, 'But obviously it's some other woman you're hoping to marry?'

'That's right.'

He was giving her no help, but, needing to *know*, Loris pursued, 'And I think you said *soon*?'

'Very soon.'

'But there are still some problems?'

'One or two.'

'Presumably you're waiting for this other relationship she's involved in to come to an end?'

'That's over, thank the Lord. But I may have a job persuading her to marry a man that her family will undoubtedly object to and who's just been fired.'

'Will either of those things bother her?'

'Wouldn't they bother you?'

'Not if I wanted to marry the man.'

'Do you?'

'Do I what?'

'Want to marry me?'

After a moment, she asked huskily, 'Is this some kind of joke?'

'It's more in the nature of a proposal.'

'A proposal!'

'I admit it's not the tender, romantic kind you read about in novels. If there'd been a rose garden handy, and a spot of moonlight, I could have gone down on one knee and asked for your hand in the traditional way. But as it's February, and pitch-dark…'

'I wish you'd be serious,' she said faintly.

His green eyes glinted. 'I've never been more serious in my life'

'You can't mean *I'm*…'

'The woman I want to marry? The woman of my dreams? The very same.'

Hardly daring to hope, still unsure whether he might just be teasing her, she said, 'But it's barely a week since you set eyes on me.'

'It's rather longer than that,' he contradicted. 'I saw you

when I first came over to England nearly six weeks ago. You came into the offices one day. I gather you had a lunch date with Longton. I knew then I wanted to marry you, and that helping Linda was a secondary consideration. But planning takes time, and I couldn't afford to make any mistakes.

'Of course it helped things along enormously when you and Longton quarrelled during the party and he went off with Pamela Gresham. If that little plan hadn't succeeded I would have had to think of some other way to get close to you…'

'What do you mean, *"if that little plan hadn't succeeded"*? You couldn't possibly have influenced what Mark and Pamela Gresham did…'

Watching his face, she knew she'd been wrong. 'I don't see *how*…' she faltered to a halt.

'I have a confession to make. As a matter of fact there's no such person as Pamela Gresham. Her name is Pamela Bradley, and I hired her from an—er—escort agency.'

Half-amused, half-appalled, Loris shook her head in disbelief. 'You hired a *call-girl*! How could you *do* such a thing?'

'All's fair in love and war, darling. And if Longton had been halfway decent he wouldn't have acted the way he did. Don't look so appalled. You must see he didn't love you any more than you loved him.'

Loris raised an eyebrow at his arrogant statement. 'What makes you so sure I didn't love him?'

He replied confidently, 'You're not the kind of woman who would cheat on a man she loved. The fact that you spent the night with me proved you didn't love him. But I wanted you to realise that for yourself, and admit it. However, after one look at your face the next morning, I knew I was in for an uphill struggle. Later, when we talked in the pub, though you *said* you loved Longton I knew you were just fooling yourself, and I was hoping against hope that if there was a showdown you'd come back to London with me. But when you told him the truth about sleeping with me and he magnanimously ''forgave'' you, despite not really believing you, I was back to square one. That's why it was necessary to involve Jane. What she did, she did for *me* as much as for Linda.'

'You still haven't told me why you allowed me to go on believing that Jane was the woman you were hoping to marry.'

'I wanted to see if, believing that, you would still sleep with me. The very fact that you did told me a lot.'

'I don't understand,' Loris said, bewildered.

'Leaving Longton out of it, you didn't seem to be the kind of woman who would make love with another woman's man unless you couldn't help yourself.'

Watching the colour come into her cheeks, he said, 'I needed to be sure so I could complete the arrangements.'

'What arrangements?' she asked suspiciously.

'For our wedding. I'd already got a special licence, but there were still things to organise. That's why I went over to Harefield. Then again, you shook me rigid by trying to run away the minute my back was turned, and insisting you still intended to marry Longton. That's why I was forced to take you to Bladen Place instead of shopping for a wedding dress, as I'd hoped. And, speaking of wedding dresses, you haven't said *yes* yet…'

He sounded so confident, so sure of her answer, while all Loris could feel was dazed, incapable of coherent thought. He already had a special licence!

Looking at her quizzically, he added, 'I must warn you that if you don't say yes at once I shall have to take you in my arms and kiss you until you do.'

'You can't kiss me here, in front of everybody,' she protested thickly.

'Do you want to bet?' He rose to his feet.

'Yes.'

Still standing, he asked, 'Is that yes you want to bet, or yes you'll marry me?'

'Yes, I'll marry you.'

'Good.' Resuming his seat, he added with a twinkle, 'That means we'll be able to come here again.' Then, watching her expressive face, 'What's wrong? Don't you like the place?'

'Oh, yes…' A shade awkwardly, she added, 'But it's bound to be very expensive.'

'I see. Will not being rich bother you?'

'Why should it? I've never been rich.'

'Your parents may not have loaded you with money, but you come from a rich background.'

Something in his tone made her ask, 'Does *that* bother you?'

He smiled at her. 'Not any longer. Now let's get out of here. I'm dying to kiss you.'

CHAPTER TEN

LA RONDE'S organisation was super-efficient, and by the time Jonathan had paid the bill and they had got outside his car was waiting, one of the attendants holding open the door.

A generous tip changed hands, and within seconds they were drawing away and joining the busy traffic stream to head out of town.

Sitting still and silent, Loris struggled to get her thoughts and emotions into some kind of order. The fact that everything had miraculously come right and she was going to marry the man she loved had barely sunk in.

Stunned by the speed at which things had happened, and the sheer unexpectedness of Jonathan's proposal, she hadn't even had time to feel happy.

Remembering his quiet admission of what lengths he'd gone to to break up her engagement, she gave a little shiver that was part excitement and part unease. Such ruthless determination scared her a little...

They had left the suburbs behind them and were on a quiet country road, their headlights picking up bare hedgerows, when she surfaced to ask, 'Where are we going?'

'Down to Harefield Farm. We're staying the night with Jane and David. Then all the arrangements are made for us to be married in the village church at twelve o'clock.'

Casually, he added, 'Though it will be a very quiet wedding, I expect you'd like your family to be there?'

'Yes, I would. But I can't imagine they'll want to come.'

'Wouldn't you like your father to give you away?'

'I doubt if he will,' she said honestly. 'He won't be very happy.'

'No. I dare say that after Longton I'll come as something of a shock.'

Knowing there was no point in denying it, she said quietly, 'For one thing it's so sudden. There'll hardly be time to let them know.'

'I'll either phone or email them as soon as we get back to Harefield.'

'I think you'll be wasting your time.'

His voice like polished steel, he said, 'I'll get them there.' Then, with a quick, sidelong glance, 'But just at the moment I have something more important on my mind.'

Drawing into a lay-by shielded from the road by a stand of trees, he stopped and switched off the engine and the main beam.

Her heart began to race with suffocating speed as he unfastened both their seat belts and took her in his arms.

In the greenish glow from the dashboard she saw him smile. 'There's no need to look quite so apprehensive. It's a shade public to do much more than kiss you.'

He kissed her lightly, almost playfully, but when her lips parted beneath the gentle pressure of his he began to explore her mouth with a hungry passion that made her stomach clench and sent her heart racing.

When he finally lifted his head she was past thinking, and if he'd suggested making love exactly where they were she would have offered no resistance.

He must have known she was his for the taking but, true to his word, he drew back and reached to fasten first her seat belt and then his own. A moment later they were on their way again, without a single car having passed.

Shaken to the soul by that brief interlude, she wondered how it was that no other man had ever been able to move her in the way this man did. His briefest kiss could summon up a storm of emotion, his lightest touch make her burn for him.

He had such power over her that it would have been frightening if he hadn't loved her as much as she loved him. But he must do, otherwise he wouldn't have gone to so much trouble to marry her.

She felt a warm glow of pleasure and excitement just reminding herself that by this time tomorrow she would be his wife...

As they approached Harefield Farm, and the security lights flashed on, Loris was surprised to see a large country mansion, rather than the homely farmhouse she had been expecting.

It was a square building, dignified and gracious, with creeper-covered walls and long windows flanking a handsome front door.

But, thinking back, Jonathan had told her that his sister had married the son of a local landowner.

As he helped Loris out and collected her case, he explained, apparently reading her mind, 'David's parents died a couple of years back, so he and Jane run the estate now.'

Having led the way into a spacious hall and up the stairs, he opened a door to the left. 'Jane said if all went well she was putting you in here.'

It was a pleasant room, with black oak floorboards, well-polished antique furniture, and a log fire burning cheerfully in the grate. A modern *en suite* bathroom had been added.

'I'm next door.' Dropping her case on the bed, he went on, 'I've a few things to attend to before I come up, so I'll say goodnight now.'

When she lifted her face for his kiss, he shook his head regretfully, 'I'd better not. If I kiss you once I may not be able to tear myself away.'

Disappointed, she reached up, and with her index finger

traced the curve of his cheek and jaw and the cleft in his chin. 'Would that matter?' she asked softly.

'Woman, are you trying to tempt me?'

'Yes. I've a lot of catching up to do.'

He laughed softly. 'Well, as I can resist anything but temptation, I'll be back in about half an hour.'

A little shocked by her own boldness, she had decided against a nightie, and, her hair loose around her bare shoulders, she was lying watching the flickering flames when he returned.

He was freshly showered and shaved, and wearing a short towelling robe. Discarding it, he slid in beside her and nuzzled his face against her breasts. 'Mmm...you're all scented and sensuous, like a velvety summer night.'

His warm wet tongue coaxed a pink nipple into life, and with a little murmur of appreciation he drew it into his mouth.

Shivers of pleasure ran through her, which were intensified when his fingers found its twin. Just when she thought she could stand no more of such exquisite torment his free hand slid down her flat stomach and began to explore.

She gave a little gasp as all sensation was dragged downwards and started to build and spiral into a growing need. When, without conscious volition, she began to move against his hand, it was withdrawn.

She whispered his name pleadingly.

Raising his head, he kissed her lips and said softly, 'There's no need to rush things, my love. Taking it slowly can mean maximum enjoyment. It will give me pleasure to experiment a little, to find out what pleases you most, then I can make our wedding night truly memorable.'

His index finger had been moving almost imperceptibly,

and now it paused and applied a light pressure. 'Do you like that?'

A little moan was all the answer he needed.

When Loris awoke she was alone in the bed and daylight was slanting in between the heavy velvet curtains.

Instant remembrance brought a fresh flood of happiness, and she sighed blissfully. Last night had been made up of love, tenderness, passion and ecstasy and, like the icing on the cake, today was her wedding day.

It didn't matter that it was to be a quiet wedding with no frills; it didn't matter that neither of them had much money; it didn't matter that Jonathan had no job. The only thing that mattered was having his love...

There was a knock at the door and she called, 'Come in.'

A young maid came in, carrying a tray of coffee and toast, and put it down carefully on the bedside table before drawing back the curtains.

'Mrs Marchant asked me to say that she's sorry to disturb you, but it's almost eleven-fifteen.'

'Eleven-fifteen!' Loris exclaimed, pushing herself upright. 'I'll never be ready in time.'

'She said that when you've had your toast and coffee, she'll be along to give you a hand... Oh, and Mr Drummond said you're to be sure and eat something, as he doesn't want you fainting at the altar.'

With a little bob, the girl scurried out.

As soon as Loris had eaten a slice of toast and swallowed a cup of coffee, she laid out the suit she'd brought, found some stockings and a set of dainty undies, and hurried into the bathroom to shower and clean her teeth.

When she emerged a few minutes later Jane Marchant was waiting, dressed in an elegant navy suit and hat. On the bed there were several boxes of various sizes, and a lovely bouquet of scented spring flowers.

'I see you have a suit ready,' Jane observed. Then, a shade diffidently, 'But I wondered if you'd like to wear this.' Taking the lid off the largest box, she lifted out an exquisite ivory silk wedding dress. 'We're pretty much of a size, and though it's seven years old these classic styles don't really change.'

Loris swallowed, momentarily too full to speak.

Noting the hesitation, Jane said hastily, 'Please feel free to refuse if you don't want to. I promise I won't be offended.'

'I'd *love* to wear it.'

Her pleasure obvious, Jane helped Loris into the dress and fastened a row of tiny covered buttons that ran down the back from the neck to below the waist.

It fitted perfectly.

Looking at her reflection in the cheval-glass, Loris said huskily, 'It's *beautiful*.'

Jane beamed. 'The accessories are all here if you want them. Shoes, headdress, and this.' She produced a garter embroidered with blue forget-me-nots.

When Loris had eased the garter into place, she tried the shoes. Luck was with her, and they too fitted.

'Are you wearing your hair up or down?' Jane asked eagerly.

'Up, I think.'

When her chignon had been pinned into place, Loris found that the headdress, a simple rhinestone coronet that held a veil as fine as gossamer, sat as neatly as she could have wished.

'All ready, with five minutes to spare,' Jane said, handing Loris the bouquet, 'and you look absolutely gorgeous.'

'If I do, it's thanks to you...'

A knock at the door cut through her words.

'That'll be David,' Jane said. 'He's offered to escort you to the church, if that's all right by you?' Then, seriously, 'I can't tell you how pleased I am that you're marrying Jonathan. He's one of the best.' Her eyes full of tears, she hurried out, just as her husband came in.

Having looked Loris over appreciatively, he nodded his approval. 'You look absolutely beautiful. My brother-in-law's a very lucky man... All ready?'

'Yes.'

Offering her his arm, he said, 'Then let's get going. We've a Roller waiting.'

When he'd helped Loris into a ribbon-trimmed Rolls-Royce, they made the short drive in pale winter sunshine, to find the small church full of flowers, the village organist playing Bach, and a grey-haired priest waiting to welcome them.

A mere handful of people were present, amongst them her mother, who was seated in the front pew, and her father, who was standing at the back of the church.

To Loris's surprise, he took David's place, and walked her up the aisle, while Simon, clearly about to perform the duties of best man, waited at the chancel steps with Jonathan.

As she reached her bridegroom's side, he turned his head to smile at her.

Knowing he must have moved heaven and earth to get her family here, she returned his smile, her heart overflowing with love and gratitude.

The short service passed like a dream—the quietly spoken vows, the exchange of rings, her bridegroom, handsome and self-assured putting back her veil to kiss her, and finally the signing of the register.

In the vestry, looking unexpectedly tearful, her mother kissed her, and said, 'I hope you'll be happy.'

Her father, unsmiling and terse, added, 'I just hope you know what you're doing.'

Simon gave her a hug and wished her, 'The best of luck.'

Then a tall grey-haired man she had never seen before came up to take her hand and say, 'So you're Loris. My nephew has very good taste.'

Moments later they were out in the weak sunshine, and the local photographer was taking pictures.

'Time we were going to get changed,' Jonathan said in his bride's ear. 'Jane and David and Simon, who know what's going on, will take care of the reception and explain our absence.'

'Why are we leaving so soon?'

'We have a plane to catch, and we're cutting it rather fine.'

He took her hand and, showered with rice, they ran down the church path to the waiting Rolls.

By seven o'clock that evening they were in Paris, at the Hotel L'Epic, being shown into the luxurious honeymoon suite by the manager himself.

This was yet another surprise in a day full of surprises.

When Monsieur Duval had bowed himself out Jonathan opened the waiting champagne and poured them each a glass.

Watching Loris while she sipped, he asked, 'Tired?'

'A little,' she admitted. 'It must be the excitement.'

'Hungry yet?'

'Not really.' They had eaten a sandwich on the plane.

'So, shall we say dinner at eight-thirty?'

'Yes, fine.'

'Do you want to go downstairs? Or shall we have it sent up?'

'Oh, sent up, I think.' She had nothing suitable to wear for dinner in a first-class hotel.

Once again reading her mind, he said, 'As soon as the shops are open we'll go and buy you a trousseau.'

Knowing the honeymoon suite must be costing the earth, she said hurriedly, 'Oh, no, I don't need any new clothes.'

'As you've virtually nothing with you, if you don't buy *something* we'll have to spend the rest of our honeymoon in bed.' A glint in his eye, he added, 'Not that that's such a bad idea... But first, in order to keep up our strength, we'll need to eat, so is there anything special you'd like me to order?'

'No, I'll leave it to you.'

While he ordered the meal, in fluent French, she put her glass on the coffee-table and went to the window to look out over the Place Chaumont, a quiet square with wrought-iron lamps and elegant buildings.

The last eight hours had had an unreal, dreamlike quality that made her feel as if she wanted to pinch herself to make sure she was really awake.

Instead, she looked down at the plain gold band that Jonathan had slipped onto her finger. Everything had happened so quickly that there'd been no time to wonder if she'd done the right thing in marrying a man she scarcely knew.

Suppose she'd made a dreadful mistake? Suppose what she felt for him was just sexual attraction rather than love? Suddenly racked by doubts, she clasped her hands tightly together.

No, if what she felt for him wasn't love, then there was no such thing. Sexual attraction was there, certainly, but there was so much more—warmth and caring, a liking and respect for the kind of person he was, a deep and abiding need to be with him, to be a part of him...

So long as he felt those things too, their marriage would be a happy one... But *did* he? All at once she was beset by fresh doubts. He'd never once said he loved her...

Though surely he must do, otherwise why would he have bulldozed her into marrying him?

Replacing the phone, he came to stand behind her and kiss her nape, before turning her into his arms and covering her mouth with his.

His kiss was passionate and searching, a devastating mixture of possessiveness and desire that made her body tremble and her head spin, so that she was forced to cling to him.

Sweeping her into his arms, he crossed to the sumptuous couch and laid her on it. Then, sitting by her side, looking down at her, he said with undisguised triumph, 'Mine at last.'

'You sound as if you've waited for years,' she remarked huskily.

'I have. Almost as long as Jacob waited for Rachel.'

She thought for a second or two that he might be teasing her, but something about the way he spoke made her know he wasn't.

Suddenly, clearly, she recalled him talking about unrequited love, and saying, 'I wasn't good enough for her... However, that was a long time ago.'

Pushing herself up, so she was half lying back against the cushions, she said, 'You knew me in the past.' It was a statement, not a question. 'When?'

'You'd just started at the School of Art and I'd finished college and was working for your father. The minute I saw you I knew you were what I'd always wanted. I started going to Bohemian Nights—if you remember, it was where a lot of the art students went for coffee or a cheap pizza—and after weeks of worshipping from afar I plucked up enough courage to talk to you. When I discovered you liked the cinema, I asked you to come to the Carlton with me...'

'*Johnny*... Of course...' Though both had been shy there had been an instant affinity, and she'd thought he might be the someone special she'd been waiting for. 'Ever since I first saw you I've had the feeling that I once knew you...'

'But I was of so little account that you didn't even recognise me.'

'I half did. If you remember, at the party, I asked you if we'd ever met before, and you said no.'

He shook his head. 'I said, *"If we had, I would have remembered"*.'

'And you were angry that I didn't?'

'Let's say disappointed.'

'But it was years ago, and I only knew you for a very short time. You told me your name was Johnny Dudley, and you looked so completely *different* then. You were *boyish*... Diffident and unassuming...'

As though curious, he asked, 'Why did you agree to go out with me?'

'Because I wanted to.'

His voice cool, he pointed out, 'You didn't come.'

'I intended to, but it happened to be my father's birthday. He'd made arrangements to take some friends to Maxim's, and because their son was coming too he insisted on me going to even up the numbers. When I told him I had a date, and who with, he said if I wrote you a note he'd see you got it.'

'Can you remember what you said in the note?'

'I explained why I couldn't come, and suggested we met the following night at the same time and place. I asked you to phone me if you couldn't make it. I didn't hear from you, so I went to the Carlton and waited for over an hour.'

Jonathan's face looked so hard and set that her voice wavered as she continued, 'The next day I went into the offices, hoping to see you, but I was told you hadn't come in to work. A few days later, when I asked again, my father told me you'd left without a word. Why did you leave so suddenly?'

'I didn't exactly *leave*, I was thrown out.'

'Thrown out?'

'For getting too familiar with the boss's daughter.'

As Loris stared at him, aghast, he went on, 'Instead of giving me your note, your father gave me my marching orders. He said he didn't want one of his workforce "trying it on" with his daughter. Like a fool, I denied "trying it on", and admitted that I was serious and I wanted to marry you. He roared with laughter before pointing out that I was a nobody, with no money and no background. That I wasn't, and never would be, good enough to clean your shoes, let alone marry you, so I was wasting my time trying to date you. I told him you were of an age to make up your own mind, and that you'd already agreed to meet me that night. He said, "Don't think for a minute she'll turn up, boy. She's just been enjoying a bit of fun at your expense. Tonight she's having dinner at Maxim's with the son of Sir Denzyl Roberts". I didn't want to believe him. I waited outside Maxim's and saw your party arrive. You were escorted by a handsome fair-haired man. He had his arm around your waist.'

Taking a deep breath, she said, 'That was Nigel.'

Jonathan muttered something under his breath that might have been an oath, before saying, 'I hope your father was proud of himself.'

'To be honest, it was more likely to have been my mother's influence that made him act as he did. I don't think my father would have cared enough.'

'He cared enough not to want you to marry a penniless nobody. I would have given a lot to have seen his face when I first broke the news to him.'

Understanding at last why Jonathan had railroaded her into this marriage, Loris went icy cold, as if every drop of blood had drained from her body.

He hadn't married her because he loved her. It had been to settle old scores.

How many times had she said, 'I wish you'd be serious'? Now she knew he was, and had been from the start. Deadly serious.

She felt a crushing despair.

Slowly, she said, 'So that's why you were so determined to have my parents there, to savour your triumph. You hate them both.'

'Not at all,' he denied smoothly. 'Your mother can't help being the kind of person she is, and your father has actually done me a great service. If it hadn't been for him I might have lacked ambition. He gave me the incentive to get where I am today.'

'In a Paris hotel that neither of us can afford,' she said bitterly. 'Well, as far as I'm concerned you don't have to worry, because I'm leaving right now.'

When she tried to struggle up, he stopped her. 'I'm afraid I can't let you leave.'

'Why not? After all, you've done everything you set out to do. You've married the boss's daughter, and given your sister-in-law a chance to keep Mark. What else could you possibly want?'

'A lifetime with you.'

'I've no intention of staying with a man who doesn't love me. Who simply used me to get even with my father.'

'I admit that getting even with your father was part of it, but only a tiny part. I fell in love with you when you were eighteen, and I've never stopped loving you. For the past few years I've worked fourteen hours a day with one thing in mind. You. I hardly dared hope that when I got where I wanted to be you'd still be free. Luckily I was almost there when Jane told me about your engagement...'

Dazed by the rush of happiness, Loris said nothing.

Watching her bemused face, Jonathan asked quizzically, 'Don't you want to know where "there" is?'

She didn't really care. The only thing that mattered was that he loved her. But she said dreamily, 'If you want to tell me.'

'I think I'd better, so you won't keep worrying about how I'm going to pay the bill. I don't work for Cosby's; I own it.'

Thinking she'd misheard, she said, 'What did you say?'

'I own Cosby's,' he repeated patiently.

'Own it?' Her jaw dropped, 'Then why did you pretend to be Mr Grant's PA?'

'I wanted the takeover to go through before anyone found out who I was.'

'But after it went through why didn't you tell me?'

'I needed to see if you'd marry me thinking I had nothing. When you agreed, I knew you must love me.'

He leaned forward to kiss her.

She put her hands flat on his chest and held him off.

'Something wrong?'

'I want the answers to some questions before you kiss me.'

'You're a hard woman,' he complained. Seeing she wasn't about to relent, he agreed, 'Okay, shoot.'

'I take it my father doesn't know you're his boss?'

'In the end I had to point it out to him to get him to come to the wedding. Anything else?'

'Is your name really Drummond?'

'Yes.'

'Then why were you calling yourself Dudley when we first met?'

'My grandfather, a dictatorial old man, ruled the family with a rod of iron. Even when his two sons were grown up he tried to run their lives. His eldest son, my uncle Hugh, gave in to pressure and took the course Grandfather "suggested'' he took. But my father wanted to be a doctor, and, what was worse, a GP rather than a Harley Street specialist, which infuriated Grandfather. There was a blazing row and he accused his younger son of wanting to debase the name Drummond, and said if he didn't toe the line he could get out. My father left the ancestral home, and, deciding to cut all ties with the old man, changed his name to Dudley, his mother's maiden name.'

Suddenly putting two and two together, Loris said, 'So ''Uncle Hugh'' must be Sir Hugh Drummond, and the ancestral home Merriton Hall...'

'That's right.'

'But when my mother asked if you were related to Sir Hugh Drummond, you said—'

'Ah, but she went on to ask specifically if he was my father, and I said my father was a poor GP. Which was the truth. He never made any money, but he was loved and respected, and when he died from an infection he'd picked up from one of his patients the whole town turned out to mourn. Grandfather, who was a very old man by then, came to the funeral. It seems he'd regretted the rift for some time but had been too proud and stubborn to make the first move. Hugh had never married, so I was his only grandson. He begged me to change my name to Drummond, to carry on the family name, and promised that when Hugh died everything would come to me. I told him politely that I wasn't interested, whereupon he told me a great deal less politely that I was as pig-headed as my father. My mother, who oddly enough felt sorry for the old man, and thought it would be a shame to let the name die out, wanted me to do it, so in the end I agreed, to make her happy.'

A thought occurred to Loris, and she began, 'The tall grey-haired man in the vestry—'

'Was Hugh,' Jonathan confirmed. 'Any further questions?'

'One thing puzzles me,' she admitted. 'You've only been in the States a few years and I was wondering…' She hesitated.

'How I come to own a firm the size of Cosby's?'

'Yes.'

'Well, I had a flying start. Can you remember me telling you that my mother's parents owned a small business in Albany? Well, that was Cosby's. By the time I went to live in the States my maternal grandparents were on the point of retiring. I took over from them, and when there was a huge boom in electronic communications I was able to buy them out. As a result of luck and a lot of hard work business increased tenfold, and profits soared…'

'When did you decide to take over Bergman Longton?'

'That had been one of my goals since the day your father told me I'd never succeed in marrying the boss's daughter.'

'Well, in a way you haven't.'

He looked at her, his sea-green eyes quizzical. 'What exactly does that mean?'

Flatly, dispassionately, she said, 'It means I'm not Peter Bergman's daughter. My mother was already pregnant when she got married. She tried to pretend I was his, but he knew she was lying. In the end, to save looking a fool, he agreed to pass me off as his own. But I don't think he's ever really forgiven her, or me. My mother still doesn't know I know.'

'So how *do* you know?'

'Understandably, perhaps, the man I still call Father has never liked me, and one day when I'd particularly annoyed him he told me the truth. I was thirteen at the time.'

'It must have come as a shock.'

'In some ways it was a relief to know I wasn't his child.'

'That fact certainly explains a lot of things—why he didn't help you through college, why he left you to fend for yourself, why he didn't care overmuch about your happiness…'

'But a lot of good's come out of it,' she said quietly. 'It's because of him that I worked so hard to become a designer and be independent…'

A thought struck her, and she asked, 'You won't mind if I keep on working?'

'My love, you can work to your heart's content, though I'd like you to take Fenny Manor as one of your first assignments.'

'So it really is yours?'

'Ours. And when we eventually get back from our honeymoon we'll buy a nice place in town, for when we want to be in London.'

'Eventually? I thought we were only in Paris for a few days.'

'We're here for as long as you like, and after Paris I thought a trip to New York, to meet my mother and the rest of my family, then on to San Francisco, Hawaii maybe…'

'For someone who's a self-confessed home bird that sounds like pretty good going.'

Taking her in his arms, he held her close. 'You'll be travelling with me, and you know the old saying, ''Home is where the heart is…'''

When he kissed her, in a haze of happiness she kissed him back, until kissing was no longer enough, and, on fire for him, she whispered, 'What time is it?'

'Eight-fifteen.'

'Oh…'

Hearing the disappointment in her voice, he left her for a moment to hang the 'Do not disturb' sign on the door. Then, taking her hand, he led her towards the bedroom.

Conscience stirring, she asked, 'What if they bring the meal?'

'They'll have the sense to leave it outside,' Jonathan said firmly. 'After all, this *is* France, and we *are* in the honeymoon suite.'

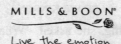

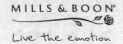

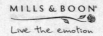

0706/03a

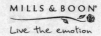

MILLS & BOON®

Live the emotion

_Medical
romance™

THE SICILIAN DOCTOR'S PROPOSAL
by Sarah Morgan

Mediterranean Doctors
Passionate about life, love and medicine.

Dr Alice Anderson doesn't believe in love — no
matter how much the new doctor Dr Giovanni
Moretti tries to persuade her otherwise. Gio's
feelings for Alice are undeniably strong. But will
the impossibly charming Sicilian be able to make
Alice realise that she has done the unthinkable
— fallen in love?

THE FIREFIGHTER'S FIANCÉ *by Kate Hardy*

Kelsey Watson loves her firefighting job, is happily
single and she has a wonderful friend and house-
mate in paramedic Matt Fraser. Then Matt notices
how deeply a fierce fire in a local school affects
Kelsey. And as he tries to help her, a deeper
connection between them emerges…

EMERGENCY BABY *by Alison Roberts*

As part of the Specialist Emergency Response Team,
paramedic Samantha Moore has always been one
of the boys. But now her biological clock is ticking
— and she wants a baby! Sam begins to search for the
perfect father…and discovers him right under her
nose: her SERT partner, Alex! Soon Sam begins to
see Alex as the perfect husband too.

On sale 4th August 2006

*Available at WHSmith, Tesco, ASDA, Borders, Eason,
Sainsbury's and most bookshops*

www.millsandboon.co.uk

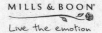

The child she
loves…is
his child.

And now he
knows…

THE SEVEN YEAR SECRET BY ROZ DENNY FOX

Mallory Forester's daughter needs a transplant. But there's
only one person left to turn to – Liddy's father. Mallory hasn't
seen Connor in seven years, and now she has to tell him he's a
father…with a chance to save his daughter's life!

HIS DADDY'S EYES BY DEBRA SALONEN

Judge Lawrence Bishop spent a weekend in the arms of a sexy
stranger two years ago and he's been looking for her ever since.
He discovers she's dead, but *her baby son* is living with his aunt,
Sara Carsten. Ren does the maths and realises he's got to see
pretty Sara, talk to her and go from there…

Look for more *Little Secrets* coming in August!

On sale 7th July 2006

www.millsandboon.co.uk

The child she
loves…is
his child.

And now he
knows…

HER SISTER'S CHILDREN BY ROXANNE RUSTAND

When Claire Worth inherits her adorable but sad five-year-old twin nieces, their fourteen-year-old brother and a resort on Lake Superior, her life is turned upside down. Then Logan Matthews, her sister's sexy first husband turns up – will he want to break up Claire's fledgling family, when he discovers that Jason is his son?

WILD CAT AND THE MARINE BY JADE TAYLOR

One night of passion doesn't make a marriage, but it could make a child. A beautiful daughter. Cat Darnell hadn't been able to trample on her lover's dream and kept her secret. Joey was the light of her life. And now, finally, Jackson Gray was coming home…was going to meet his little girl…

On sale 4th August 2006

www.millsandboon.co.uk

M&B™